ny

Austria

Castle von Eschenbach

Salzburg

To My Dear Friend—
Jean,

Celebrate Life,
Love and Lily
Pads!

We should
be enjoying
ourselves, Jean—
Your Friend,
Charlotte
Bush

Grave
DISORDER

Charlotte de ne Guerre

Eschatology, LLC

Published & distributed by:
Eschatology, LLC

in association with
IBJ Custom Publishing
Indianapolis, IN
www.ibjcustompublishing.com

ISBN 0-9776675-2-9
First Edition

Printed in the United States of America

Acknowledgements

In the long years during which this book was written, I enjoyed the cooperation of many scholars, libraries and friends who offered me their help with a love of learning and a warmth of feeling that always evoked my deepest appreciation and joy beyond words.

First, the incomparable Heidi Newman of "Mark My Word" who worked diligently correcting the many errors, typos and conversions many of which were created during new computer and new computer program transfers. Her meticulous perusal led to many stylistic refinements and artistry of editorial work left its traces in more than a few places.

My son, Jeff continues to be of immeasurable help to me. His ingenious computer techniques and command of the English language never ceases to amaze me. His contribution to this work reaches the point where it would have been impossible without him. His patience, intelligence and understanding are peerless.

My attorney's and close friends David Canmann and Eileen Sims, the forces behind me and Norm and Nan, Laura and Ray, Helen and Boyer, and Agnes and Jim – all of these for the comfort of true friendship. Drs. Dolan, Dean, Munson, Honan & Pierach for medical advice and guidance. Thank you to Kathy and Vivian for their responsible and loving assistance in our daily lives without whom we would be lost.

Thank you to Erika and Leslie for religious and esoteric contributions and wisdom beyond the ages.

To my own daughters, Nicole and Cheryl whose support and love have sustained me throughout our lives. My extended family who here remain unnamed for fear of the stigma. They know who they are and how much I love them.

Our granddaughters, Sarah and Jenny make our lives joyous, and to share in their lives is an incredible gift. To my father who talked to me only after he went to the other side and my fabulous mother who was the fount of all knowledge.

I cannot fully express my gratitude to the exceptional team at IBJ Custom Publishing (*Indianapolis Business Journal*) for their generosity and guidance – Pat Keiffner, Matt Maynard, Jennifer Turner and Brad Dixon for an education in Publishing and an astonishingly beautiful jacket. Special thanks to Matt Maynard for his faith in me and this work.

And the best for last – my cherished blessing – my husband, Stan whose constant abiding love has rendered our lives to be phenomenal, exciting, unique and extraordinary. The scientist, Pharmacist, executive and artistic talents in him have been the source of any basis for intellectual thinking I may have.

Courage, understanding

Inspiration, optimism

Insight, authenticity

Gentleness, kindness

Wisdom and heart

Prologue

To my readers,

This testimony contains a controversial concept of a moral, philosophical and intellectual nature in the areas of science and religion.

To some of you, this concept will be inspiring – to others, it will appear strange and startling – to others still, it could be deeply disturbing, and yet others may go off the deep end because I am advocating they lose one of their demons for which they might be blaming their misfortunes.

I am sharing my personal discovery of truth with you because I believe that any kind of search implies an obligation to exchange with others what has been found. This is in the interest of hastening harmony on earth.

> *Then Jesus spake again saying, "I am the light of the world; he that followeth me shall not walk in darkness, but shall have the light of life."*   *John 8:12*

"…Would to God your horizons may broaden every day! The people who bind themselves to 'truths' are those who are unable to encompass the whole truth and try to catch it by the tail…"   Leo Tolstoy

Charlotte de ne Guerre

The LORD is my shepherd; I shall not want.

He maketh me to lie down in green pastures: he leadeth me beside the still waters.

He restoreth my soul: he leadeth me in the paths of righteousness for his name's sake.

Yea, though I walk through the valley of the shadow of death, I will fear no evil: for thou art with me; thy rod and thy staff they comfort me.

Thou preparest a table before me in the presence of mine enemies: thou anointest my head with oil; my cup runneth over.

Surely goodness and mercy shall follow me all the days of my life: and I will dwell in the house of the LORD for ever.

Psalm 23

Charlotte de ne Guerre

Chapter I
The Dream

Mourners duck out of the funeral home into a gray wall of water, by themselves and in pairs. Women hunching their shoulders are held close under the strong arms of men wielding umbrellas as empty promises of shelter. One woman stretches her leg past the curb to overstep the river speeding through the gutter. "Such a shame," she whispers at the lapel of her husband's raincoat. A second woman grasps her spouse's elbow as she navigates the water-slicked sidewalk and remarks, "She was so young." A lone older woman follows close behind, bobbing to dab at her cheek with a handkerchief, murmuring to no one in particular, "Who will look after the children?"

The rooms inside betray the Gothic limestone facade with their soft light and pastel cushioning. The view from the windows is oppressive and bleak, revealing only the pounding rain on the asphalt parking lot, while the pictures hanging on the wall show divine swords of light piercing cotton-candy thunderheads.

Dark doors open into the chapel. A few friends and relatives linger, paying their respects to Claire Foster. Doleful organ music hums as they pass a flowerbed of wreaths and arrangements to approach the coffin. Gladioli tower over roses; chrysanthemums vie with carnations; and sprays of orchids preen in front of fountains of lilies.

Three children sit in the front row of the sanctuary. The eldest, Victoria, wears a white-collared navy velvet dress with an oval gold locket at her neck that displays her initials. The girl is fragile in appearance but has a core of iron that will be needed for every waking moment of the oncoming weeks as she faces one of the greatest possible tragedies of childhood: the loss of a parent. Holly rubs the toe of one Mary Jane with the heel of the other and gnaws at the end of her braid. In between them, young John curls up to Victoria's right arm and presses his nose into the dress's comforting nap as he swings his feet. Normally, it would be Victoria's job to tell him to stop fidgeting or she'd tell Mom, but now she knows that she can't tell on him. She tries to swallow the quarter-pound lump in her throat and keep her face dry. She wants to be brave for him and Holly, to show her father that she can help care for the younger ones. But it's too much to ask. As she gazes into the back of her father's black coat, two hot streams squeeze out of her eyes.

Stuart Foster stands at the head of the coffin and greets mourners.

To the children he looks like a magician, in a costume he might wear to a Halloween party, with mother as the beautiful, sequined assistant with her own tricks up her sleeve. He's about to cover the coffin with a big silk square, wave a wand over it and say "Abracadabra!" After the magic word their mother would spring to life and step out of the box. As he kissed her hand, she would curtsy to the audience's applause.

Victoria snuffles as a neighbor steps up to her father. "She looks so peaceful, Stuart. Natural. Resting." Stuart's ears grate from so many repetitions of trite sentiment. He wants to grab Mrs. McDarien and shake her until her glasses fall off, her false teeth rattle, and all the wads of Kleenex fly out of her purse. He knows that the imagined fit of hostility is not him.

The open casket suddenly strikes him as barbaric and he shudders. *What is the matter with you people?*, he wants to scream in fatigue and sorrow. *Don't you believe that she's really dead?* Stuart pauses to understand, as if being robbed of your soulmate, partner, sometime adversary and always-cherished mate is a trigonometry problem only requiring assignment of appropriate functions. When his hand is grasped by a skeletal claw, he sees his own reflection in old Jack McDarien's spectacles. He looks like hell. His usually robust face is now gray and haggard. Pouches cast shadows beneath his eyes. His mouth gapes as he forces himself to speak: "Thank you, Jack." He reaches forward to grip the man's shoulder. "I know she'd appreciate you coming."

Stuart moves on to confront the last mourner, a fellow volunteer from Claire's charity work. She collapses on Stuart's chest, sobbing. Stuart feels the head of this woman on his collar and leans in to hug her as if he's burping a large child. How odd that this stranger is hiccupping grief all over him while he is the one desperate for comfort—and the three children sitting on the hard pew more so than himself.

"Such a tragedy. I know she's in a better place." Stuart steps back from her, looking at the remains of his wife in repose. Claire is pale, but not with the wax-on-ashes pallor common to the dead. She is wearing her favorite dress, a stylish steel-gray gown. "My warrior goddess," he had teased her whenever she wore it. "My iron-eyed Athena." His mind raced in all directions: no justice in this world, nor rhyme, nor reason. Like Job, he had an impulse to hide his children. What would his maker take from him now? What loss could occur next?

At last the woman leaves, trailing in the wake of the neighbors. The undertaker appears and reaches into the coffin to remove Claire's jewelry. Stuart steps forward and says, "No, no—leave the wedding band." The plain gold band had meant everything to them when they were starting out: a simple circle for eternity, the purity of gold, the metal that most conveys warmth.

"From her father's mother," he explains. He is handed her charm bracelet. "Each charm represents a line of ancient lore from family tradition, and..." *Damn.* He should have had her write it down so he could pass the history on to Victoria or Holly. Of course, he never would have imagined he'd be left to raise the children alone.

Stuart holds it up to the light, the better to examine the small creatures and odd items hanging from each link. A small clove of garlic, a bunch of grapes, a miniature bottle, a cross, a tear-shaped drop, an arcane coat of arms on a shield and a bat-winged dragon all hung in a row like so much gold laundry on a fairy-tale clothesline. Stuart is reminded of her inherited dragon ring tucked away in the bank's lock box.

The necklace he is handed next is one he bought for her on their last trip to Europe. His eyes dampen as he recalls their voyage on the Rhine. They had embraced as the tour boat passed the cliffs where the Lorelei sang, luring sailors to their deaths on the river.

After the Lorelei's perch there was the Mouse Tower, der Mausturm. He held her from behind as the boat rounded the corner and approached the landmark. "Europe is covered with history, Stuart," Claire observed. "Layers and layers of it. I wish I could scrape off a little and take it home, nibble a bit of a kingdom. Could we put a stained-glass window in the breakfast nook and dine in a cathedral every morning? Or perhaps get a set of medieval wooden trenchers and eat heartily like ladies and courtiers? Would you like to take lute lessons?" Her uncharacteristic whimsy drew a tighter squeeze from Stuart. The spray from the boat made her blouse adhere to her camisole, barely serving to camouflage the fullness beneath.

Once they disembarked in Frankfurt they wandered past a shop full of antiques and curiosities and stopped in to see more, to perhaps find a piece of history to grace their shelf at home: a Dresden figurine of a porcelain shepherd girl wooed by a harlequin painted with black and white diamonds, or a spinning wheel, or a little bell of Austrian cut crystal. He had been attracted to the necklace at once. Stuart was nothing if not a practical man, all too knowledgeable about negotiating the hard bargains of the business world, and it was odd that he felt so immediately drawn to an object. The necklace was made of heavy gold links with a medallion attached, a gold piece that was obviously centuries old. "Claire, she looks like you. Look." Stuart held the disc under the light for closer examination and his cheek grazed hers as they gazed at the distinguished profile of the woman depicted in bas-relief. "A strong lady for my strong lady," he murmured in her ear.

Years later, Stuart wipes a fallen tear off the profile of this same resolute gold woman, and the necklace follows the bracelet into his left jacket pocket, accompanied by the ruby earrings he had purchased for her after John was born—reminding him they are five years old. Stuart turns and looks at his five-year-old son swinging his feet back and forth as he waits on the bench. What do you say to a child? No lying, no coddling, no room for misunderstanding. Mom may be in a better place, she may be resting with God...no, more likely she'd be up there all set to organize and improve things at once, full of initiative—but could John understand that he wouldn't see her again, that his job was to live out his life in a way that would have made her proud? Stuart needs to make sure that all three of them understand this in the years to come. He extends his right arm and beckons Victoria. "Come say good-bye to your mother, now. She loved you, and gave you the gift of life, even though she lost hers so young."

Victoria nudges John's forehead and leans on him to get him to sit up straight. John immediately scoots over and leans on Holly, who has stopped chewing on her braid and is now curling its end around her finger. Victoria looks at her feet as she approaches the coffin, trying to step in the center of the parquet blocks instead of at the corners. "Step on a crack, break your mother's..." Was there anything she could do to reverse this? Never step on cracks? Do even better in school? Confess that she had taken that Snickers from the checkout line of the grocery when she was six—the chocolate that had gotten her in trouble for staining her new shirt with the daisy appliqué? She feels the weight of her father's hand on her shoulder and looks up from the parquet. "You must remember her," he says. "I will, Daddy." Victoria kisses the forehead of her mother's corpse. Her lips make a small crater in the powder and make-up. She touches a stiffened lock of her mother's hair.

The undertaker's assistant appears and passes a small pair of scissors over the coffin. Stuart takes them to cut off a curl of hair. He kneels in front of Victoria, opening the plain gold locket that rests on the bodice of her velvet dress. He places the curl inside. "This way she'll always be with you, sweetheart."

Victoria's fingers clasp the locket, as if to keep the tendril from escaping like a wisp of smoke. Then Stuart looks at Holly and the younger girl steps up to the edge of the dark wooden box. The dampened end of her braid looks like a paintbrush. Her hands grip the edge of the coffin to steady herself, then she spins around to her father who kneels to embrace her. Holly collapses on his neck, crying. "I miss her. Daddy. I already miss her so much."

"I miss her too, sweetheart. I miss her, too." His eyes glisten. He holds her head to his shoulder, stroking the girl's fine hair. Corn silk— just like her mother's.

As Stuart releases Holly, John steps up to the edge of the coffin, places both hands on the wood and stands on tip-toe to peer at his mother. Then John turns, terrified, to his father and grinds his face into the black wool of the man's pants leg, sobbing. Stuart signals to the undertaker to close the casket. Still holding Holly with his right arm, he gathers John in with his left. The boy smells like summer and hay, despite the cold rain outside.

Claire Foster can smell nothing other than the chemical finish on the acetate of the coffin lining. It is sickly and surreal. If only the air were clean, not this manufactured vapor competing with the already decaying flowers and a note of lingering sawdust. If only she could have fresh air maybe she could lift her hand to the lid of the coffin. She tries to scream, but all she can do is emit a low moan. She can hear Stuart murmuring to the children.

Then the box shifts and she knows that it is being moved to the hearse. Her mouth is sore; her gums feel as if they're made of sandpaper, that opening them to scream would tear her face apart. She wrenches her mouth open anyway, but only a gasp escapes.

The undertaker and his assistant wheel the coffin out to the car in the hammering rain, their hair sticking to their foreheads in plastered hanks.

Stuart leads the children outside toward the vehicle. "Come on, now. She wouldn't allow us to be late," he admonishes them, but Victoria is busy zipping John's coat up to the collar.

Another assistant runs ahead of the family to the back of the hearse, trying with limited success to use an elaborate swag bouquet as an umbrella. He reaches in to place it on the coffin, and a white rose falls from its nest of ferns and lilies. Holly lets go of her father's hand and steps forward to pick it up out of the puddle. It is perfect, but without scent. The smooth white reminds her of the paper plates at picnics, baked beans and corn on the cob, coleslaw and chicken. No more picnics now, no more family reunions with Mother in Iowa, no more long picnic tables covered with flapping paper tablecloths of red and white checks, stretching out in the yard before the cornfields and even rows of golden wheat.

The grass at the cemetery is short-clipped and deep green, well-manicured for a harvest of nothing but memories. Now at the graveside, the coffin is lowered into the earth, past the astro-turf-lined edges of its maw.

Victoria is sobbing as the pastor intones. She can't help but look over the edge: John follows, and then Holly, who takes the white rose out of her pocket, squeezes it, and drops it onto the casket. Then Stuart takes a spade full of dirt to throw a ceremonial farewell on top of the coffin. The ritual makes sense to him. He has to prove to himself that she's not coming back, that she really is dead, that she is beyond his salvation. Even if he jumped in, tore the lid off and promised God to trade places with her, it wouldn't do any good.

The falling clay sounds like hail to Claire inside the pall. She tears open her mouth to scream, "No! NO! I'm not dead! There's been a mistake. Stuart, can you hear me? Stuart?" Minutes pass. Claire feels her blood passing through her veins, chilled and slow. It isn't too late…if she just had the strength to clench her fists, to pound at the inside of the box. The ground around her starts shaking. Is it an earthquake? No—they must be pulling up a small bulldozer to fill in her grave. They had been waiting for Stuart and the children to leave. Now she is entirely alone, and the clumps of falling clods coalesce as they close the earth over her.

Claire Foster bolts upright on the lounge chair, hyperventilating. She has awakened in a state of disorientation, but soon realizes she is aboard their boat enjoying a picture-perfect holiday at their lake cabin. She presses her open left hand on her sternum and grasps the arm of the flimsy aluminum recliner to steady herself. After a couple of deep breaths she stops panting and replaces the straw hat that was knocked off during her nightmare. Then Claire reaches over to the deck of the boat and picks up her oversized sunglasses. Once she puts them on, her companions, two couples and her husband, are reflected in the silvered lenses.

Mary Norton, that sweet woman from the bungalow at the east end of the lake with twin boys who are in that angst-ridden, sullen stage of black t-shirts and wandering off by themselves, waves at her. Claire waves back, relieved that she's alive and visible, still terrified, her heart racing, but now exhilarated with the growing realization that she is not confined, not trapped, that no one heard her scream.

Her husband, Stuart, stands in the center of the flybridge, knuckles on his hips, head thrown back as he roars with laughter. He holds a bottle of beer by its neck with two fingers. "Oh, Stu, you're such a card!" Mary slaps her knee, doubling over and almost losing her wine cooler in the process. "You could not possibly have said that to him. That's too clever. You must be making it up." It's their neighbor and dear friend, Irene, whose husband Chip is passing her a fresh cocktail, while Mary's hubby Joe is at the helm. She stubs her cigarette as she winks at him, then stirs the chunks of fruit against the ice cube with the red plastic straw.

Chip elaborates, smacking Stuart on the back as he singsongs, "Beeeelieve it. You should have heard what he said to the CFO of DB Corp last week at the shareholders' meeting. The opening volley started with a reference to 'so-called leadership' and picked up steam from there." Stuart shakes his head and grins, reaching over to turn up the music. The boat unfurls a sharp-ridged wake and the engine splutters to compete with the mellow tune of the song.

Claire surveys the sky, water and lakeshore. A few thin cirrus clouds reflect in the choppy waves, but otherwise all is pristine blue. The weekends at the cabin mean so much to her; she gets time away from the house, her job, the children's need to be chauffeured from lessons to events or girl scouts or church youth league. Trying to raise well-rounded, responsible young people is an occupation in its own right.

Stuart gets a well-deserved opportunity to relax on the small "yacht" they had purchased. Even though it was preowned, the craft was just the right size for Apple River Lake, giving Stu the chance to teach the kids to waterski. And most of all, the children get to play and enjoy nature and wildlife, even if John's version of that includes putting garter snakes in Victoria's bed.

One afternoon their first summer there Holly collected tadpoles in a mayonnaise jar. She left them on the windowsill in the sunlight and went off to go rowing. When she returned and discovered that the swimming little commas had simmered to death, she was almost inconsolable. Stuart told a fanciful white lie out of sympathy for his daughter's grief: he told her that refrigerating them overnight just might do the trick. Holly looked so solemn as she reached to the top shelf, moving aside the milk carton to put in a jar of dead tadpoles. "Will it work, Daddy?" she asked, rocking back on her heels. "Well, sweetheart, it doesn't work very often. I'm just trying it tonight because it's the waxing crescent moon and these are rare, grey-spotted black tadpoles. So, cross your fingers and remember them in your prayers."

Once the children were asleep, Stuart snuck out and filled the jar with live replacements, catching them with a Styrofoam cup and cursing under his breath as he held a flashlight in the mucky shallows of the water's edge. The next morning he put them in the refrigerator for Holly, and the girl clapped her hands with glee at their resurrection.

Chapter II

Christoph
de la Violette

"Y"ou can go now." The young man turned to look out the window as the afternoon sun dropped nearer to the horizon. The bare branch of an apple tree almost scraped the sill, and the dark arm of its shadow folded down onto the floor.

Christoph's nose twitched from the down of the pillow, so he rolled onto his back and stretched in indolence. The pink heap was still to his right, the moist and spent servant girl, Marta. "You're still here?"

"I want to stay." The silly thing was trying to nuzzle up to his shoulder, as if wrinkling her pug nose could be more endearing than ridiculous. She looked at him from beneath raised eyebrows, an attempt at coquetry from one who possessed no grounds for such a luxury.

"Are you deaf?" Christoph started to raise his voice and then caught himself: this one is luscious enough for some regular rides, attractive in her hearty, broad-faced way and enthusiastic to a fault. He could afford to be a little kind. He extended his hand to the side of her face and stroked back three long yellow locks, each one turning itself in a spiral. He twined the soft rope around his fingers and lowered his voice to explain.

"Marta, Marta, Marta. I wish this idyll could last forever, or at least until supper, but I must deal with that pretentious fossil of a baron. I want to be ready." Her lip stopped quivering and she placed her splayed fingers on his chest. Christoph stopped playing with her hair and pressed her hand there for a moment. He gathered the fingers together, squeezed them firmly, and replaced them on the quilted satin which covered the lower halves of their bodies. "It is time for you to go," he reaffirmed. "Now." The maid sat up and pulled her hair back from her shoulders, holding the mass over the back of her head mimicking an elegant lady's coiffure for evening. "How did you do it, Christoph?"

She was wearing nothing other than a narrow ribbon bearing a small gold cross, and it glinted in the dull shadow between her breasts. "Like this," he grunted, and turned onto his side, fingers planted firmly between her legs, mouth to her right breast. "Oh! None of that—not if you're going to banish me." The girl batted her eyelids and curled her lower lip into a pout. Then she raised herself onto one elbow, tightening her thighs around his hand. "Really, now, Christoph. The little baroness was constantly chaperoned."

"You, my darling illiterate peasant," Christoph leaned up to Marta and with sarcasm, said, "You fail to appreciate the immense power and spiritual intensity of true love." He rubbed the tip of his nose against hers, and then sat up straight. *Hands off:* even his formidable theatrical skills were almost exhausted. The girl rolled onto her back, flopped her arms over the side of the bed, then snorted like a mare in a stable. She didn't even have the sense not to act like livestock. *Ahhh, patience—* Christoph remembers the afternoon's amusements. "Well, my most materialistic little slattern, I will tell you. You noticed that new gown Tante Sophia brought home from Vienna?"

"Noticed? Every girl in the castle was drooling over it. The pleats, the rucking, the silk—it must have cost a fortune." Marta's chest shook with excitement. "Did you buy it for her?"

"My generosity is as limitless as my regard for my beloved baroness." Christoph reached up to scratch his chest and pulled two, long, straw-colored hairs from his damp skin. "It was worth every schilling. Tante Sophia, of course, upon receiving the present of such a gown knew that it must be fitted by only the best of dressmakers, but our usually efficient Jean-Marc encountered difficulty after difficulty in the attempt. Perhaps these spinsters like Sophia dry up and get all sorts of figure problems." He yawned, chuckled, and slumped further into the pillows. "Well, the fitting took hours—a bit longer than usual." The shadow from the branch had risen to the canopy over the bed.

"Hours? Wasn't she suspicious? Didn't she insist that the girl be brought to her?" Marta slumped down next to him and tried to put her head on his shoulder. Christoph shrugged, continuing with his explanation. "Like most humans, her good sense is second to her vanity. Jean-Marc is a shameless flatterer as only a seller of elaborate gowns can be. He lavished her with attention and champagne in equally heady doses. That old bat, in all her life, has had neither attention nor champagne, as you were so kind to inform me." Christoph kissed the top of her head.

"What of the maid, Jutte?"

"What of her? Jutte was more than happy to retire early at my behest and a handful of coins.

"And our baroness, Elysia?" Marta hissed the name.

"I'm used to eager virgins, but she was exceptionally energetic,"

Christoph replied as he sat up again and stretched his arms out in front of his head, fingers twined together. "Her vigor is a credit to the von Eschenbach line."

"You are confident." Marta gathered her legs up and rested her cheek to her knee. She could not resist a last attempt at flirtation and another chance to outcharm the baroness.

Christoph's face hardened as he weighed the situation. "My confidence is warranted. My mother's plan is unfolding perfectly. Soon everything here at the von Eschenbach estate will be mine as well." He reached over to tweak the tip of her breast. "Including you." Marta's hands rose up to shield her chest, but then she remembered to mew, "But I am already yours, Christoph." He rolled his eyes to the canopy above them. She did not know what perversity drove her to ask, "Do you love her?" She unfolded herself and arced her toes toward the end of the mattress.

"Love is not an issue here. I am about to enter into a gentleman's agreement." Marta snickered, covering her lips with the back of her hand, then let slip, "The baron is one gentleman. Who is the other?" Christoph spun around, planted his foot on her hip, and shoved her off the bed. She landed on the floor ass-first, hands and feet splayed up in the air before falling to her sides. She had to clamp her hand over her mouth to keep from laughing despite her smarting rump. "Bastard!" escaped with a giggle as she prodded at the tender spot on her backside.

Christoph's face was instantly over hers, but creased and dark with anger. His fingers became talons and encircled the back of her head, pulling her face up to meet his darkened and razor-narrow eyes. He hissed like a snake.

"Never," he jerked her head for emphasis, "*never* use that word again. You forget your place. You are a servant. You are here because your company amuses me. I will be master here and you will learn to be respectful. Do you understand?" He gathered her hair into his fist and yanked her head. She could smell the old wine on his breath. "Yes." Marta's voice broke on the word. She had to force the utterance out past the tears held back in her throat. "Yes, what?" Christopher retorted. "Yes, Christoph." She looked up at him, aspiring to her best Sunday impersonation of meek and mild, the one summoned when she serviced the youngest prelate, the one with exceptionally broad shoulders for a man of God. "Wrong again." Christoph yanked back on her head so that her throat was exposed. He could see the inside of her nostrils. They flared quickly now that he was frightening her. Good.

"Yes, I mean, Monsieur de la Violette." He let her hair go, but she waited until he sat back on the bed before she gathered herself up. Her hand traveled up to investigate the soreness of her scalp.

Pleased with himself, Christoph lifted his elbows over his head and stretched, twisting and yawning. The wardrobe gaped open at the foot of the bed, so he rose to select his costume for the evening. The scarlet brocade waistcoat would be too flamboyant. The gray silk moire, too decadent. The beige linen with embroidered trim? Perfect. Quality, yet restrained and plain—at least by the standards of *his* clothing. But first, the full-sleeved blouse and knee-buttoned breeches.

Marta scuttled to the far side of the bed, gathering her far-flung clothing. She would have to mend the seams of her bodice. *Damn*. She had to get on all fours to search for her lost slipper under the bed. She wished she could bundle her clothing to her chest and dress in the hall instead of waiting for this debaucher's permission to leave. In her heart, she was jumping up and down on the bed, shouting, "Bastard! Bastard! Bastard! Whoreson! Commoner!" Her cheeks burned with shame and anger. Anger at his rough treatment, yes, but that was the sheerest cloak to cover the shame of her own fancies. As if she were at her mother's knee, still believing in fairytales of poor but honest servant girls elevated by the love of the prince. Well, she might not be honest, but she wasn't hiding much. She would never be invited to the ball except to clean up afterwards. The best to be hoped for in servicing Christoph de la Violette, for not even she could deny that was all he sought from her, was the tolerance of a man of increasing importance in her master's house— perhaps a master-to-be. As they dressed she could hear the steps of horses on the stones of the courtyard. A crow cawed from the gate.

"How do I look?" Christoph whirled to her and extended his right foot forward in a point, arched with a straight calf, as if he were a dancer. "Very handsome, Monsieur de la Violette." With a little kick, he pranced side to side in front of her then crossed his arms over his chest like a Russian. She saw that the buttons of his breeches were covered with the same suede as the pants themselves.

"Stand up!" Marta flinched to hear the command. Baron von

Eschenbach ordered the same to make his favorite hunting terrier rear on its hind legs for scrap mutton. So be it. Her hands smoothed down the front of her skirt as she rose.

"Eyes closed!" The girl feared she would receive a ringing slap as a reminder against her earlier insolence, but instead she felt the cool familiarity of a coin fall into her cleavage. Felt like a five-schilling piece. His lordship was generous. His lips grazed her forehead as she opened her eyes. "Now leave." Her knees bent in reflex curtsy, but she halted in mid-turn. "Should your...do you want...will you need me later?"

"Unlikely." Christoph was before the mirror, splashing lavender oil into his hand and then smoothing down his hair. "Tomorrow, perhaps. You are dismissed." His left hand flapped in her direction twice, and then went to straighten the lace at his collar.

Marta took the bundled laundry and returned to the hall. She braced the burden on her hip and used her free hand to fish the coin from her dress. Five schillings, indeed! Well, then Monsieur de la Violette would retain a household spy and rambunctious bed mate. "We each use the other," she told herself as she descended the stairs. "That is the way of the world."

-

Chapter III

Fun in the Sun

C laire rises from her chair to enjoy the spray of the boat's wake. Then she becomes faint, and not in a giddy, lightheaded way, but as if some inner suction has decided that her stomach and brains must switch places at once. Her face feels flushed and prickly: a thousand little men with invisible swords trace patterns connecting the pores of her cheekbones. Her headache becomes intolerable, and brings memories of fruitless visits to doctors in hopes of a diagnosis for these symptoms and those awful recurring dreams.

Feeling a rush of nausea, she slams the back of her hand to her lips, stifling an urge to vomit. As she closes her eyes and grabs the rail to steady herself, she hears Joe cry out a captain's warning: "Hold on!" The boat banks, and the sudden change in the craft's trajectory throws Claire into the water. She yells but is unheard because of the noise of the powerful engine and pulsing radio. The blue of the sky becomes underwater deep and green and her arms flail in a vortex of bubbles. Claire's life falls in snippets before her eyes as the desire to breathe liquid grows stronger. She is so tired; the water is so soothing and cool.

Claire is a three-year-old with a single blond braid and a dark dress. She looks at the toes of her shoes as her mother leans over her. They are in a place with candles and flowers. Her father is gone, they tell her, despite the fact that she can see him right there in a box. This is for the trip to heaven, a trip when they pack you in a fancy crate and give you flowers and cry because you aren't coming back. Her mother's hand is on her shoulder. "Your father loved you very much. You have to say good-bye to him now."

Claire leans against her mother's hip and a lady she doesn't know comes up. "Poor dear. And with the other two as well. How will you ever manage, Evelyn?" Her mother tries to smile but her face is a mask, the skin around her eyes puffed out as far as her nose. The woman touches her mother's hand, then Claire's head, and walks off.

Claire must be eight because she has a treehouse and she opens the back screen door to run to it through a lush Midwestern garden. Skirting columns of hollyhocks and eluding bumblebees, she scales a maple to her private refuge, careful, careful—the rungs are scraps of board nailed into the tree. Once inside, she strains out its window to pull a coffee can from the crook of a branch. The can holds a small diary, pencil stub, three hard candies, a large green cat's eye marble and a photograph. The picture shows a thin-faced man smiling from beneath a jaunty fedora. Claire licks the pencil lead, opens the leather-covered diary and writes.

"Mother says father was handsome and exotic. He wore his hat like a movie star. If he had been in the movies he would have played a general or a spy, wearing either a uniform with an eagle on the front of the hat or a long raincoat and a hat like the one in the picture. I have been half an orphan for five years now, and I have to help my mother who works very hard but I wish that she would let me go to the movies without taking Richard and Helena along. Especially Richard because he whines. Now I can hear her calling us for dinner. Chicken and biscuits—the best!"

Claire thinks *I'm swimming away now; I'm going to bob up to the surface and call out and they'll stop the boat. Even if they don't hear me, I'll just stretch my legs and arms, and propel myself through the water to shore. Just a healthy stretch. Nothing too remarkable, nothing that I would think about twice, really. Any second now. Just catching my breath, just drawing up that last oxygenated reserve...*

Stuart, always the thoughtful husband, takes a can of Sprite to Claire. He steps down to the main deck and opens the can. Her lounge chair is empty, towel wrinkled on the seat, paperback face down to one side next to the brown plastic bottle of sunscreen. Where could she have gone? "Claire? Claire!"

He drops the can of soda and runs to the side, rushing back to call up to their friends. "Hey! HEY! Turn the radio off. Joe, Irene, have you seen Claire? She's not here." Joe cuts the engine and Irene steps over to the deck's edge. "She was there just a minute ago."

"She said she was feeling a little queasy and might take a nap," Mary Norton says as she raises her sunglasses to the top of her head. "Maybe she was getting burned and went below to get lotion?" Irene suggests. "Claire is so fair-skinned, Stuart, you should get her to wear a caftan every time you come out here."

But Stuart isn't listening. He ducks below to survey the small cabin. He can hear the steps of the others as they walk across the decks calling for his wife. No Claire. He returns and scans the water to see her straw hat floating in their wake, waltzing to the center of the lake, passed from small wave to small wave. "Joe! Over there! Now!" Joe nods and starts the motor, turning the boat around to the straw beacon.

Once upon a time there was a woman, Claire remembers, who looked behind and was turned into a pillar of salt. If she were made of salt, she would be dissolving now, but she has become the woman made of Sakrete, and her limbs are slowly stiffening, concrete setting in the water. They are plumb lines pointing to the bottom—this way, this way—surveying the deep green of the lake where freshwater mermaids swim, the twisted seaweed hiding them, the ghosts of unforgiving souls of virgin maidens wronged by trappers centuries ago kicking up from the depths to take her by the ankles and teach her to dance with them. This is ridiculous, she knows, some phantom of a summer camp legend coming to her, but why can't she swim? *Just try not to breathe.* The image of a yogi she saw on television appears in her mind for a split second. The Indian man had a long gray beard and wore nothing but a cloth rag. The yogi folded himself into a clear plexiglass box and stayed there for a week. Physicians had taped electrodes to his body to monitor his heart rate. That man knew what to do—knew what not to do—knew how not to breathe. Claire imagines her lungs, twin tanks of clean, frothy bubbles, and the gauge running lower and lower. She opens her mouth and a small trail of bubbles rises up. That way…that's the way she has to go: up to the light with the spheres of air.

Claire's eyes lose focus and the candle flame she is gazing at dissolves into a wash of light. She blinks, and it's a flame again, a yellow tongue eating a wick. The church is filled with candles for Christmas Eve, and she stands in the choir with her sister, Helena. They look like pilgrims to the North Pole with their big square white collars over red velvet gowns. Santa Claus is not on the stained glass behind them, but Jesus is. He wears white robes instead of a red suit and stretches out his arms to gather them all in. Claire knows the quiet strength of a good shepherd because her cousin, Skye, raised the prize-winning lambs for the county fair. Months of careful attention means a 4-H ribbon and the proceeds from sales of the tender meat. Not that Jesus is the kind of shepherd who takes followers to market, of course, just that he pays careful attention and works hard to take care of them. Like fathers are supposed to do: take care of their flock of children, make sure they have plenty, be certain they learn to do what's right, tuck them in at night. "Silent night," Claire falters and then rejoins the chorus, "Holy night. All is calm...." The children have finished singing and all calm is gone.

They want cookies shaped like Christmas trees with green sugar on top, gingerbread men (bite off the head first, then the hands, then the feet), cider and peppermint canes. All these delights and more await them, once they're out of the performance gowns and back into their street clothes. Claire found her gloves, the scarf that Aunt Nicole crocheted for her, and her coat right away, no problem, but Helena has lost her mittens. Where are they? She has looked from one corner of the coatroom to the other, and there isn't a sign. They were from Aunt Nicole, too, and were attached with a long cord like those unfortunate twins she read about in the Centropolis paper, but this just meant that Helena lost both of them.

Claire opens the door to the basement. The door whines like their dog yawning and the steps smell of must and old wood. Snow dances on the other side of the windowpanes, and the thin light of the street lamp shows the shadow of a man at the top of the stairs in front of her. He is exotic, handsome—standing just like a movie star but not smoking a cigarette. His clothes are all wrong for winter: thin cotton pants and a wide-brimmed hat worn at an angle. It is the man in her hidden picture, the unknown father.

"My Wild Irish Rose, you sing like an angel," he says, leaning down over her. She can see the stubble of his beard. His hand is almost on top of her head, but she feels neither pressure nor heat. The shadow-father has no scent, but she senses a calming, warm reassurance emanating from him, like the memory of something good that you've just been promised—walking by a bakery at the moment that the wind changes direction. "Do not be afraid of me." He smiles the same smile as in the photograph; kindness with a hint of swagger. "I have a message for you." Claire listens with rapt attention, no longer afraid. Isn't there a rhyme? 'Once I came upon the stair and met a man who wasn't there?' But this man is here, is speaking to her and smiling. "You must have faith and believe. There is a reason and purpose for all things. I tell you now that you must always be a good person, honest and kind. There is a heavenly secret that has been entrusted to us. In time it will be revealed to you."

Claire keeps standing still, expecting the man to disappear, but he remains, eliciting an intense reality. "Claire," the man says, "Have courage. I will always be with you." His eyes are warm and safe, not shadow eyes, nothing like the vacant caves in the faces of ghosts that she's read about, nothing so cold and empty. She can feel his fingertip graze the skin between the parted hairs on her head, and then she is alone.

Stuart's sharp eyes rake the water with grief. Claire is such a strong swimmer, there is no way she would succumb in the smooth middle of an inland lake. Suddenly his gaze catches a patch of red, still on the surface but beginning to fall. He dives into the water and reaches Claire with three strong strokes, scoops her up and turns around to swim back to the boat. His arm is wrapped around her ribcage as he lifts his precious cargo aboard. His shins scissor the water as he passes her to Joe: "Here. Here. No, not that way." There is a patch of rust on the side of the boat shaped like the island nation Cyprus. *What a bizarre thing to notice*, he thinks, his hand covering the patch as he braces himself to lift the inert column of Claire up to the deck.

The cold forceps of terror are on his stomach and his eyes are peeled open with hooks. Everything around him seems more real in his deadly urgency, and yet he has never been more indifferent to it. Every splinter of time is a timber; every second, an hour. The minute to fumble her over the edge of the boat is a decade. Stuart grasps the metal railing and hauls himself up. Joe has flipped Claire over like a fish and Stuart sees the trail of water run from her mouth onto the deck, mingling with the spilled soda from the can of Sprite he dropped, a can that he opened at the end of some innocent and joyous era that is now passing into oblivion. Joe lifts a strand of hair away from her nostrils—the water darkens it to the color of broom straw—and then begins to administer mouth-to-mouth resuscitation. Joe checks her mouth for any debris and then lifts her chin with two fingers of his right hand. His left hand pinches her nostrils shut. Stuart can see her chest rise like a bellows, and then Joe pounds the bellows down with the heels of his hands on her sternum, one hand on top of the other.

The top of Claire's swimsuit has a gold knot on the chest, and when Joe lifts his hands Stuart can clearly see the red welt of its imprint embossed on her chest. Again. Two breaths, three punches. Again. "For God's sake," Stuart hisses at Joe through clenched teeth. He stifles the illogical urge to scream at the man trying to save his wife. Mary and Irene hover behind, mute witnesses. How many tries are mandated by the Red

Cross? Stuart has to wonder if there is a minimum daily requirement for trying to save a life, if good Samaritans and fire fighters are ever off the hook, because if he knew cardio-pulmonary resuscitation instead of Joe, he would blow and thrust, too afraid of loss to be gentle. It's good that Joe is the rescuer here: Stuart knows he is too torn, that he could pop her lungs like balloons or break the bones in her chest. Again. Again.

They are pounding on the lid of the coffin. It has splintered and a fist grazes her chest. Claire screams. She wanted to escape being buried alive, but not like this, not this way, not from a dark box to the tense pounding and throttled growl above.

Chapter IV

The Baron Ignatz von Eschenbach

ho is that exquisite fellow?" Christoph continued to admire himself in the mirror, musing. "What a handsome wretch. He already has looks, a fine physique, splendid wardrobe, deft way in the boudoir, a charming personality. A magnificent dancer, masterful horseman, and sackloads of gold. What else could he possibly achieve? What is the one thing left for such a man? Well, he is not a nobleman. Not until now." He bowed to his own reflection, allowing his knuckles to scrape languidly over the carpet. Then he stood upright to inventory his corporeality, so self-vaunted. His shoulders were stretched back and he tightened his abdomen, taking a deep breath to expand his chest. The effort flushed his cheeks a little. Very good, the entire ensemble: soft suede knee-breeches; silk stockings in a classic ecru; cordovan shoes so new they lacked any scuff or scrape, buckles so polished that a mouse might see its reflection. And no shortage of mice in this drafty old stone barn.

The lace at his cuffs and throat was new, so there was no need to be concerned with either sweat stains or over-bleaching. The waistcoat was a fine linen embroidered to subtle and charming effect with thread of the same color. What coat to wear over all? An obvious choice: the deep and trustworthy blue with plain brass buttons. A bit on the dull side, but these old fuddy-duddy, petty royalty types were never ones for fashion. A green scarf for the waistcoat pocket could serve to bring out his eyes and liven things up a bit. Perfect! Christoph placed the folded cloth into his vest pocket and arranged it symmetrically. He held his breath again and examined his profile. Was his nose a bit too sharp? No matter. Any prominence would be balanced by the fullness of his lips. Not too boyish, but appealing. He puckered and threw a little kiss to the face in the mirror. Then he kept puckering and proceeded to whistle.

His whistle echoed in the corridor. At various spots along the way, he could see his reflection in a polished shield or suit of armor. The metal stood out in the general gloom. The walls were covered with threadbare tapestries, prancing stags and rampant bears fading into shadow as the knots that made them faded. Well, he could select new tapestries. Purple, for the house of la Violette, with stalking leopards flipping hunting dogs over to tear out their vulnerable bellies, or unicorns vanquishing the breasts of innocent maidens with their soulful eyes. Or no tapestries at all: perhaps just curtains, swaths of silken drapery to be changed to a new color every season. No, no—they would keep the old furnishings so that there would be no doubt in anyone's mind that this was the home of the baron. Hell, perhaps he would run about on occasion, unshaven and slightly rank with a pack of baying hunting dogs, just to maintain the appearance of rustic nobility.

His mother taught him the absolute importance of appearances. In only three generations his family had gathered one of the largest fortunes of any merchant house in the entire Austrian Empire. However, they were still merchants to the haughty affected eyes of the nobility, silly swine with their pedigreed lineages and formal balls and hunting. The Violettes would show them. Christoph smirked at his image distorted in the shine of some ancestral breastplate. If a title is no more difficult than impregnating the daughter of a baron, it was a wonder that every family didn't have one. No, this would require a little tact, a little negotiation. But the bargain would be forthright enough, he was sure of that. Then the lands and the title of the von Eschenbach estate would all be theirs— and Mama Odile could use the weight of property and nobility to secure Christoph's rights to an inheritance from his step-father, Rene de la Violette.

Christoph's footsteps rang out in the stone hall, but the bass picked up a lighter pitch as he passed onto the parquet of the dining hall. Instead of a long feast table, two places were set near the fireplace. The Baron Ignatz von Eschenbach awaited him.

"Christoph de la Violette, a pleasure." The baron granted a courteous smile. "It is a pleasure to see you and to welcome you to our home."

"And likewise, Baron. The pleasure is always mine." Not wishing to display too much respect for the baron, Christoph timed his bow more to show off his own flair for charm and grace: *bow from the waist, right arm extended, brought over to touch the left shoulder, count one, two, three, four, and then back up with the arm descending in a flowing arc.*

Patience, now—he knew he was going to have more than enough opportunities for insolence that evening. The meal's first course was plain but delicious. The competent but ancient Griselda had concocted a parsnip soup seasoned with sage and a bit of bacon. Tasty though it may be, she would have to go. No such hearty food could stain the dining table of the house of la Violette. Christoph imagined their own coat of arms hanging over the mantle, discreetly covering the insignia of the von Eschenbachs carved into the mantelpiece.

First course in his household would be a veal broth with slices of hard-boiled quail eggs garnished with scallions and some cress for color. Yes, and Odile would select a gold-edged china instead of this antiquated pewter and brass. Masculine, to be sure, but can there be too much of a good thing? The entire castle would have to be re-done and refined so it would be a true palace, not a hunting lodge inhabited by fading gentry. Still, the silver had an authentic heft in his hand, and things did possess a certain value in durability and association. He had to smile at his inventory. If he and his brilliant mother had been shopping for a duchy for the taking, and indeed they had, they could not have done better than the estate of the von Eschenbachs. Title, land, acres cultivated and forested, a castle with reasonable grounds, vineyards, game, and a lovely and seduceable daughter. Congratulations to the de la Violettes. Congratulations to Christoph. He smiled at the old baron with barely restrained glee.

The venison came from the property, of course. Christoph took mental notes as the baron complained of poachers and the difficulty in keeping the fishing ponds stocked. The apple tart was from fruit harvested from the orchards. Quite an industrious lot of peasantry here, even if the place seemed a bit shabby. There was nothing fashionable; perhaps affecting a disinterest in fashion was requisite in aspiring to nobility. He shook his head at the prospect of explaining this to his sister. She would stamp her slippered foot and insist that she dress as flamboyantly as ever, and of course she would.

"Will you join me in an aperitif?" The baron moved his hand and a manservant instantly materialized, bearing a silver tray with five bottles of liqueur. The candlelight refracted in the crystal stoppers of the decanters, making a hundred tiny flames float in the air between them. The baron felt as though he were about to walk on flames, to so sacrifice his only precious child, and thus poured himself a generous glass of cognac. He knew that alcohol did not agree with him, but the ensuing conversation required liquid fortitude. He could not bear to listen to this vain and pretentious young man trying to flatter him as he attempted to price every surrounding item. The baron should have served him mutton stew on wooden trenchers. Bah! This unsavory business must be gotten over with, that much was for certain. To cleanse the palate in preparation for unpleasant words, he reached at last for a plain green glass bottle. "Ice wine," he explained to Christoph, smiling despite himself. "A rare and precious vintage grown on this estate. Our vintners made it from the final harvest after the cold winter sleet froze the last grapes on the vines— hence the name.

"This estate is the origin of many rare and precious things. If I may suggest a toast to your daughter, Elysia." Christoph hurriedly raised the goblet to his mouth in order to camouflage any inadvertent smirk of victory.

"Yes. Elysia." The baron saw his daughter in his mind's eye, an infant at her mother's bodice, a toddler on his knee, a young girl dancing in a circle in the garden at the beginning of May. Now he saw her as a serf for sale in the eastern lands, the poor thing. "Of course, a marriage necessitates a dowry."

"I eagerly anticipate joining your family. The honor is a dowry in itself." Christoph knew that there was no risk of his attempts to charm being regarded with seriousness. No von Eschenbach daughter would enter a union with nothing to offer but herself.

The baron sighed, rubbing the edge of his wine glass. A thin high note rang out. It could be the sob of his departed wife from some ghostly plane, crying for him at the sacrifice of their daughter. "Then you will accept the honor of one quarter of this estate?" He looked at the embers of the fire to hide his expression. The fading flames reflected orange on the baron's forehead and cheeks, an effective camouflage for the fury burning within him.

Christoph did not hide his disdain. "If I knew how to farm or hunt, such an offer would be useful to me. However, you know that the la Violettes are the toast of Vienna. Such a parcel without authority or the means to manage it would be useless at best, and quite possibly a drain upon our household."

The orange cast on the baron's face now glowed ruby red. He took a deep breath. So be it. *May this also purchase Elysia's happiness*, but that struck him as a futile prayer at best. "You are aware of our financial condition. There are adjacent acres on the other side of the river."

"My dear Baron…" Christoph could sense the silver-beard's

embarrassment and relished his discomfort. "I beg your pardon: the last thing I desire is to insult this family by stating the truth. Another unfortunate truth is that our time to work these niceties is limited, well, depending on how public a wedding is desired. Of course, if I withdraw my offer of marriage now, perhaps you can find another candidate, one who would not test the means of this barony and would be delighted to welcome your virtuous daughter into his home." Christoph drained his glass of ice wine, and his tongue slithered out to catch a drop at the corner of his mouth.

Baron Ignatz set his glass down on the table. Damn this scoundrel. Damn, damn, damn. He shifted and his chair creaked. This impudent pup should be kicked by the seat of his pants down the front steps, and then only after a thorough beating. Instead, to give up everything... he could only pray for his daughter's happiness. He rotated the ring on his right hand, the insignia of the family glinting back at him. So be it. "Monsieur de la Violette," the baron paused and took a deep breath. "Monsieur," rub it in as long as he can that this pipsqueak is untitled, if it means so much to him. "I am an open-minded man. No matter what your family origins, the humble start has been overcome to an admirable extent. An alliance would serve us both well. What dowry would permit this alliance?"

Christoph turned from the fire and took the baron's glare head-on. "Title and land. You have no sons. I have no title. We do, however, have the means at our disposal to return this," he waved his hand at the vaulted ceiling above them, flicked his wrist at the fireplace, and let his hand rest on the arm of his chair again, "to its former glory. Confer title to these lands to me and I will marry Elysia. Your daughter's child..."

"And yours!" the baron snarled and leaned forward in his seat. Christoph stiffened then corrected himself. "*Our* child will be born with honor and will benefit from the prestige of your family and the wealth of mine. Do we have an agreement?"

The baron's eyes did not leave the flames. This is the bitter wine of pragmatism. Wealth was no abstract lure. It could be translated to real things all around him. To restore the grounds, tend the forests, rebuild the collapsing east wing, fill the garden with new stock, an arbor as befitted his daughter. Fie! At first he had relished the opportunity for Elysia and la Violette to wed. When he had first received dispatch that sought permission to court the girl, he raised his eyebrow in speculation, noting the smooth touch and heft of the scented cotton paper that the messenger had presented. "Freshening the bloodline" was the polite euphemism, an acknowledgment among the propertied that association with nouveau riche did carry certain advantages. If only he did not have the unfortunate pregnancy playing into la Violette's hands.

A replacement groom might be found, but the implications of the individual's inevitable lower rank, combined with the speed of the nuptials, would cast a pall of shame on the couple's beginning. Besides, there was no guarantee that a new groom on short notice would be better than this one, and at least la Violette had money. A great shame that he was such an obvious and silly swine. The baron took another swig of wine. He would pay in the morning, but he needed the grease of liquor to slide through the exchange before him at present. Very well, marrying off his daughter to this common Frenchman would be a trade of gold for title with the darling child as the pawn.

He turned to face Christoph and folded his arms across his chest, sitting upright. "You will restore these estates?"

Christoph sat up straight to be polite, responding "Entirely." A little show of courtesy on the brink of such a coup did merit an indulgence of the old man. "Such an undertaking will require considerable resources. You are willing to make such an investment?" With squinted eye, the baron watched Christoph. *May as well attempt to think charitably of this man, if he is to be family.*

"All family resources are at my disposal. This is no paltry amount. We could begin immediately after the wedding. Say, for instance, by repairing the eastern part of this palace, installing quarters for Elysia and myself, a balcony overlooking the pond, freshly restocked with swans and other fowl. Those cattails would have to be cleaned up, but a willow planting would be pleasant..." Christoph realized that the details of his proposed renovations were too proprietary and trailed off.

Well, there was no questioning his commitment to the castle. The baron looked at the wax pooling at the base of the candelabra. "My daughter?" he asked Cristoph, "Do you have any feelings for her whatsoever?"

A placid grin spread across Christoph's face as he placed his hands together before his chest. The fingertips touched in a mockery of prayer.

"She is the light of my life, my reason to live. I will cherish and protect her for all our days together on this earth, God permit."

The baron's guts curdled to listen to this mewling churl. A tapestry depicting a hunt hung on the wall behind la Violette. Five small dogs are bringing down a boar against a crimson field. The turning leaves of autumn are edged in gold and one floats down, about to be speared on the boar's tusk. The first arrow has entered by the boar's third rib, causing it to turn to its wound in indignant rage. If only the baron could remove the arrow of this wretch from his own side, and replace him instead with a man of honor, but this was not to be. His was the cruel sacrifice demanded of Abraham, to turn over one's child. At least her child will know comfort, if it will not follow the example of its father's weak character and dedicated pretension.

"Baron von Eschenbach?" Christoph lowered his hands to his lap and leaned forward.

The baron focused on the bottom of the glass, swirling a remaining sip of wine into a small whirlpool. "Very well, Monsieur de la Violette. I will have the solicitors draft the appropriate documents detailing our respective responsibilities, disposition of the lands and provisions for the future inheritance of the child."

Christoph noted all the trust the baron placed in him, to seek a written guarantee that the offspring shall be tended. No matter— whatever allowance he deemed necessary for the whelp, as long as he had the land and title. "And the rights of succession?"

"Yes, that. As consort to the future Baroness von Eschenbach, title shall be conferred upon you. The child shall be heir to our title and our lands."

The sardonic edge had worn off of Christoph's smile now that the prize was in reach. He would be the next Baron von Eschenbach. "Time will not be wasted in planning this wedding."

"That is good," the baron concurred. "It is only fitting that my daughter have a wedding that will not set the tongues of gossips to wagging. The nuptials should be as soon as possible."

"The wedding will be in Salzburg." Christoph drained the last of the wine in his glass. He swished the sip from one cheek to the other before he continued. "My family is there, after all."

The baron frowned. "So far away from Elysia's homeland?

"The wedding has already been arranged. My mother has handled everything." Christoph let the empty goblet hang from his fingers and then swung it up to rest it on the table between them.

"A bit presumptuous."

"She had a premonition." Christoph winked at the baron whose cheeks again burned red. Then the boy slid his chair back from the table, placed his hands upon the edge and stood up.

The baron looked up at him. "So, clairvoyance is a family gift? Every family has its special traits."

"And I eagerly anticipate our families joining." Christoph moved away from the table's side and straightened his jacket. "Thank you for sharing your table with me, Baron, and for the exquisite meal. If I may beg your indulgence, I wish to retire, although it has been most edifying chatting with you." He clicked his heels and inclined his head slightly. "Bon nuit, mon pere."

"Insolent bastard," the baron muttered, expecting Christoph to be out of earshot. But Christoph heard and he smiled. In this one particular case, the word had no sting. Baron Ignatz von Eschenbach could call him whatever he liked; he was going to hold the title to the estate. He would play holy family with Elysia and their child, and all would be blessed with the new name of de la Violette. Every tree in the forest, every foal in the stables, every rat in the larder, and every fresh new country wench to service. Christoph danced towards his room.

The plan had unfolded just as his mother, Odile, had designed. She had researched all the nobility in the region, poring over dusty registries and marriage records. Having selected the von Eschenbachs as presenting the perfect combination of grandeur and near-destitution, she arranged the letters of introduction and lectured her son on the appropriate behaviors to this particular courtship.

"Pregnancy is key. You need the extra weight in bargaining to guarantee the title. He will not risk his daughter's honor, not to mention his own. Once you have the title, you have an advantage over your half-sister. She does not have the sense that God gave a goose, for business or anything else. But your stepfather is not overwhelmed in his adoration of you. I'm not saying a thing that either of us does not know. Once you are a baron, you are the obvious heir to the la Violette fortune."

The young man's self-righteousness was not contained as he returned to his chambers. He lingered, touching almost everything he passed. Dust had collected on the bottom of gilt-edged frames. Well, soon they would have enough staff to keep things in order. *This is all mine,* echoed the jubilant cave of his thoughts. His palm encircled the great bronze globe of the bedroom doorknob. *This all belongs to me.*

The baron's chambers must certainly be larger. *This may do for some transient guest, but he was soon to be family. He would investigate the other suites in the morning. It was doubtlessly all shabby, but the baron's rooms would most likely offer the most space and relative warmth.*

Drafty old caverns, these ancestral warrens. He threw his jacket on the bed and turned to the mirror, hands thrown up and back in delight. His facial expressions graduated from a leer to a full-blown, idiotic, toothy grin. "Brilliant." His breath left a small cloud on the mirror-glass. "He never had a chance. I will be Baron. Mama will be delighted. It was fated. Fate!" Christoph reached under his lace collar and began unbuttoning his shirt. He removed his breeches and folded them, situating his undergarments within their folds. He rolled his stockings down over his calves and placed the balled silk in his shoes. As bare as the day he was born—the perfect costume to play the child of nature in his next performance. He turned to face the mirror again and smiled so that his teeth showed in spontaneous delight. His hands cradled the back of his head as he turned his face to one side to have a better view of his jawline. "This is what drives the women mad." His eyes inventoried the bundles of his upper arms, the cannonball solidity of his calves, the symmetrical hills in his stomach muscles. "They are like brioche," Juliette had giggled in the attic so long ago, tracing each one with her tongue. Or his mother's friend, Madame Cecilia, patting his chest after an afternoon bout in her parlour, acres of lace and taffeta tossed over the back of a chaise lounge and now rustling in the breeze. "You are exceptionally well-developed for a young man of leisure." She tweaked his left nipple beneath the thin down of chest hair. "Stay active, so that your charms will not desert you."

Christoph admired his own image once more. Humility be damned as a distraction for fools; he had so few obstacles to limit his character, so much accomplishment and grace to laud it. Christoph removed the red glass stopper from a bottle of rosewater on the stand and poured it into his hand. He put the bottle down, releasing half of the bounty from his cupped left hand into his right. Then he slapped each side of his chest, feeling the liquid flowers pour down his sides. He scraped up the rivulets to polish his arms and shoulders; he tried to smear some down his back to the unreachable hollow between his scapulae and then slapped his stomach with the perfume. With an extra handful, he doused his crotch, and the flow drizzled down his legs to the arches of his feet. He grabbed his risen shaft for a flowery polish and then dabbed an extra drop on its hungry eye. "There."

Christoph dried his fingers on the fur beneath his navel and then raised his arms to let the air dry the scent upon him. "Little rosebud that I am, but now a bee to my favorite blossom. Where is she? Buzz, buzz." He removed his robe from the wardrobe. He had specifically selected the emerald green velvet to set off his eyes. The golden silk rope around his waist ended with tassels that bounced from knee to knee as he entered the passageway leading from his room to Elysia's quarters. A quiet tap befitted the hour and the occasion. "Darling...Elysia," Christoph whispered. "C'est moi."

The door flew open. "Christoph!" Elysia fell against his chest and dug her nails into his shoulders. "What did he say? Is it to be?" Christoph kissed her forehead and drew her back from him, then took her hands between his, smiled, and kissed her fingertips. "Oh, Christoph!" Elysia exclaimed. "I was so afraid he would refuse, and that you would argue with him, and all would be ruined! Tell me it as it happened."

Christoph opened the top of the gown of the raven-haired beauty who had appeared before him and grappled her breasts as he spoke. Elysia could feel his hot breath in her ear as he proceeded.

"Darling, I never expected such a warm reception. It is a true blessing, to be so graciously accepted into this family, considering the current state of affairs." He squeezed each breast tighter, pressing them together and rubbing the underside of each areola with the base of his thumbs. His tongue arced on the top edge of her ear to nip it. "Your father appears to be pleased, my beauty." He moved his mouth from her ear to her lips and pried them apart with his tongue. Her robe fell open and his hands moved down her back to grab Elysia's derriere.

"The generosity of this family knows no bounds. Your father said I would be like the son he had lost. I thanked him for this honor on bended knee and assured him the only things of importance are your happiness, our child and our love. Oh, Elysia." He let a finger rest at the top of her peach cleft and moved his other hand back to the breasts, shoving one up against her ribcage and feeling the nipple pop out from between his fingers. "Oh, my dearest treasure, if we had been disinherited for our love, the passion and kindness you offer would sustain me until the final judgment. Tell me you love me. Say it. Now!" Elysia opened her mouth to say it, but his lips covered hers and she felt herself falling towards the floor. Her rump had barely landed and he was already in her, leaning onto her chest with all his weight and scooting them both across the floor with his rammings. "Yes, my darling, I love you, I need you, you are the one for me, oh yes, I am the one for you, we were made for one another." He reached back to grab one of her ankles and then flung her leg over his shoulder. "Tell me now, tell me how much you love me, how much my love means to you, how much you need me, how much you desire me, tell me, tell me now. Tell me, Elysia. Elysia!"

"I...I love you, Christoph." Her words gasped out between her quick breaths. The back of her head scraped the wood floor. Her hand reached out seeking some garment or cushion, but finding none, returned to press into Christoph's back. "Again! Tell me you love me. Does this feel good?" He leaned into her and then shifted upwards. "And this? And this? Tell me again!"

The top of her head bumped against the wall. Elysia did not know love would be so rough and demanding. She felt more mauled than pleasured, but if this is what the man who loved her wanted, it must be right. The first love, the only love of Elysia von Eschenbach, was this dashing man. He said he loved her, and so all was perfect in the world.

Chapter V

Baron Ignatz von Eschenbach's Sorrow

The baron watched the embers on the grate fade from roaring yellow spikes to dull orange squares, and then finally dull grey-white ashes. By then he knew that the scoundrel would have celebrated in his daughter's chambers and returned, but it was now of little matter. The girl could not become more pregnant. He looked over his shoulder at the dark outside the window. At least may the child have some pleasure in the handsome appearance of the mongrel, for there seemed to be little hope for his character. If there were some way the baron could raise the child instead of the la Violettes, that is what his wife would have desired.

Ignatz von Eschenbach was a hollow man, as coreless as the iron maiden that they kept in the town hall basement in Magdeburg, and with the spikes inside piercing the remnants of his heart. He cradled his beard in the palm of his left hand and stirred the remains of the fire with a poker. A spit of sparks twisted upwards. To build another fire? No, it was time for the baron to drink a pitcher of water and go to bed. His head would be pounding in the morning; he could feel it already. The liquor lent an edge to his melancholy.

If he were a peasant or a merchant right now he would be at the inn, spending his wife's egg money and crying into a crock of ale with his arm around some stranger, commiserating on the injustices of life—that his heart had been so broken, or his children so ungrateful and foolish, or that they were sitting in a wattle-daubed hut of a crossroads inn instead of a mountaintop palace like the baron's. But he was not this simple salt of the earth, man of the soil. No, the Baron Ignatz von Eschenbach was born to his fate as much as any of them under the sun, and so he would try to preserve his family's honorable history despite whatever cruel tricks and dark jokes were concocted by chance.

The same chance had deprived him of his wife almost a decade earlier. "Dorothea..." he sighed, running a finger about the edge of his empty goblet. If he wanted to play Job, he certainly had good cause. He had lost his only son, Peter, afflicted with a mysterious ailment after a day spent inspecting the grounds. The widower would eventually lose the company of his daughter, he knew that, but he had shut his mind to this day. Of course she would blossom into womanhood, but to lose her to such a shallow schemer was a dark and bitter prospect. He poured some water from a carafe and cupped the glass in his hands. The portrait of his wife watched him from over the mantelpiece.

"Dorothea," he started again. "If I could only speak with you, receive your wisdom, fulfill my dream that I have made the right choice instead of sitting here pierced with a quiver's worth of doubting arrows. Christoph de la Violette will restore our lands. He will have the pond cleaned and the garden replanted. He will most likely tear out the gooseberries and the small orchards and replace them with a useless hedge of box laurel trimmed like a maze, a topiary menagerie of animals almost as queer as the court life in Salzburg, but so be it. He will have his display of arrogance and gild the stones of this castle in order to escape the stain of his bastardy. Whoreson. Well, hush, so Odile's father did not have castle lands to offer a seducer, eh? She most likely did not know her father, either —sailor, soldier, tinker, peddler, vagabond? I will try to remember charity, but it would have so much less sting if Christoph were a good man.

Some moments I wonder if Elysia would be better off tending chickens in front of a shack as the bride of a swineherd, or perhaps marrying some steady functionary from the village, a pragmatic minor official who would overlook the cuckoo's egg in the nest that he was about to tend and be awed to be inside a castle at all. Sometimes, Dorothea, I wonder if I could give her at least that—someone who would respect and cherish her, but we all know too well how the young are wanton in their errors. Fie! Their energy is wasted upon them, to spread gems in the dung heap and not know that they cannot pass that way again." He drained the goblet of water and refilled it. His head felt a little clearer; perhaps it was cleansed by these maudlin rants.

"Our grandchild will at least be assured material comfort. If it survives. I fear for Elysia, darling, and I cannot stain her hopes with the telling of how many more brothers or sisters she would have had if God had been willing. The ones lost early, the ones lost late. My treasures, Elysia and Peter, the two surviving children reached adulthood, only to have one carried away by death in his prime, and the other to be lost to a calculating fop. It is an indignity, but I feel shame to even consider my injured pride when compared to the certainty of Elysia's heartbreak. If the baby lives, she will have solace, our line will survive, and in the continuation of our history may I see the recapitulation of your beauty." He laughed to himself despite the water collecting at the inner corners of his eyes—himself, the Baron Ignatz von Eschenbach, to sound like a nursemaid about to tell fairytales to her charges. "And the child will be born with your storm-gray eyes and raven-wing hair. All the church bells in the land will ring in their towers, and the grandchild of you, my most precious darling, will grow to be as strong as a stallion and wise as an owl. His counsel will be sought before he reaches maturity." He laughs, "Or she will become a noble beauty with the bearing of a queen and the wisdom of all ages."

He turned his face from the fireplace, tilting back to see the empty void to the ceiling above him. Damn. If only he could fling Christoph de la Violette into a void as dark as a vault and a hundred times as vast. The abandoned copper mines near Eichensdorf would do nicely. The man's monstrous ambition would probably sustain him through such a fall. He thinks he is so cunning; once the grounds are restored, he may learn that he cannot move in this circle as fluidly as he first thought. This aspiring nobleman may be forced to realize there are risks beyond the boudoir that will test him. Bah!

He speaks to Dorothea's portrait, "To so pursue a young girl and turn her into but a bargaining piece for his own vanity, or perhaps his mother's vanity...ah, worse yet, that such a young man would become a marionette for his mother, whose powers are so superficial, so restrained to a show of couture for a season. Christoph's mother would evaporate when exposed to the vast and frightening legend of your deceased family, my beloved.

"Dorothea..." he began again, "I am hard-pressed to continue life without you." The eyes in the portrait gazed down upon him with patience. They matched the gray watered silk she had worn when she sat for the artist. Her image had been captured with perfection. The pearl-drop earrings and the ruby signet ring with the dragon were medieval and strange, but beautiful beyond words. He had been so blessed as to know the spirit of the one portrayed. "My darling, Elysia has no idea of your family history, and the Violettes have even less. The tales would turn the heart of a good Christian, but that appears to be no reason to keep it from the grasper. No reason to tell them, either. I will enlighten Elysia as soon as she regains her senses. Having a child among la Violette's family and their assorted hangers-on with all their escapades will be enough of a sobering experience.

"Our son, Peter, was to be the keeper of the secrets, and was shown the relics in their hiding place. But Elysia, her I have sheltered. These are the secrets I must convey to her now: The Knights Templar, the Merovingian, long-haired kings of the Rhine Valley, the Holy Place, the planet alignment in the year 2019 when all humanity will be free. The baron closed his eyes and visions unfolded behind them: pale ones swimming through darkness, a crowd with torches, a cobweb-curtained crypt.

"This ignorant foreigner and pretender to our lands does not know your ancestry, does not know what name he marries into. The impalers would never have tolerated this fancy Frenchman's insolence." The baron could not help but smile at the thought of this seducer in torment, his tenderest parts wrapped around a stake that raises him aloft at castle ramparts, eyes glazed and rolled back, tongue lolling a string of saliva and blood to his lace collar. And that would only be the beginning. At the end of these mythical rites and violations there would not be enough left of Christoph for the worms to bother with.

A cold wind rustled the tapestry and interrupted his gory reverie. The fire was out. It was time for the baron to retire. So much to sleep on, and so little he could do about it upon waking. He would tell his manservant not to let anyone disturb him in the morning. A lapse, but the broken spirit required it. How could he tell Elysia the dark truths? How could he stand powerless and watch his daughter serve as sacrifice for the preservation of their line and lands? How could he keep a history alive when it tended to decay by the growth of nature around it, like the neglected castle wing? The wing that la Violette was at this moment redesigning as a brothel in his dreams. The baron stood and cursed, threw his goblet on the grate, turned heel and left the hall.

Chapter VI

Claire

"Yes, darling, oh my God." Stuart is hovering over her, pushing wet hair back from her forehead with his fingertips. Claire turns her head to the side, coughs up water, then turns on her side and moans. Stuart's hand is on her shoulder. "I thought I had lost you." His lips graze her before he rises from his knees to take a dry towel from Mary Norton. He doesn't know whether to dry her or wrap her in it, or both, or neither. His hand shakes as he dabs at her hair then unfolds the towel to cover her. The towel's graphics depict three sailboats racing into a setting sun and a sky strewn with stylized seagulls.

Young doctors fresh out of med school are annoying. They are taught presumption of privilege; they assume a mandate of control over the bodies of others; they poke and prod to tell what's wrong without the mellowing delicacy of time and experience. The physician at the emergency room is one of these new M.D.s. Whenever addressed as "Doctor" he startles for an imperceptible moment, back straightening and eyes widening, and then grimaces with pride at the appellation. He shakes his finger at Claire, looking over the glasses that slide down his nose. She suspects that he didn't even need the prescription and just wears the frames to look dignified.

"Mrs. Foster," he starts, "you need to watch this vacation partying. Every week we have people fall off boats up here at their summer homes. Next time you may not be so fortunate. You could have hit your head on a rock. If there had been more traffic on the water, you could have been maimed by a propeller. Or if your husband and friends had been further along in their celebrations and hadn't noticed your absence..."

Claire knows the doctor is an ass. Such condescension—and how could she possibly hit her head on a rock when they were at the center of the lake? She appreciates his cautions in general, but not in particular. They come up to the cabin to unwind and let the kids run off some steam, not to have some sort of transplanted suburban bacchanal brouhaha. She nods politely throughout the remainder of his lecture.

"You're not immortal, you know. I prescribe a day or two of bed rest. If there is no marked change, or if you have any other episodes of fainting, see your family doctor." The last admonition falls over his shoulder as he leaves the examination room and the door swings shut behind him.

It is dark as they drive home and there is a certain charm about the highway median, a narrow lawn that the highway department is attempting to fill with trees and flowers. The lights of passing semi trucks illuminate thin-armed saplings on a bank of some flowering bramble holding up a hillside from sure erosion.

Their own faces are illuminated by the lights of the dashboard, veiled with a green cast. "For Pete's sake, how could you be so careless? Walking around on a moving boat…you were sneaking beer, weren't you?" Stuart's brows are knotted over the bridge of his nose.

"I was not!" She resented the implications.

"Dammit, you just can't hold your liquor," her husband growls. "When are you going to accept that?"

"Stuart, we both know that beer makes me ill. I had a couple of Cokes and that was it." Spouses squabble with the precision of chess— they know one another so well, the board with its set patterns and parameters; both players know that each piece is moved according to rules. Her voice is smooth and even, but a note deeper.

"Dad, you know that Mom doesn't touch beer." Victoria puts down the magazine she's trying to squint at under the passing lights.

"That's right," adds Holly.

John can't let the girls comment without being included in some way. "Yeah," he huffs, slumps down in his seat, and resumes racing a matchbox car over the knee of his jeans.

"Quiet. This is between me and your mother." Stuart's eyebrows have unwound a bit and he pauses to choose words carefully. "Claire, I'm just upset because I'm worried. That punk doctor couldn't tell me what was wrong. Can you? He seemed to think that you were drinking. Am I qualified to question his judgment?"

"Stuart Foster, I am insulted. We have been to the cabin weekend after weekend and you have never seen me indulge. Tell me when you last saw me drink. I just get off-center at the cottage. Friday when we arrive I'm ready for the adventure, but by the time we pack up on Sunday I have a headache and can barely hold my breakfast." Claire turns from him and looks out the window at the median. The empty rubber husk of a semi's blown tire litters the side of the road. Her reflection shows a set jaw, purposeful eyes. "I become so ill I am disoriented."

"Great. So the cabin makes you sick. What's it going to be next? Do you have any idea what an investment that was? You know that we saved so we could have this—it's the pinnacle of our success, our team, and you tell me you can't go there? To our dream retreat?"

"I know, but I'm just trying to consider possible causes. You want an explanation, but then you blow up when I start considering things."

Stuart's knuckles tighten on the steering wheel. "I buy a special get-away for us, and then you tell me that it makes you ill? How am I supposed to respond? 'Oh, no problem, honey, let me get us another expensive thing to share so that you can become allergic to it.'"

"Don't yell at me, puh-leeeze."

"You think I'm being unreasonable? Maybe you're unreasonable! Maybe you need to talk to someone about these 'spells,' make sure they're not all in your mind."

"What!" Claire's head spins over her left shoulder and she glares at Stuart.

"Fess up, Claire." Stuart's voice is lower and quieter now. "You just don't want to come up here with me, do you? Is that it? Any excuse will do. Invent an illness so I'll come up here by myself, or take the kids off your hands, leaving you alone in the house for..."

"That's right, Stuart, I intentionally fell overboard and lost consciousness in a near-drowning just to get some space. Every illness, every pang, every stubbed toe that I experience is a reflection on you. For God's sake—may my nausea escape the reach of your ego? May I have some stomach flu to call my own?

I had a fairly severe cold in January. That probably meant I really wanted to take the kids and run away to Arizona to live in an Airstream and work incognito in a greasy spoon under the assumed name 'Flo'."

"You hate omelettes." Stuart looked at her with alarm.

"We both know something is wrong. Tomorrow I'm going to go to the doctor and find out what. All right?"

"Fine."

"Good."

All the way home the car is a quiet box on wheels. The kids have fallen asleep despite the fight, and Claire has turned her back to him. He laments his anger and he wants to cry—even more so when he flashes back to his mad scramble to locate her in the water. God, how he loves this woman. He fights back tears by fluttering his lips. How do these things happen, the storms that spiral out from the wrong words? All he had wanted was to make clear that they needed to find out what was going on, needed to investigate the reason for these episodes. He depends on her so much it frightens him. He imagines coming home to an empty house looking for her, wandering down a stretching hallway, opening door after door only to find her gone. He meant to tell her that they had to find out why, to be detectives for her health, but instead he came across as the selfish grand inquisitor, so judgmental and damning. That is not what he had meant at all. Not at all.

The nightmare returns to Claire that evening with its sickening familiarity. She is smothered by the cloying sweetness of lilies and the sad spice of decaying carnations. Leaden paces of different weights drum by on the floor, some timpani bass, or women's high heels clattering like snares. People parade past her coffin and lean down to whisper, "What a shame. What a shame." She can feel their breaths on her cheek, a series of small warm clouds drifting across her mouth at regular intervals. The breath of some makes her want to close her nostrils, but even that small movement is beyond her.

Claire is frozen stiff, but not frozen, just as cool as the scratchy lining of the pleats beneath her hands. Why are her hands at her sides? Don't they know that her hands should be folded on her chest in prayer? Sometimes the air they exhale on her face smells salty, like a day on the coast at the gulf. She knows they have been crying. The smell of sour cabbage has to be old Mrs. Jankowicz, bless her heart. The pace with an uneven gait, step heavy then light, must be Renaldo from the car wash. There are sounds of hissing, then like a woodwind section checking its pitch, a string of high notes rasps in the sound of human tears, a chorus of sobs as they close the lid on her casket and she hears the final click. The last scent carried into her is the tang of brass polish on the hinges. Then she is hermetically sealed in this metal-lined box and they are going to take her away for burial.

She slides from one side of the box to the other as the casket is carried outside, her body crumpling against the mock padding. She is inert but still able to feel the sting from the bumps through the nerves above her elbow. As the wide back door of the hearse slams shut she regains some small scrap of her voice and tries to call out: "I'm not dead. I'm not dead!"

Chapter VII

Odile
de la Violette

S he stood on the balcony overlooking the Koenigstrasse, counting the couples who lingered beneath the lindens and noting who returned to the coaches with the best steeds. The Stallenbachs now rode with two courtiers. Christina von und zu Wittelsberg appeared to be in a liaison with the young man from Trent, the trickster who was the toast of the scientific circles for his experiments with vapors in the parlors of the under- amused from Nice to Grasse and back. Three young women were wearing gowns from her house, the house de la Violette, but only one could afford this season's. Odile's palms polished the top of the stone railing with their vibrations, her entire body taut like a harpsichord string. The face of Christoph's mother, Odile de la Violette, was stretched back as if it were too small for her skull. Lines, lines, she remembered, and attempted a smile so the creases of her spirit would not affect her face. It was a day of victory. Let her countenance beam a rosy glow upon the returning son and his delightful bride-to-be, God be damned. She gave voice to her curses in a rare moment of class slippage, a facade as fastidiously maintained as her appearance.

"Damn this son of mine! Where is he?" Her hand plunged into a fold to retrieve the letter the messenger had brought. If the ink could fade from her gaze the letter would be invisible by now, just the echoing ghost of the following phrase:

Cher Mama, je vais arriver le six de Mai, avec mon fiancée!

Tout est tres bien. Christoph.

So, things unfolded, legs uncrossed as planned, and he was returning home with a fiancée. This fiancée had better be the baroness Elysia von Eschenbach or she would not let him in the house. But there was no way that even her indiscreet son would be so foiled and trapped, was there? No, the baron's daughter was coming home with him, they would marry, and the la Violettes would become nobility. Nobility!

The eye of Odile's memory unwound a scroll of scenes: in her youth, the man on the tall horse and his scowl of dismay and disdain that looked upon her rags; the young men who would leer at her as if she were common property. Only the rich could sneer at Odile in years past. But now not even the gentry could smirk with her son and her grandchild among their own. The wedding and the christening would have to be in the biggest cathedral in the city. When she first read this letter she held it with both hands, as if it might fly away and take the tidings with it, a white piece of paper disappearing over the horizon to steal Elysia from the side of Christoph, return her to her father's lands, turn back the hands of the clock and strip her son's seed from the girl's belly. All had occurred as planned. Now it must come to pass.

Her own passage had been no less remarkable. Odile was born to a family of laborers in Lyon. Her father had been a rag-picker, junk-dealer, and sometime petty thief. He was also a notorious drunk, cleaning the swill from any abandoned barrel left behind in the town's taverns, grasping at the silver-buttoned cuffs of the prosperous and claiming to need centimes to feed his children whenever things were particularly thin. His greatest gift to his family was passing out cold in the pigpen one winter evening. Even without his stupor, he would have been no match for a half-ton of angry sows. The three pigs approached and snorted. Pickled and immobile, he became short work for this mob. The family had one less mouth to feed, and the livestock was better nourished in the bargain.

Odile's mother had a pragmatic heart that had been more hardened by circumstance. She did not waste time mourning the gnawed remains, but set out to the cabinetmaker's to purchase a coffin. She muttered to herself that it would be more fitting to use an empty cask from some rotgut red wine, and it would be a resting place her husband would have preferred. She laughed at the suggestion of a cherry or oak wood coffin. When shown the plain pine boxes, she ran a fingertip down the splinters of the unhanded edge and asked, "Do you have anything smaller? The pigs are not so well fed as to have left much of him—they nearly starve on our leftovers." That same day she balanced the wooden box on her hip and took Odile, only six years of age, by the hand to the pauper's graves. "My darling child," Odile's mother drew her close as the first scattering of dirt and clods of mud fell, "that you would have had a whole father and I would have had a whole man, but it was not to be. Now we are alone, and I think we are the better for it. This is one of those rare occasions when the hand of God has moved with wisdom and justice. Remember it well. That thief will no longer search my apron pockets for change to feed his drunkenness instead of his daughter." She looked from side to side and quickly spat into the void before her. In the years that followed, Odile's fostering and upbringing were punctuated by her mother's crude boast that she had 'buried half a man in half a box,' and that one incident was cited as evidence of every scrap of education or achievement from her widowhood to her business acumen.

The family business that the women tended was sewing piecework. They arose in the morning to throw desultory grain in front of their few thin chickens, rinse their faces in icy water from the basin, say a prayer and then sit to pierce their fingertips again and again as the needle danced through whatever haberdashery or frocks they had to repair. Every hole made by the tiny metal stake was marked by a complaint from mother to daughter. "Never forget this, Odile," her mother would note, tearing off a strand of thread in her teeth and knotting the end. "Love is a fool's game. I wasted my youth on the pretty words of a man who turned out to be the town drunk. Used and wasted, and for what? To scrape for scraps the rest of my life with no consolation except my daughter. You must do better than me. Do not allow yourself to be distracted by such fancies as young women think are their reward in this world. You are the only one who can provide for yourself. I try now, but..." and sometimes her mother would shrug and extend her hands, palms up, over the wicker baskets of cloth before them.

On other days her mother would be a little more reverential and optimistic, clasping her hands in prayer and beseeching Odile to try on one of the smaller gowns among their jobs. "Oh, mon petite cher," her mother would smile in rare frivolity. "If only we had a mirror that you could see yourself. This red suits you entirely, although it is a scandalous color. It flatters your dark hair and brings some color to your face. Now if you wore gowns like this we could pass you off to some man of means. It is as easy to be with a rich man as a poor one, and all cats are gray in the twilight, sweetheart. When the sun rises, you can admire his purse. You should have a better life than I, God willing, and wear such a dress all the time, a different one for every day of the week and two for Sundays, and they will be mended by miserable fools in dank cottages."

The sermon would continue over an evening meal of thin soup and barley bread. "You are a clever girl. This we can tell, even without effort. You are quick to flatter those who bring us the most work. It is a pity that you waste words on the servants' servants, for that is who they are. Flatter a wealthy man, and you may escape." Odile wiped her soup bowl with a crust as her mother continued. "To accomplish this, do not listen to the trills of the heart. They are but an echo of the groaning of untended loins, and both are second to the growls of an empty stomach, I am sorry to know from experience."

This instruction was the extent of Odile's education, but she remembered it well. Her mother taught her that men were a means, not an end, but the unfairly selected guardians of wealth and property. To achieve any comfort or status, she would have to use her appearance to manipulate men into taking care of her. Odile had enough confidence in her own abilities to believe that she would eventually take care of the means possessed by the men without their intervention. But even the virtuoso does not first raise the violin to his chin and break hearts with a solo tremolo singing on strings from the pit of the king's own orchestra. First there is practice, perhaps even a fiddle, and many less ambitious attempts before a grand performance.

The Marquis de Lyon had three sons, the youngest of whom was Guillaume. He was a thin and bent lad given to reading small leather-bound books of poetry and sighing beneath willows. He was particularly given to sighing beneath the willow near a bridge that Odile traversed almost daily in returning dresses to some of Lyon's more established households. She started to check her hair more carefully before leaving their hovel, applying rose petals to her cheeks for color and a dab of vanilla behind her ears as perfume. Odile reconditioned a bodice that modesty would recommend be abandoned and commenced to wearing it as she went about these errands. Sometimes she would sing, trilling selections of ballads, or a hymn. If Guillaume tried to catch her eye, she would blush and turn away.

Odile found a small book of verse in the vestibule of a client's home during the return of some dresses. She slyly pocketed it to display on top of the baskets of clothing she carried. By now Guillaume arose at her approach and stood to watch her pass, both hands clasping a book to his heart, his upper lip trembling like a leaf as Odile smiled at him with her greatest attempt at mustering shyness. The next week she carefully dislodged a piece of clothing to fall from the top of the bundle she carried. He followed her with the retrieved blouse in hand.

"Mademoiselle, Mademoiselle!" He offered the blouse on bended knee, and looked up to see a beautiful animal. Odile's face was heart-shaped, with sharp features and wide green eyes beneath a delicately arched brow. Her eyes had the most heart of anything about her, but she gladly reciprocated Guillaume's abashed romantic cooing throughout their courtship. She even managed to expand her acting talents by feigning awe at the poetic efforts he recited for her at midnight beneath the oak behind the family chateau. The third son of the Marquis' seed became her seed money, for nine months into this grand affair she presented the Marquis de Lyon with a bastard grandson, and the Marquis, with embarrassed generosity, presented her with a comfortable sum with which to raise the child.

Nothing could appeal to Odile less than the prospect of raising the Marquis' grandson in the shadow of a chateau that she should rightfully occupy. The financial settlement became the trappings of a life that a woman of property facing temporary misfortune might possess. Her mother helped her purchase secondhand goods, haggling with the maids and menservants who had brought them bundles of sewing from wealthy homes over the years. "Fie, Pierre!" Odile's mother would curse a manservant with newfound familiarity. "I may be losing my sight, but even I can tell that your mistress wouldn't let the scullery maid wear this to peel potatoes! Now, just show me something with which her ladyship is bored, or has outgrown, not such a tired rag for MY daughter. If a blind woman can feel the holes in it, no child of mine is going to wear it to Paris!"

Such bargaining for couture items with half-thieving servants also successfully produced a trunk, a candelabra, two place settings for household meals, (more whimsical than practical), and a wardrobe of only slightly provincial dresses and slippers. Odile kissed her mother good-bye with an obedient thank-you, and took the first morning coach one misty spring dawn to the town of Regretteriens to the southeast of Paris. It was a cluster of many simple country homes for some of those at court. Odile sought lodging where she could present herself as the tragically bereaved recent widow of a son of a marquis from the far south. In tribute to her father, she decided that her "late husband" was killed by a boar. He was hunting when he was thrown from his steed and hit his head on a rock, knocking him unconscious. Had he not been out cold, he would have been more than a match for such a rough beast, strangling it with his bare hands. Odile knew far better than to talk about herself too much.

People want to talk about what is truly important in their hearts: themselves. Such was the case with Courtier Stefan le Poisson, her first lover from the Parisian set. He was happy to keep her for his amusement in a cottage on the grounds of his country place, but Odile was not going to languish away behind the orchard in what she knew were her strongest stalking years, for the vanity and lust of men who crave youth. Within two years she married the elderly Monsieur George de la Violette, a lace importer who had visited Regretteriens to tend to some accounts and was instantly stricken by her charms. After his demise—he seemed to have overexerted himself not long after the honeymoon—Odile sought comfort in the arms of his eighteen-year-old son, Rene.

Odile knew all too well the feel of quality cloth versus thin rags from the hours of piecework behind her. A mere glance could tell her whether a bolt was reputable, whether a spindle of lace would hold up as trim on a gentlemen's jacket or only be fit for trimming the lapels of the footmen's uniforms.

Under her guidance, the family import business quadrupled, and then multiplied again, until every court in Europe was decorated by some fabric or frippery from the house de la Violette. This was the weight behind her argument that she and Rene should move to Salzburg from Paris to exploit the eastern trade routes. Proximity to royalty would by no means be bad for business, for Salzburg was the playground of all nobility in the heart of Europe. And if it was a playground, oh, Odile knew all the games. No longer a flirtatious maid dropping items for a marquis' son to fetch, nor the pitiable widow of some distant noble, she held opulent balls and banquets and signed the invitations Madame de la Violette.

The more established nobles would smile at this line of script but were happy to indulge the pretense in order to attend a good party. The commoners followed the lead of the aristocracy, for none could claim to be more wealthy than this odd and alluring Frenchwoman. But Odile was not satisfied. She needed to be reassured that none were laughing at her, that no one knew of her as the daughter of a drunken rag picker, a piecework seamstress and producer of bastards. The perfect close, the gem upon the pinnacle of her crowning accomplishments, would be to join the ranks of the land-owning nobility, the true gentry linked only to the rocks of their holdings through long-ago battles clouded in legend, not in some recent trade among merchants for status—exactly the kind of trade she intended to execute.

Odile de la Violette knew her advantages. She had a fortune and a handsome, compliant, marriageable son. All she had to do was find a family of noble birth who had fallen upon financially hard times and who had an appropriately marriageable daughter. She studied histories, blew dust from hidebound sheaves of parchment kept in the catacombs of monasteries, visited graveyards to confirm the unions and deaths claimed in documentation, spent hours among the records in the basements of town halls.

Her own records became an elaborate chart kept on the wall of her private study. If the family had potential, its holdings were outlined in green. If second-stage investigation revealed a shortcoming, the interior was not colored in yellow. The lands of the von Eschenbachs were colored in red on top of yellow, making them the winners of the dubious prize in a competition to meet Odile's qualifications. The family was old and mysterious, once powerful beyond question and feared as if some magical witchcraft bound those near to them. The baron's ancestry could be traced back to the Rose Knights—the Knights Templar of the Crusades. And further to the Priere de Sion.

His late wife, Dorothea, was reputed to have descended from Vlad Dracul, the hero of Romania. Dorothea's dark and dangerous history suggested the mysticism of the occult, the frightening wizardry of Count Dracula himself.

Odile was fascinated. If respect by association could be bought, she would buy it. She penned the letter of introduction suggesting that Christoph and Elysia meet. "Now, my dear boy," she lectured Christoph before she placed the letter in the hands of the messenger. "We are sublimely fortunate in the discovery of the von Eschenbachs. Their pedigree is splendid and their holdings considerable. However, they face a limitation common among nobility: they are rich in land but not much else. If you bring me the title, I can assure your inheritance of the la Violette fortunes. You know that you are not Rene's son. You are not a son in his heart, either. You are my son: I do not need to sentimentalize and prettify things for you. If you are a baron, he cannot attempt to disinherit you."

Yes, Christoph was her son, her sun, the light of her life, joy of God's desiring, but her daughter with Rene was her competitor, and an unworthy one at that. Everything Christoph wanted was within Odile's comprehension: pleasure, adulation, food for vanity and flesh to while away the hours. And his mother's approval. Unfortunately, his sister, Marie-Ange, had given up seeking her mother's approval long ago. She had learned that she was more likely to receive attention through wily subterfuge and brash insouciance than doting obedience. Marie-Ange liked to think that in her heart Odile respected her rebelliousness, perceived it as a will of iron mirroring her mother's, but Odile was far too concerned with her own goals to consider anything positive about her daughter. Marie-Ange's displays were a distraction at best, and an embarrassment at worst.

Marie-Ange first remembered her mother as the grand and beautiful woman her nursemaid brought her to each afternoon. Odile would inspect the child, having her stand in front of her and turn around. "Slower," she would command, pausing to sip her coffee. "Ah, darling, you are too rough a blossom. Why could I not have a daughter with some refinement? Your nose is like a speckled radish. You are going to be as sturdy as a peasant, I can already tell, and your complexion will be far too carroty. Well, don't just stand there—curtsy! No, no, not so stiff. You are not a little tree trunk." Odile drained her cup and set it on the end board so firmly that it rattled. A servant promptly refilled it from a silver pot. "Now, child, a pirouette, and a curtsy. Do you want to end up mistress to a swineherd?"

Marie-Ange took refuge in the garden, at first, amusing herself with a willow hoop and stick, or planning elaborate tea parties for her dolls. The porcelain ladies would be served tiny china platefuls of clover and cups of water. One spring afternoon such a party was interrupted by a high-pitched peep behind her. Marie-Ange turned to see that a little lark had fallen from its nest among the aromatic flowers of the apple tree. It had opaque marbles for eyes and shook with fright when the child reached out to collect it, rotating the globes in their sockets and showing the red interior of its yellow bill as it cried. It was so young that it had fuzz mixed with its feathers; little tendrils of fluff rimmed the edge of its beak. "Poor little bird!" Marie-Ange cooed. "We must get you back to your mama! You must not miss tea-time or your flying lessons! My mama will help—she knows everything."

The tiny drum of the creature's heart beat against her palm. The girl lifted the bird to her face and scrutinized it: the even ridges of the emerging wing feathers, the silken trail down the back, the warm belly fluff, the patch of color on the throat, the fan of tail feathers. Eesh! The terrified thing voided itself on her hand. Marie-Ange made a face but knew to clean her hand with a leaf before putting the bird in her outer skirt to carry it to her mother.

"Mama! The baby bird fell out of its nest and I cannot reach to put it back! It may have hurt its wing! Could you tell Klaus to help me? Should he get a ladder? Where is he?" The girl stamped her small foot, but then remembered not to disturb her pleats. Odile put down the quill with which she had been recording discrepancies in an order of Chinese silks that had been shipped through Constantinople and blew on the page lightly to dry the ink. Really! What a ridiculous interruption.

She knew that the infidel must be trying to cheat her, perhaps taking one bolt from each bale, or perhaps it was one of his camel-drivers, but did he really think she would not notice?

"Give it to me." Marie-Ange sniffled as she simpered up, stretching out her overskirt before her. The fledgling peeped again before the woman snapped its neck with her thumb and tossed the limp remains over her shoulder into a bed of parrot tulips. There. Now the broken thing would not starve to death. She had already picked up her quill to resume her calculations when the child flung herself at Odile's legs.

"You killed it! I hate you!" Marie-Ange wailed and flailed, punching her mother in the stomach and tearing at her hanging lace cuffs. The girl turned heel and fled, not giving Odile a moment to explain that the bird would have starved to death. Even if its wing was undamaged, the mother would reject an infant that so reeked of humans, and might even flee her nest, causing all of its brothers and sisters to starve. There was nothing to be done—a quick end was the best. The child just did not understand. Odile shrugged, then squinted at the table of figures before her.

Marie-Ange ran down the path toward the house, rubbing her fists in her eyes and tripping on the edge of the lawn. "What is wrong, mon petite pomme-orange?" Her father picked her up and tossed her in the air. "Why is our darling Princess de la Violette crying?"

"Mother killed the bird!" the child sobbed. "Papa! This dress has a grass stain now! It is torn! I must have a new one!"

"Yes, you will have a new one. I'm sure it was a bad bird. Your mother always has her reasons. Perhaps it was not nobility. What color new dress would our little flower like, hmm?"

The girl spied a daffodil at the edge of the lawn. "Yellow!" she cried, pointing past her father's shoulder with one hand and grabbing at his beard with the other. "Yellow with red trim like that flower."

"So, my baby would look like a gypsy, eh? All the better, we'll get you a bangle of coins and a tambourine to match and it will grieve your mother to no end. Let us go to the swatch room and look at all the yellows." He held her to his side and carried her to the house. "If you are to be a gypsy, you should learn to dance. Would you like dancing lessons? I know: We will stop by the kitchen to get pastries before we go to the sample books. There may be some sugar-coated brioche with almonds and rosewater. Now there's a dainty dish for a dainty girl." Rene kissed her hairline until the girl smiled. From that day forth she never asked her mother for anything but knew to approach her father to have no whim go unmet. Every slight, every criticism from Odile was another strangled bird, a pile accumulating near Marie-Ange's feet, a trail of mite-ridden broken bodies scattered down the parquet halls behind her.

"Madame! They are here! He is home!" The chambermaid breathlessly approached through the boudoir to the balcony where Odile stood. Odile's reverie was broken, snapping her back to the present.

"Then get out of the way!" Odile returned the letter to the folds of her gown, gathered up its folds in her fists, pushed the maid aside and rushed to the stairs. At the top she paused, released the fistfuls of brocade, and smoothed the fabric before her. Her hands adjusted her cuffs then flew up to pat her coiffure. No stray strands, no crooked seams, nothing other than perfection was permissible.

She could hear the footsteps of Christoph and Elysia entering the foyer. Odile inhaled to quiet her nerves, and then took the first step down the stairs, stopping to count three pulses before taking each step. They were to be welcomed, but not with rushed anticipation. Besides, there would be plenty of time for her to survey the prize of her effort, or the means to the end of the barony, more accurately.

Odile was enchanted. It was like when she was a young girl in Lyon, the first time she had accompanied her mother to return some repaired garments to the house of Henri Lesceaux. Lesceaux owned a vineyard, and his wife was a woman of rare poise and charm. Seeing Elysia reminded Odile of that first glimpse into a world that was not hers: the view out of the kitchen at the wide clean hall, pleasant furnishings, and then the sweep of the mistress's broad skirts as she entered. "What a darling child!" The woman smiled down at Odile and handed her mother some coins. "Elisabeth, give this girl some of the custard from last night, if you did not already give it all to that rogue stable hand who enjoys your favors." She winked at Odile and then patted the child's head. "This one is going to be a heart-breaker. You keep an eye on her."

"Oui, madame." Odile's mother curtsied.

Odile's first glimpse of Elysia struck a thrill in her bosom. Elysia was beautiful—a vision of exquisite bearing. This young woman would more than serve Odile's purposes! What a prize to present to the world of Salzburg. Elysia emanated a strength without any implication of crude labor or vigor. The girl had a bluish tinge which reminded Odile of the myth of the woman carved from a pillar of marble who had come to life. But if Elysia had been made under the palms of some Pygmalion, it would be as a gift from Pallas Athena, not seafoam-spittled, weak-kneed Aphrodite. This girl was obviously sheltered, but had an edge, the suggestion of some sharpened steel core. Her gaze returned Odile's without hesitation, and Odile suddenly felt self-conscious, struggling to stay in control. She began to inventory Elysia, thinking of her as a prize mare to establish the distance between them. This girl may have a bewitching hyacinth complexion, but there was no need to be so distracted, no cause for trepidation at all. *So, whose characteristics would the child have? Christoph's green eyes or the deep, cool gray ones of this creature's?* Odile was surprised to find herself remembering the words that the Marquis' third weak son had simpered to her. "Raven hair. Petal skin." Christoph coughed, and the young couple started walking toward her. Elysia slid soundlessly, without perceptible movement.

"My new sister!" Elysia suddenly found herself assaulted by Marie-Ange. The buxom young woman pressed an armful of apricot roses upon her. "For you. Welcome to our humble family!" Marie-Ange emphasized 'humble' as a certain way to annoy her mother, for whom humility was an accessory to be used on Sundays and not recalled under any other circumstance. The choice was as deliberate as her selection of the orange gown that her mother despised.

A salmon, mused Odile. *That girl looks like a swollen salmon flinging itself upstream at some glacial pool. Not even the sense to cultivate some restraint to compensate for her lack of grace and delicacy.* Odile stepped forward to greet the group. Her back was to Marie-Ange. No reason to look upon that repulsive orange shade a moment longer than necessary. Such an ignorant choice for a redhead to make. Christoph stepped forward and kissed his mother on both cheeks, knowing to be careful not to dislodge or mar the area near the precisely placed beauty mark.

"Madame Odile de la Violette, permit me to introduce my bride-to-be, and thus your future daughter-in-law, the Baroness Elysia von Eschenbach. May you love her as well as I do.

Odile smiled, and then leaned forward to kiss the air above both Elysia's cheeks. She gathered the girl's fingers together and held them to the gold embroidery above her heart. "My darling child," her voice was barely above a whisper. "I welcome you into my home, my family, my heart...."

Chapter VIII
Exercises in Futility

Bickering couples can call a truce and are frequently well-advised to do so: a temporary break in hostilities in order to accomplish the business of the day. An evening's slight is passed over because someone must pick up dry-cleaning; two suits, three cotton blouses, four shirts (light starch), and a cocktail dress with elaborate blue beadwork scrolling down its side. A cruel jibe is filed for later reference, sometimes after the checkbook has been balanced, or the dog has gotten his shots, or the kids have been collected from soccer practice. Domesticity necessitates detente, and there is a diplomatic understatement in a cursory morning greeting, an averting of eyes, coffee placed on the table but not near the hand.

Stuart sighs and teases the lacy brown edges of his eggs with a fork. They are dry and overdone, the vinyl consistency of the white breaking to little rubbery flecks in his mouth instead of sliding down his throat in warm, intact strips the way that eggs should. Instead of gazing back at him like featureless smiley faces, the yolks are cracked and much too firm on the parched terrain of the white. The toast is coated with the carbon of Claire's discontent, and the orange juice had not been stirred, leaving him with a glass of citrus-tinged water. He reads all the signs but does not escalate conflict, instead holding his territory by a silent perusal of the paper. The Browns won, so he's ahead in the football pool. The stock of his employer continues its steady and healthy climb. A zoning conflict is holding up development of a local shopping center.

Normally, all this would be shared with Claire within a reciprocal banter about the tasks of the day, but today they cultivate their silence and let objects speak for them. Stuart rattles the business section and ostentatiously folds it over to read an article in the lower half, his glasses sliding to the tip of his nose. Claire drops a pan in the sink from a height six inches higher than necessary, causing food-flecked water to leap out onto the counter with a splat. Cabinet doors slap wood on wood, and cleaned glasses chime as they are returned to the cupboard.

"I'm seeing Dr. Land today.'" Claire's statement is a nonchalant announcement of plans, in no way related to the tenor of her near-drowning or the exchange in the car.

"Is that so?" Stuart responds, suddenly becoming more engrossed in the newsprint photo of a dignitary cutting a ribbon in front of the renovated public library. "Sounds like a good idea," he says, an olive branch sprouting from the general brambles of the day so far. He coughs and puts the paper down. "I may be late tonight. There's a meeting about the possible O'Donnell acquisition." Normally Claire would ask about Stuart's business obligations, offering her incisive comments and sharp observations, inquiring about the particular foibles and motivations of the players, but today all he gets from her is a brief nod and a cheek turning vaguely in his direction. He puts a coffee kiss on it, picks up his briefcase and leaves.

Dr. Land's office is in a stark complex on the periphery of Libertyville's hospital. Its exterior is white concrete, and the doors slide open to reveal an atrium where red lace maples surround a meditative rock garden. The carpeting still smells new in its expensive way, like a car interior. Being ill would seem like an affront to the architect, the gardener, and the maintenance staff. The offices are more like a consultant's than a physician's: the magazines are actually current and the houseplants in the waiting room shine with vigor.

"Why, hello, Mrs. Foster." Judy, the receptionist, smiles. She's been with Dr. Land nearly as long as the Fosters have. Claire pauses to inquire about Judy's little boy, Roger, leaning over the counter to admire his latest picture in its wooden heart-shaped frame. Roger smiles back at the onlooker, the gaps in his teeth giving him a goofy adolescent smirk. The mischievous boy is always up to something, and whenever the Fosters have an appointment, Claire always has to hear the latest diagnosis of Roger's attention deficit disorder, how he got up on the roof at Sunday School, and how alternate weekends with his father always aggravate the boy's misbehavior. This time Roger has been caught heaving cats into the neighbor's swimming pool with a catapult he constructed from scrap two-by-fours and a bungee cord, a generally harmless but more ominous prank with some admirable technical innovation.

"I don't know, Claire." Dr. Land leans against the wall opposite the examination table while scratching his head. "You seem to be your usual healthy self: your constitution would be considered as tough as they come. I'm just troubled by the history of these episodes. Did it happen again?"

"At the lake, yesterday." Claire's fingers fold together and she takes a deep breath. "We had only been out for an hour and a half. I was wearing a straw hat and sunblock—it couldn't possibly have been overexposure. I don't drink. I became nauseated, dizzy and then I lost my balance. Once I was in the water my limbs felt stiff and unbearably heavy. I couldn't move. I was paralyzed. Otherwise I could have easily made it back to the boat, or back to shore, even."

"Well, even the strongest of us can fall prey to the unexpected." He stands up to rest his hand on her shoulder. "The emergency room doctor at Geneva probably sees things like this all the time. Just the change in environment, the excitement of the weekend—just one of those things, Claire, because I'll be damned if I can find a thing wrong with you, and I've been your family's physician for over ten years." He looks out the window and coughs. "I'm at a loss. I would call this a 'stress-related incident.' How about if you just slow down, take it easy for a bit? Perhaps you could get away and visit family, have somebody dote on you for a change."

"Dr. Land, I become *so* ill…this is not in my head. I know it. And there's nothing less possible than my abandoning my duties at home." Claire sits up straight gathering resolve. The nerve! As if she's some indolent housewife who sits around all day in a chenille bathrobe. Donald Land should know better. "I don't have the time to slow down. We are breaking ground on a new business. I'm supervising the construction as well as the planning. Stuart's executive position gives social engagements a particular relevance. The children are active and in their formative years Their demands are constant and I do not want to neglect them in any way. Their character is my responsibility. Rest and recreation are not regular options."

"Claire, you have no idea how many people come in here every day saying "I don't feel well. Look, I'm at my wit's end. There isn't a magic diagnosis for this." Dr. Land fishes a prescription pad out of his pocket, clamping it to the top of his clipboard. "You won't do Stuart or the kids any good if you're at the end of your rope, tense and irritable. What I'm writing for you now is a prescription for a relaxant. I want you to take two a day."

"I do not want happy pills! Tranquilizers seem pointless at best when I know that there's something physically wrong with me."

He responded, "Stress and depression are physical conditions, Claire. They alter the brain chemistry and eventually affect its structures. There's nothing wrong with taking medication to relax. Think of it in evolutionary terms, how quickly human technology has outstripped our bodies. Why, it used to be that the most stressful thing humans faced was the occasional predator, or having to wander farther to gather roots during the dry season. Now, our systems are under constant pressure, and it's inescapable, relentless, day after day. Please consider this prescription. It's for your own good."

"Please, Doctor Land, if you can't tell me what's wrong with me, refer me to someone who can."

Chapter IX

The First Attack

R ene de la Violette was a quiet man with carefully cultivated interests that were of no concern to his wife: his garden and his daughter. His daughter may have perhaps benefited more from training than the clematis, but it was now too late. A reminder of this fact nicked his consciousness one summer day as he examined the roots of the new Bourbons, the latest addition to the rose bed. This green world was shattered by the shrieks of a red-haired dervish, his darling daughter. He sighed to hear her squawk like a parrot, and stiffly raised himself up, clippers in his right hand. "Papa, Papa! You would not believe what she is doing now...." Marie-Ange stood in dismay, panting and disheveled with sweat plastering red curls to the sides of her face.

"Your mother has always been a woman beyond belief." Rene furrowed his brow at a stream of tiny bright green dots trailing down the stem of a plant. Aphids. Too bad. They must be eradicated at once. "What has she done to upset you now, rosebud?" Marie-Ange fanned herself with her hands under the shade of a large lilac. "She is planning, not the third, not the fourth, but the fifth reception for that pale stiff of a new sister-in-law that Christoph impregnated and hauled out of some heap of stones in the forest. Ooooh, it makes me SO angry!

Papa, people will think we are like peasants who come to town once a month to sell turnips and buy ribbons with which to seduce milkmaids. I cannot believe it. My mother has no restraint, no dignity whatsoever." She kicked over a toadstool that had erupted through the edge of the flowerbed.

"Now, now, do not let your mother's excesses render you unkind to the poor girl. She is already with Christoph—this is punishment enough, let alone perhaps feeling a bit on display. The last thing she needs is more enmity."

"Fine, Papa." Marie-Ange plucked a leaf from the branch above her head and folded it in two, and then tore it into small pieces as she spoke. "Fine, if you do not care that we are certain to be the laughingstock of Salzburg. At least listen to me. Do you have any idea how ridiculous mother is acting? She practices to look like Elysia in front of her mirror. She does everything except follow the woman around the house taking notes and measuring the ratio of her limbs like one of our dressmakers. I actually caught her in Elysia's room going through her personal belongings!"

"And what were you doing going into Elysia's rooms to so catch her there, my darling rosebud?" Rene leaned over and started to scrape away the pests with the tip of the clippers. Damn! He would have to tell Klaus to come out here with some soapy water and clean off the Bourbons at once.

"I was just walking by and heard something." Marie-Ange pouted. "Besides, Papa, someone has to pay attention to what is going on inside that house. Mother powders herself in an attempt to look like Elysia, looking more like she's been laid out for last rites. Are you listening to me?"

"I hear the chorus of every sweet note from your lips, my angel. Your mother is stricken with the temporary delusion that she is royalty. We have a baroness in the house. No one in the house is allowed to possess higher status or prestige than your mother. Therefore, your mother aspires to surpass the baroness in noble characteristics, but the most that she can do is flatter the girl and wear too much powder. If no greater evil comes from this farce than your embarrassment, we will have done well, indeed. It's the unborn child I fear for." One of the new roses appeared to be a bad strain. Rene cupped the unfolding flower in his hand and examined the green fingers of the sepals connected to the petals. No, no—it wouldn't do. The specimen was faulty; he would have to order a new one. What was the name of the violet variety? Vanity—that was it. He would order a replacement for the defective plant at once. He snapped off the bud and placed it in his pocket as a reminder. "All this entertaining should appeal to you at least, right darling?"

"Papa, I have nothing to do with it." Marie-Ange stuck out her lower lip and traced an arc on the lawn with the tip of her left shoe. "All come to admire her grace, the Baroness Elysia." Marie-Ange rolled her eyes skyward and then bent to the lawn, drawing the back of her hand over the grass in a caricatured bow. "Oh, oh, oh…the baroness has such refinement, such an air about her. Have you ever seen such pale skin? So unblemished! So pure!" She spoke through her nose, trilling the occasional 'r' in a crude parody of the last traces of Odile's southern dialect. "You would think that she was hawking rare antiquities, not speaking of a human right there in the room. She even said that Elysia's skin is like 'moonlit alabaster.' Please, Papa, I am trying to eat during all this drivel. It is enough to make one lose the food already consumed, never mind sustaining any appetite throughout.

"So then everyone has to gawk at the contrast, my dotted ruddiness next to the lady of the cool-blue-ivory tower. Papa, it is so unfair." She made her hands into fists and drummed the air in front of her chest.

"You are a beautiful girl, Marie-Ange." Rene tried to console her. "You have lovely coloring. You look healthy and vibrant. Look..." he waved his arm out over the rose beds. "Which do you see first among these flowers? The yellow? The red? Or the white?"

"I am not sitting still with my feet in manure, covered with thorns, waiting for someone to smell me!" Marie-Ange stamped her foot. "Papa, I am not one of your roses! I am a young woman who is trying to be the toast of Salzburg! With our money, that should be no challenge—but mother will not help me. She spends all her time following this strange visitor. She's never cared for me, you know it!" The young woman turned her face to the hedge behind her. Rene knew her eyes were filled with tears.

"Your mother has just never had a use for you, sweetheart. This is as close as she comes to caring. Christoph is helpful in her ambitions. I'm certain that the moment she can think of a use for you, you will be as valued. Do not envy the puppets for the attention of the puppeteer." Rene fingers the petals in his pocket.

"At least they get to be on stage," she sulked. "I do not like this Elysia. She looks as if she has been visited by the barber-surgeon every day. Perhaps she puts leeches on her arms at night. She is as listless as one bled all the time, too. And I cannot stand to speak within a foot of her: it smells like something has died in her throat. How Christoph can kiss her, I do not know. He must place a handkerchief perfumed with rosewater between them whenever she demands his affections. I swear it has worsened since her arrival."

"Well, if your mother is stalking her as you say, it's no wonder that the poor thing is nervous and ill. Perhaps she is keeping still, hoping that Odile will lose interest and leave her alone. You should be more kind toward this woman. With Odile mimicking her and parading her around from reception to party to ball, and in her condition, the girl is no doubt too fatigued and beleaguered as it is. She does not need your abuse. Try to think of her as a sister that you never had, an ally, perhaps, at some point. Do not bother trying to fight your mother. It is easier to go around her. Just nod and smile and go about your business, doing what you will, out of her way. There is no glory in her machinations, either perpetuating them or inflating their significance through your reaction."

"But, Papa," Marie-Ange turned around to reveal her tear-streaked face. "She ignores me for years, and now I am the ugly stepchild in my own house. Everything I do is no match for the grace and beauty of Elysia. What's worse is having to hear about it, having her harp on and on all of the time." Her face crumpled as Rene drew her to his shoulder and rocked her side to side.

"Yes, darling, I know, I know." His hand smoothed her curls. "But you can do better. You needn't be like your mother. Try to charm her and she may leave you alone. You are your own shining beauty, not some cave-bound pale creature. Elysia is a stranger among us. Be kind to her."

Marie-Ange snuffled against her father's collar. "Yes, Papa. I will visit with her this afternoon. Perhaps we can go out to the park in the carriage."

"Very good, my dear. Don't they have a quartet performing in the gazebo each day at three?"

"I will see. We could just stay here and have a sisterly talk—your garden is so lovely."

"Yes, my darling, that it is. Good-bye now," he called after her as she turned and trotted off towards the house. Rene sighed over his carefully tended shrubs. Concentrating on the plants always seemed futile after the distraction of the dramas in the household. Elysia's arrival threw off the delicate balance that he strove to maintain between Marie-Ange and Odile. The common focal point of the baroness drew them into conflict, and Odile would compare her child unfavorably to anything or anyone, let alone a striking young woman like Elysia. It was really too bad, the way she had to insult her own child, not just fawn over the newcomer. The best that could be hoped for was that Odile and Marie-Ange avoid one another, but with all of these parties there was going to be even more competition and rivalry.

Baroness von Eschenbach had no idea that this drama was unfolding before her, inspired by her presence. The young lady most likely hadn't any knowledge of the possibility of such chicanery and pettiness. Rene could only hope that she had the good judgment to stay away from the inevitable conflict between mother and daughter.

There was much more he had hoped for, but Christoph had yet to be stricken in some accident. He knew it was not Christian to consider his adopted son so uncharitably, but mon dieu, it was a wonder that they had not been petitioned by an army of young women bearing bastards by this bastard. And he is so little his own man that he just runs off to stud whomever his mother directs, thrusting away to further Odile's ceaseless ambitions. Who knows what perversions he might engage in upon her demand? Rene blushed to consider, and then crossed himself. God had made this day: let him enjoy it in the garden likewise created. He returned his attention to his roses. "Odd," he mused, "in this light, you do actually note the white ones first." Perhaps it was the bank of laurel behind them, or the late morning light. That new variety has a bluish tint near the petal base. What was it called again? His head shook with chagrin to remember the name assigned by some gardening poetaster: 'Moonlit Alabaster.' He would not share this gem of knowledge with Marie-Ange.

Rene stepped through the hedge of smaller, hardier blossoming plants to examine the flowers. Full and even. And the scent? He leaned over and inhaled, closing his eyes. The petals were smooth beneath his moustache, and the smell, incomparably clear and heady. Not too fruity, nor too flowery. As ridiculous a criticism as that was to apply to a flower, some of the blousey English cabbage varieties almost reeked. No, this one smelled like a good dessert wine.

In her chambers, Odile stood at the window with a glass of wine in her hand. She was having a drop to celebrate the planning of her next grand reception, a party in honor of the baroness's entry to their family. Not the wedding itself, which she had arranged months in advance, just an introduction to the most select two dozen families in Salzburg. The first course would be turtle soup, and then a terrine with morels and borage flowers, followed by potted larks with fennel, and then ginger-glazed piglets in aspic for the main course, each one carrying a little apple covered with gold foil in its mouth. It may seem a little ostentatious to Elysia, but she would have to get used to their ways here in Salzburg.

They would spice up that old castle, indeed. Just because one was nobility, that was no reason to be restricted to a lifetime of venison on pewter served by brawny-armed women. No, not at all. Odile felt almost childish around the baroness sometimes, as if Salzburg were a music box she was about to give Elysia as a present, but she wanted to make certain that the woman liked it prior to its presentation. These moments were of course rare when compared to Odile's overwhelming pride, her sense of accomplishment at having actually found a title for the Violettes. She was in the midst of such planning, gloating, and admiration when the voices of two servants drifted up from the courtyard below.

"Well, whatever his lordship wants..." The one voice trailed off, covered with the giggles of both women. If Odile had a schilling for every maiden ravished by her son among the staff, she could hire a whole new retinue. She felt a surge of annoyance at the overheard report. So let him be amused. She drained her glass and rolled the small cylinder of crystal in her palm. Suddenly, she pricked up her ear—they were discussing Elysia.

"That's why they call them 'blue bloods.'" Odile leaned over the balcony to see Rosamunde elbowing Giselle. Knowing the help, if only for matters of surveillance, was not unwise.

"You!" she barked at the wenches. The two spun in surprise.

"Madame?" They both curtsied, flustered. Rosamunde was trying to hide a half-gnawed leg of chicken in her apron pocket.

Odile blared, "Up here! At once!"

"Yes, Madame," the two squeaked, and bumped into one another entering the downstairs door from the courtyard. She opened the door before they arrived and queried them as they mounted the top step.

"You were talking about the Baroness von Eschenbach. You said that there was something odd about her passed water. What is it?" Odile raised her right eyebrow in inquisition as her fists nested on the points of her hipbones. "I am waiting for an answer."

Rosamunde glanced at Giselle, and then stepped forward to the lady of the house. Bowing, she addressed the floor. "Madame, we were simply concerned with the health of the baroness. Since she is with child, we..."

"And what makes you think that?" Odile snarled.

"Oh, we do not believe it at all, it is only that the companion of the von Eschenbach aunt made a remark to the cook, who told the..."

Odile waved her palm with disgust at Rosamunde. "Enough. Tell me what you were discussing about the baroness."

"Her pis...her water is strange, Madame." The servant drew herself up in an attempt at authority. "I have raised five children and tended countless others. I have shared quarters with women from England and even once a Nubian, and have watched lords and carriage-drivers alike pass water, begging your lady's pardon," Rosamunde remembered herself and bent her knees, "but I have never seen anyone with purple night water."

"Have you yet to tend her chambers from last night?"

Rosamunde turned to Giselle, who slowly shook her head side to side, twice. "Hmmph," snorted Odile. "Very well, slatterns, bring me the chamber pot of the Baroness von Eschenbach." The two women hesitated. "Move!" she demanded. "Now!"

Upon their return, Odile rolled up her sleeve and dipped in her empty wineglass, holding its contents to the light. The liquid was purple. She turned to the servants. "Has it always been so?"

"It is darker now than when she first arrived."

"Curious." Odile rotated the glass in the sun.

Rosamunde and Giselle exchanged glances. "Is the baroness alright, Madame? We were worried, with the child and all..."

"Nonsense. You have no concern, just a gossiping interest in the most intimate leavings of your superiors. Shame." Her back stiffened and she set the glass down on the balustrade. "The von Eschenbachs are a long-established line of nobility. You cannot be expected to understand, but such refinement affects the inner workings among those of our heritage, not just the outer bearing." She emptied the contents over the balcony, right on top of Rene's prize Dutch iris and handed the empty glass to Giselle. "And where is the baroness now?"

Rosamunde replied: "She is in her chambers, Madame."

"What? And you intruded for this pot? Never mind. What is she doing there so late? It is almost noon."

"The baroness is not given to rising early, Madame." Rosamunde bent over to collect the blue and white porcelain pot as Giselle stood, uncertain, with the wineglass.

"I see." Odile returned her gaze to the window. "You may go now."

In the hallway, the two women commiserated over having to speak with the mistress. "They are all insane. Blue-pissing, purple-wearing show-offs. They still have to squat to use the pot." Rosamunde hunkered down with the willow-patterned china balanced on one hip and waggled her bottom at the top of the stairs.

Giselle giggled into the back of her hand. "I thought she was going to taste it, at first, or demand that we bring her the pot every morning." Then they heard steps behind them and rushed down the stairs.

Elysia slept wrapped in white linens. Her hair fanned out toward the top of the bed, forming a lacy lattice over the folds of the pillows. Scenes unfolded before her eyes, each one as bright and sharp-edged as the stained glass in the windows of a cathedral. Her brother, Peter, played with a new puppy in front of the family hearth. He was showing her how she was to pet it, stroking its face and chest before scratching its ears. The little dog's tail whipped back and forth; its hot tongue left little circles of spit on her cheek from his happy lapping. Her father rode into the courtyard, dismounted, and reached into the pouch affixed to the saddle's side, removing a wooden top for Peter and a fabric doll for herself. Then she and Peter chased one another through the autumn orchard, avoiding the fallen fruit abuzz with hornets.

The buzzing changed to humming and she knew she was leaning on her mother's lap. Cool, smooth fingers stroked her forehead, tracing a wave of hair falling in front of her ear. Her adoring mother, Dorothea, encircled Elysia's body with her arms. Elysia pointed to the ring on the hand covering her own. A dark red stone sat in the middle of a thick gold band, a dragon sculpted in gold at its upper border. The hum ended and her mother's voice deepened in seriousness. "Elysia, remember: the dragon is the blood. The blood is the dragon."

The little dragon opened its eyes and flapped its webbed wings, then grew to astonishing size, exhaling a ball of fire into her face. Elysia raised her hand to shield her eyes. The orange blast was racing toward her. She knew that her eyebrows were going to be singed at any moment. Her forehead burned.

"Good day, Baroness." Elysia cracked her eyes and saw Odile de la Violette standing over her. "You have slept well, I trust?" The sunlight pouring in through the opened curtains made her eyes smart. She wished that she could roll over and ignore this woman, but winced a soft smile instead.

"Very well, yes, thank you." She sat up among the linens. "With such a thoughtful hostess, how could I not?"

"Now, now, is that any way to speak with your new mother?" Odile clasped her hand. Elysia recoiled but gave Odile a gracious smile once more. The woman sat on the edge of the bed and patted Elysia's foot through the covers. "You would not be so formal, of course, as to not tell me if you were feeling ill?" She knit her brows together and pursed her lips in doting sympathy. Elysia sat up, straightening the silken coverlet. She had trouble moving her limbs.

"Why no, Madame, but thank you. Why do you ask?"

"Well, my dear, I am a little concerned. Your appetite is normal?"

"Yes—if I may inquire as to why you would think otherwise?"

"Well, it's only that you eat so little. Is the cuisine here unpleasant?" "Oh, certainly not. On the contrary, it is exquisite in the extreme. I have never sampled such delicacies as I have tasted here. Some of them are seasoned beyond my previous dining, but I am flattered to have my palate so educated." Odile held on to Elysia's foot and began to rotate it in an arc beneath the covers. "Have your little feet been hurting? Pardon my concern, dear, but it just seems that you stay in your chambers, only coming out for meals and receptions. Have our ways become tiresome to you?" Odile's eyebrows moved up in their interior corners in a sarcastic show of dismay.

Elysia smiled at the concern her mother-in-law displayed. Such lavish attention was not something that appealed to her character, but she was flattered nonetheless. "Madame," she drew her knees up to her chest under the covers, and Odile's hand relinquished her foot, "Your generosity is unparalleled. You have so many friends…it is an honor to meet them all, and I am truly charmed that they might want to make my acquaintance, but it is a pace of life to which I am unaccustomed. Please forgive me if I sometimes fail to meet the standards that the whirl of life in Salzburg demands."

"As long as it is nothing exceptional, my dear." Odile sat down on the foot of the bed and drew her knees up to copy Elysia's posture. Odile was wearing a necklace of cloisonne beads and began to trace the floral pattern on each one with the tip of her fingernail. As she examined the beads, she lowered her voice and inquired further, "You are certain that is all?"

Elysia extended a hand over the bed cover and smoothed a crease in the brocade spread. Now the solicitousness was passing into prying. What did this woman want? Was she going to bring a physician to prod her all over like someone examining a mare for purchase? She replied with measured words: "The excitement is somewhat of a demand for me. So many dances and receptions—I am a bit breathless. Each day, I seem to sleep in a little later and later. I am embarrassed to admit that I have not heard the cock's crow since my arrival."

"We city folk do not judge people by rising with the dawn," Odile leaned forward and grabbed Elysia's knee as if it were a doorknob that she was considering turning. "What I would like to know, truly, is that you are all right, as one woman to another."

Elysia felt her cheeks grow warm. She plucked at a loose thread on top of the coverlet. The answer had better satisfy Odile. Surely this woman did not intend to poke and prod her? "As one woman to another, all is well."

"Tres bien! Very good, my sweet." Odile winked at the blushing girl. "I do not mean to intrude; it is just so important to me that my favorite guest and new daughter be well in all respects." Elysia's picking at the coverlet had grown more aggressive: the girl now wound a length of thread around the index finger of her right hand. Still, her fingertip had turned to a light coral, not the radish color that most people's tied-off finger ends would obtain. She looked up at Odile, and then turned her eyes to the uncovered window. Odile followed her gaze and continued. "There is still much of a lovely day for you to enjoy. That pastel silk moire is so flattering to you. Will you be wearing it today? Shall I call your servant to assist you?"

Elysia nodded, "Oui, Madame. Merci beaucoup."

"And what is her name?" Odile stood up and straightened her gown. Such familiarity as sitting on the bed might have been inappropriate, but the posture seemed necessary to broach such intimate topics. Elysia snapped off the errant thread, replying, "Marta."

"She is pretty, for a servant." Odile tucked the length of cloisonné beads into her bodice, and then rearranged her cuffs. "How long has she worked for your family?"

"Since her birth. Her people are Slavs who were kept by my mother's family for generations. She will be charmed by the compliment—I will pass it along to her."

"No need to do that." Odile's palm curved around the bedpost. "There is no need to flatter the help. It would only interfere with the performance of their duties if you let these people acquire airs. If you become too familiar, well, my dear, I need not explain to you these matters of class." The bell-pull cord hung next to the door. Odile swung its tassel back and forth and looped the rope around her hand. "By the way, is your water moving as it should?"

Elysia felt her cheeks grow warm again. Really! Next, would this woman ask to see it? "Yes, Madame." Elysia rose from the bed. Marie-Ange burst in, a flurry of color, causing her mother to stumble backward, yanking too hard on the cord. The top hook wrenched out of its holder and the rope fell limp at her feet.

"Hello, Elysia! Oh, hello, Mama." The girl bounded to the bed and plopped onto the mattress, belly-first. "Elysia! What are you looking at out that window? How lovely Papa keeps the garden? I will have to show it all to you very soon: the roses, lilacs, healing herbs, conservatory with imported orchids that the Portuguese bring bundled in straw and linen. But first, today, I have a better idea." Marie-Ange sat up and swung her legs to the far side of the bed, bounced twice, and then joined Elysia at the window.

"You do not need the extra sunlight, girl." Odile snarled at her daughter. "Every moment that you spend under the eye of the sun makes your hair more like carrots."

Marie-Ange shook her hair in defiance. "A touch of sun would do wonders for our Baroness. Everything is arranged. Today we can go on a picnic. The cook has packed quail, parsnips cooked with apples in pastry, chilled sugared grapes, slices of lamb, brioche…just a few leftovers, and a flask of amontillado." She winked at Elysia, not turning to gauge her mother's reaction. "Josef is bringing around the carriage. You haven't seen the lake yet, have you?" Elysia moved her head from side to side, having taken her gaze from the topiaried grounds to the babbling dervish at her side.

"Well! We must change that! You can go to the park or this garden any day of the week, but a special girls' jaunt to the lake would be a particular treat. You will be a married woman under lock and key soon enough. Let us get out and see some of the area. Believe me, I know all these lavish mansions can look the same after a round of parties. Perhaps the lake is like the one your father keeps stocked with trout?" She threw her arm around Elysia's shoulders. Odile stood with the bell rope at her feet.

"Yes, of course!" Elysia blurted in response before Odile could proffer any objections. She must get away from being interrogated by this woman. "Please, Marie-Ange, you must stay and help me select my dress. I do not know what is fashionable to wear to the lake here in Salzburg." She took Marie-Ange by the hand, led her over to the wardrobe and flung the door wide open so that Odile's view of them was obscured.

"Ooh!" Marie-Ange squealed. "I did not know you had this pink! But let me see the gray—no, no that is far too somber. Wait—behind the cape. No, not the light green, the one with the blue flowers. Perfect! To think that somebody had to embroider those bachelor's buttons all over it. Oh—and the buttons match. Too precious! Mama? Mama?"

Odile was leaning against the door frame, fuming. *That babbler bounces into the baroness's boudoir, interrupting a quiet moment between us and ending a very important line of inquiry, yelping about all these ridiculous plans she's concocted.* She glared at the underskirts and shawls accumulating at the young women's feet. *That ridiculous useless goose of a daughter could never have come up with this idea on her own. It must have been Rene's suggestion.*

"Mama!" Marie-Ange shrieked. "Have you not heard me? The baroness will require Marta's assistance for her coiffure. Perhaps the bell in the next room is still working." The girl turned back to the wardrobe and bent down to collect a pair of little slipper shoes. "Also, could you ask the cook to include some of those chocolate cakes, my favorites? The ones with the candied violets on top. She could even spell out our names with the petals, like she did for me when I was a little girl. Elysia, I have the perfect bonnet to match your dress. You absolutely must see it. Come with me." The women laughed as they left. Odile could hear their footsteps receding down the hall. She leaned against the balustrade until she heard the clatter of the coach in the courtyard, and then its departure.

Odile stormed down to the garden. *Where is that useless flower-fondling cuckold? What a miserable excuse for a husband, an inert dolt who finally stirred to life only to attempt to foil my plans.* "Rene!" she shrieked. "Where are you? Ruh-NAAAY!"

The new Bourbons stood before her. She built an empire, raised the entire family, and what has this man done? Pampered expensive pansies. It was really too much. Her hand flew out and she snapped off a bloom, tearing the delicate cabbage petals to pieces. Then another, and another.

A trail of tiny scraps of red, yellow, purple and white unfurls behind her down the edge of the rose bed. "Rene de la Violette! I must speak to you at once! Get out of the potting shed, you miserable fool!" Her husband heard the echoes of her shrilling, and decided it would be an excellent time to tour the box-laurel hedge maze he designed and had tended with Klaus for over ten years. He might get lost in the labyrinth and wander for hours, or even have to sit down on a bench in the shade to rest, safely away from that cloying screech.

Marie-Ange and Elysia sat in the landaulet, enjoying the breeze that ruffled their bonnets. The horses threw up dust from the dry road and the chestnut branches kept them beneath a canopy of shade. In the gaps between the trees, Elysia saw the rushing Salzach, a gathering of mountain streams into a mighty tribe of melted ice surging down from the rivulets of the Tyrol to cut an Alpine liquid swath through the valley. It was muddied by the relative summer calm, but still broken with whirlpools and swelling waves from bank to bank. The road ran parallel to the river around the foothills at the outskirts of town, and as the horses pulled them farther from the de la Violette estate, Marie-Ange had to raise her voice in an attempt to be heard over the river's turbulence.

Elysia would nod politely, but her eyes kept veering back to the raw strength of the river, so elemental, so free. When she closed her eyes she could hear the roar of the water thrashing over the stones at the bottom of that glacial canyon, each boulder crying out to her, it seemed. Marie-Ange kept up her own torrent at Elysia's side, but the competition was too fierce, too alluring in its beauty and grandeur, for the spoiled girl to distract the baroness. Without an audience, the young woman turned to harangue the help.

"Faster, Coachman!" She hoisted a skirt to kick the back of the driver's seat. "My father pays good money to keep these nags fed and curried—the least you can do is make them run! Where's your whip? Faster!" Her gloved hand grasped the edge of the carriage and she glared in defiance to the passing trees.

"Marie-Ange! My bonnet!" Elysia's fingers tried to catch the last satin ribbon as it flickered beyond the carriage. "We must stop. I cannot go out without a hat. It is the bonnet you lent me!"

Marie-Ange rumpled her nose and yelled, "That old thing? Please do not worry, Baroness, it is just a bonnet for a country jaunt, not a Paris-designed hat with dyed feathers. There is no need for such concern." She slouched back in the seat and raised both slippered feet to the edge of the driver's seat before her.

"But a lady does not go about without a head-covering." Elysia frowned and tried to smooth her hair beneath the onslaught of the wind, but loose strands already whipped out around her ears.

"Oh, a lady doesn't, eh?" Marie-Ange laughed and threw her head back, plucking at the bow tied beneath her chin. "Ladyship is too highly esteemed." She took the straw edge of her own hat and whirled it out behind her. Both women turned to see the disc of ribbon and straw skip among the ruts and then finally wheel on its edge before coming to rest in the middle of the road.

"Marie-Ange!" gasped Elysia, "You will ruin your complexion. My mother always emphasized to me that if you go out in the sun without a bonnet the skin will dry and parch like a market-woman's.

"And perhaps these market-women benefit from the sun's rays, live a little, enjoy their lives, hmmm? The workers in the field last all day; perhaps they draw their strength from the sun. These chestnut trees tower to the light, not to caves beneath the roads, not to the catacombs behind the church. Have you ever seen daffodils grow tall beneath the moon?" Marie-Ange stretched up her arms, fingers spread wide, in impersonation of a growing flower. Then she turned to Elysia. "Besides, dear Baroness, a touch of sun would do you some good. Just a bit of roses in your cheeks and you would be even more fetching." Marie-Ange's fingers drummed her own freckled cheeks for emphasis.

"Really?" Elysia turned her eyes up and squinted. When she closed her eyes, spidery black dots filled a field of red, and white bursts of light pulsed behind her eyelids. Her head was throbbing.

"Of course. And, actually, I know that my brother is mad for women of high color. To be candid, I was quite pleasantly surprised when he arrived with you on his arm. I was too used to him becoming all slack-jawed at the sight of women who were as brown as Turks, or at least a bit too ruddy to seem refined. I used to tease mother that he was going to run away to Constantinople and start a harem. As you can imagine, that did not amuse her." Malice reeked from Marie-Ange's pores.

"Whatever do you mean?" Elysia turned to her companion, trying to conceal both her anger and her nausea. "That is a crude jest."

"Oh, is it?" Marie-Ange leaned forward to brace her elbows on her knees. "Would that my jokes were the crudest thing in the household. My dear, surely you know my brother is a man of the world. It would be in your best interest to use every feminine trick and wile in the book. Change your appearance every week, or color your hair, or send away for foreign costumes, learn new dances, suggest new vices—I have heard of a folio of engravings from Marseilles that perhaps you should examine."

Now Elysia's cheeks burned without the sun. "Thank you for your insights," she replied, voice low.

Marie-Ange smiled small and then grinned large. "Anything to help my new sister."

The carriage turned down the lake road. "Oh, look," called Marie-Ange, "There is the Viscount D'Assembrey. Last year all the girls swooned for him, but now he is engaged to some princess from Pisa. People say she is a dwarf. Yes, him in the green jacket." She waved graciously at the man. "And here we are! You'll find that this is exactly what you needed. Some fresh air, some time away from my mother being your shadow. Do not protest; I know she does not give you a moment to yourself. If Odile were sniffing at my heels all day, I would never leave my room, either. And all those receptions! To be shown off to people attending out of the most base curiosity, why, it must be all too tiring to be so on display. Please, just follow the picnic standard: in the sunlight, or else you might as well have stayed at home; but near the water, so that you will not overheat.

"Don't tell me your mother told you that ladies do not eat out of doors, either?" She gave Elysia's elbow a playful tweak and then wrapped an arm around her waist. "Close enough to the willow to admire it, but not so close that we need worry about bugs or leaves in our food, Josef," she directed the coachman. He called the horses to a halt in a sylvan stretch of grass. He unloaded a small white wooden table and carried two chairs from the back of the rig.

Marie-Ange stepped back to the carriage and lifted out a wicker basket covered with a linen cloth. "Oh, yes." Her tongue traced the interior edge of her upper lip as she removed the bowl, trays, plates, bottles and jars from its inside.

"What is all this? Elysia was used to the plain and healthy food of her father's lands, not the rich delicacies arrayed before her.

"Well, I will explain each course to you. First, we must start with this pâté..." The women indulged: pâté, pesto, wines, sweets, a liqueur to aid the digestion. The women discussed the wedding, the fashions, the foibles of the court at play. At first, Marie-Ange's salacious gossip made Elysia blush, but she found herself an accomplice to the giggles by the end of the meal.

"Look!" Marie-Ange demanded, whisking a small bottle from the bottom of the hamper. "Ta-da! The ultimate delight to toast the ultimate wedding—it is cognac from my father's cellar. Two such elegant ladies..." she tossed her thoroughly disheveled red hair, "must have such an exquisite drink. We cannot let the men hoard everything to themselves."

Elysia shook her head. The amber glass floated before her with indistinct edges. Marie-Ange pulled the stopper from the bottle and put it on the table amid the rinds, dirty china and scraps of waxed paper. Elysia tried to rest her elbows on the small table but it rocked. The once-engrossing ripples on the lake made her feel queasy.

"Marie-Ange, I feel ill. It is time for us to go back." She leaned back in her chair and braced herself against the table's edge, arms stiff from fingertips to elbow. "I do not feel well at all." Elysia turned her head to look at the calming green of the willow.

"Poor darling! Whatever you say, although you look much healthier. Just a touch of sun upon your face and your appearance is quite enhanced." Marie-Ange handed her a small glass of golden liquid. It smelled sharp and piquant. "Drink this while I have Josef pack up. Then I'll have him flog those old nags to a lather. We will return in no time at all."

"Help me to the shade." Suddenly the sun became Elysia's tormenter. "Please, Marie-Ange." She extended her hand, closing her eyes and her mouth tight against the light in the air.

"Baroness, just stay still for a moment, and we will be in the carriage. If you are in distress, it is truly better that we do not move you." Marie-Ange tilted the table over to dump the remains of the meal into the hamper. Elysia heard breaking china and turned her head back toward the lake. As she sipped the cognac, the sunlight spilt its rays across the surface of the water, a hundred blades rolling sideways, piercing her eyes. An entire army of solid light had accumulated and was threatening to crack the base of her skull in two. The rattling of the light sword was echoed by the lurid lapping of the current at her feet; the comforting rhythm of water, rolling yet confined, became a relentless series of thuds on mud.

Marie-Ange moved at a lumpen pace, bickering with Josef about the arrangement of the gear in the back of the equipage. Surprising that such details would concern her. Elysia arose and started stumbling to the carriage. Her legs wobbled as if the bones had melted. Her knees bumped into one another as she approached the door and fell against the railing. She turned to lean against it, but then shuddered and doubled forward. Her stomach rebelled and all the molten remnants of the decadent afternoon fountained to the grass before her. Marie-Ange appeared at her side and placed an arm around her shoulder.

"You ARE ill! Here, let me help you up." Marie-Ange turned Elysia around to the carriage and Josef helped lift her into the seat. Elysia's flushed complexion and panting breath made Marie-Ange wonder for an instant if she'd pushed this game too far. The driver cracked the whip over the horses and the women knocked into each other. The landaulet returned to the road. The same distance that was an amusing, bumpy jaunt shortly before noon was now a harrowing, rugged terrain that stretched before them indefinitely, punctuated only by gulches and rough sprays of gravel.

"Josef! Not so fast!" Marie-Ange commanded. "The baroness is ill." To Elysia, the yelling was just another stone thrown in the thickening sludge of her consciousness, a prickling mixture of buzzes and sharp pangs that emanated from her head and gut. The sun cooked her; she knew it had heated her corsets and that they were abetting the torture, confining her in roasting strips on the outside like a human spit. The skin on her arms scraped her sleeve interiors—she was surprised to find her dress had been lined with sandpaper all this time and she had never noticed before.

Each little blue embroidered flower carried a thorn behind it; now her skin was all prickled and punctured. Elysia raised her hand to her face. She assumed her cheeks looked flayed and swollen, as if bitten by an army of hornets. She turned to express her surprise to Marie-Ange, but only guttural gurgles could escape her throat.

"No, Baroness, do not try to speak. We will have you home soon." Elysia turned and gazed at the river. The whitewater was once again hypnotic, but this time she wished the reflected sunlight would pull her all the way into unconsciousness, that she could fold into absolute rest in some cold safety. Marie-Ange's voice was a set of harrowing shrieks at her side. Elysia gladly would have flung herself into the river to let it carry her away, away from this obnoxious harridan, the vile Odile, her suspect fiancé Christoph, and mostly, the churning of her own innards and the burning of her skin. She could not distinguish Marie-Ange's yells to the driver. The thudding of her own heartbeat in her ears drowned out the shattering octave-yelps of invectives from the woman's mouth.

Marie-Ange bit her lower lip. *Damnation,"* she mulled. *I only wanted to give her a heat rash, perhaps cause her to miss the next dance. It is not my fault the gentry are so fragile. Who would have thought? Just a little sun and a picnic; there was really no harm intended. Would such a delicate flower survive in Papa's garden?*

The carriage finally drew into the round drive on the grounds. The driver called for help and Elysia was carried to her bed by four strong men using an abandoned door from the side of the stable as an improvised stretcher. They carefully banked their cargo on the stairs, negotiating the turns and holding her feet higher to maintain even elevation. Elysia's hand fell over and brushed along the railing. Her head was turned to the side, eyes swollen shut. They deposited her on the bed.

The handlers disappeared with the door and Odile appeared with Rene, Christoph and Elysia's aunt whom she called Tante Sophia. "Marie-Ange!" Odile roared. "What happened?" The finger she pointed at Elysia's prostrate form shook with rage.

"Sh...sh...she became ill," Marie-Ange blubbered. "I do not know why. I merely wanted to take her out for a picnic."

"You witch!" Odile could not retain the pretense of refinement. She was shaking her fist at her daughter. "Why is she so flushed? Would you have her cooked?" She placed her palm on Elysia's forehead. "Mon Dieu! She is burning up! What did you do?"

Marie-Ange struggled to keep her composure. "Mama, she said she wanted to gain some color before the wedding, that she wanted to look healthier. She even tossed away the bonnet I lent her. Do not blame me for her vanity, I only..."

"Blame you?" Odile hissed, approaching with narrowed eyes. "What did you do, Marie-Ange?"

"Mama, nothing. I swear!"

A servant materialized at Odile's elbow. He did not bother to clear his throat, but announced that the doctor had arrived and that all except Tante Sophia were to leave the room, according to the physician's instructions.

Odile had been pacing the hall for hours. Rene and Marie-Ange remained on a settee near the head of the stairs. Marie-Ange alternately dozed or sought solace on her father's collar. Christoph was sprawled in a chair, cleaning his nails with an ivory-handled letter opener. It was a gift from a tutor who had been enamored of him; the gentleman admired the Greeks for more than their philosophy. Christoph was happy to receive presents and flattery. Madame de la Violette had worn a path in the polish of the parquet before Elysia's chambers. At the bend in the hall there was a clock on a stand, an elaborate gilt mechanism that chimed the time with sweet bells and had dancing Dresden china figurines of a romantic pastoral couple. The rakish goatherd and cherubic shepherdess appeared from the clock five times before a servant opened the door, eyes downcast, toting a bundle of bloodstained linens. Odile spun around and ran to the doorway. Next Tante Sophia emerged, leaning on the physician's shoulder. The blood on his forearm had stained the ecru of her shawl. "Christoph!" Odile commanded. He rose from the seat, took Tante Sophia by the elbow, and started escorting her to her chambers. The woman's sobs and prayers echoed down the hall behind her.

"May I speak with...?" The doctor could not finish his sentence before Odile shoved him back into the room and shut the door behind them. A minute passed, and then he emerged, coat over one arm, his leather satchel of implements in hand. He offered silent condolences to Rene and Marie-Ange and then descended the stairs. They turned to face Odile. She stood at the threshold for a second, wavering as if she were tempted to slam the door in their faces, but then stepped out and closed it behind her. The click of its closing was loud in the stillness. Then she stepped forward and let her hand fly across her daughter's cheek. It was not a palm like a falling dove; it careened onto the girl's face like a falcon, again and again, punctuating each word in her exclamations. "You bitch!" Odile's face was blotched purple. "I cannot believe that you, you bloated little strumpet, had the audacity to scheme away our future! My greatest accomplishment!

Rene grabbed Odile's wrist on one of its downward trajectories and twisted her arm behind her back. Her left hand shot out, with fingers stiffened. Before Rene could grab her upper arm and restrain it, Odile's nails made three even tracks on Marie-Ange's face. Her arms held against her sides, the woman tried to kick at her daughter.

"You ruined it all! You were not content to be overdressed, overstuffed, over-esteemed in your own mind as the belle of the ball!" Odile spat on the floor. "You had to destroy it!" She stood panting and Rene loosened his grip. Marie-Ange wailed into her hands.

His hands still clutched her upper arms. He let go of one arm and turned her around to face him, promptly grasping it again. Rene bent down to speak into Odile's face. "Is the baroness all right? Woman, answer me. Is Elysia dead?"

Odile lifted her chin to Rene and took a shuddering breath. There was water in her eyes.

"No…. But the baby is."

Chapter X

Torture

Claire is in another impeccable medical complex, this one bordered with azalea, a healthy maple tree near the entry, and a trio of rocks arranged in a meditative cluster. She goes to Dr. Negelmann, Suite 403, who proceeds to test whether she is allergic to any substance by either placing it on or injecting it beneath her skin. For good measure, he has her sniff a couple of vials of powder. The ragweed pollen makes her sinuses swell. Dr. Negelmann does not provide canned patter to distract and ingratiate the patient prior to injection. He squints, pinches the flesh above Claire's elbow, and plunges in the syringe. After a couple of hours her arms are covered with red polka dots of irritation: blisters the size of nickels decorate her arms, shoulder to wrist, like a row of ant hills.

Claire presses the button next to the elevator in the lobby. *The wait is interminable. Is it coming up two flights or twenty?* Claire is on the verge of taking the stairs when the doors hiss and part, admitting her to the sterile box of carpeting and dark wood. She reaches to the panel and pushes the circle labeled "L". The ceiling has recessed lighting in a brass plane, and Claire looks up at her reflection. The strain of the day is beginning to show: her eyes are as red as the patches on her arms where the skin is pillowing up into crescents.

The lights flicker. She presses the button again. Nothing. The air in the elevator is becoming thick and acrid, threatening to coat her lungs with a chemical layer and block the bronchi with carpet lint. She presses the button more fiercely now, holding it down for a count of three. The button lights up and the doors jolt, but nothing happens. Claire gasps in terror and pulls the red knob marked "Emergency" in urgent black capitals. A bell starts shrieking at once, causing her eyes to widen and her throat to grip. It is a din to run from, an emergency alarm, a warning of fire or a nuclear raid, dissonant blatting without the cry and peal of a siren, just a mechanical bark.

When had she last heard bells? Claire's tongue dries to the roof of her mouth as she recalls the nightmare, the version of live burial with a bell in it. She learned there was once a tradition of installing a bell, or even a voice tube, in a gravesite so that the accidentally interred could ring for resurrection. The elevator walls become smaller and darker as Claire's claustrophobia kicks in. Her nails make a slight scraping noise against the doors. "No!" the back of her mind shouts. "I'm not dead!"

The elevator reconsiders, shudders, and begins its descent. The temperamental trap will not open its doors, will not release her. She pounds the door with a hammer hand, and her curled little finger leaves a spiral smudge in the middle of her reflection. The doors open to a small knot of waiting would-be passengers: a UPS delivery man with box and clipboard, presumed patients having their patience tested, and a nurse with a small child in a wheelchair in front of her. Claire feels the flush rise to her cheeks—they must be as red as the welts on her arms—and stumbles over the wheels of the chair as she navigates through the group, putting out her hand to regain her balance. In an attempt at nonchalance, she swings her purse off her shoulder to fish out her keys, but her heart still pounds with the rhythm of the emergency bell, the tintinnabulation echoing the horror of confinement.

The parking lot offers little relief. The sun has made the door handle too hot to touch. She rolls down the window until the air conditioning kicks in, hissing the cold directly onto her lap. After catching her breath, she heads to the car wash, the paragon of vehicular care for the county. As she pulls up she can see the glaziers inserting the windows, a meticulous supervisor inspecting the corners of one. Car owners would be able to view their cars throughout the entire process—this was not a car wash as an afterthought with a tank of gas, but a business dedicated exclusively to the cleanliness and freshness of the vehicle. *How much time did people spend in their cars, anyway?*

A commute into the city and back could easily consume four hours a day. It made sense to give people the opportunity to have their cars as clean as their homes, since they are mobile personal spaces, after all, personalized with a vanity plate or a particular charm on the rear-view mirror for some. Claire backs her car in between the parallel yellow lines and sees Charlie, the foreman. His sleeves are rolled up over solid arms, and he's shaking his head at a man standing with him before a small heap of brick scrap. "Charlie!"

"Hey! Hello, Mrs. Foster!" He smiles and tips the yellow bucket of a helmet farther back on his head. "Everything on schedule today?" Claire asks, shielding her eyes in the bright light. Every visit to the car wash reminds her of some organic thing, a different workman for each organ system: plumbers for circulation, electricians for the nervous wiring, masons for the thick brick skin.

"Right on time, Mrs. Foster. Just cleaning up after the last of the brick work right now. The cloth should be delivered on Wednesday." Charles White is rugged and astute. She and Stuart feel secure in his competence, and he has kept every condition of the contract that she can currently recall.

Back at home, Claire finds a reminder of those less scrupulous: correspondence from their attorney regarding their disagreement with Brian Carlson. Carlson is a scammer and a thief, a confidence man with an easy grin and a diamond-bezeled Rolex, given to smattering the patter of motivational seminars.

When they first met, he punctuated concrete discussions of the car wash with phrases such as "paradigm maximization," or he would comment, "Out-of-the-box thinking, there, Stuart," with a lopsided smile. Last time they had seen one another, there had been no smiles around. Carlson accused them of breach of contract, willful malfeasance and virtual fraud. The nerve—the man expected to be able to pull up his stake and walk away without a thought to his obligations. There was no reasoning with him, so they had been reduced to litigation. Claire shudders to recall those events as she sits down at the kitchen table with the documents.

Her legs are tired with stiffness. "I'll sue!" was a cry of last resort, the most embarrassing public venting possible, the call of a small soul that can't let things go and heaps negatives upon negatives, but in the end she had been forced to realize it was the only thing Carlson would understand. Now she has to wade through the aftermath, sheaves of jargon particularly drafted for obfuscation and confusion.

Stuart arrives home. The haven, the hearth, the heart, he thinks, as he turns the ignition off. The sunset is reflected in the rearview mirror, fish scales of lavender on a field of gold. Sunsets are inherently corny, but so necessary. Stuart smiles to think of such sentiment, reaching over to gather a bouquet of red roses and his briefcase from the passenger's seat. Perhaps all necessary and important things in life are sentimentalized, but that doesn't mean that they're any less true. He sits in the front seat for a moment, surveying the front of his kingdom, at peace with himself and the world.

The kids have left some toys on the front lawn: a red rubber ball, a doll that has been made-up with markers, one yellow Tonka truck and a jump rope. The doll is taking a ride in the back of the Tonka dump truck, one of her arms bent upward to wave like Queen Elizabeth. Stuart waves back to her as he strides to the porch. "Hi, honey, I'm home." Stuart closes the door behind him. He deposits his briefcase in the armchair in the living room and enters the kitchen brandishing the flowers. Claire startles out of the legal abstract and leans back in the chair to greet him. "Can you believe this?" Claire says, holding up the crumpled paper in her right hand.

"If you're trying to tell me there's nothing that people won't pull, I am unfortunately compelled to believe you." He pulls out a chair and lowers himself onto the orange cushion. "No, what are the particulars?" He takes out his reading glasses and snaps the case shut with a click. An hour is consumed by shuffling papers, transcripts, photocopies, invoices. When he leans back in his chair again, he glimpses the array of red on Claire's right arm. "What happened?"

His fingers reach out to gingerly circle one of the raised, blister-like patches. "Who did this to you?" He leans forward to kiss the top of her wrist. "An expensive and highly qualified professional," Claire sniffs. "Dr. Land referred me to an allergist to see if he could make a diagnosis. I was stuck full of pins like a voodoo doll and had all sorts of fluids from little vials swabbed on my arms and back." Claire twists in the chair to display her left arm to Stuart, and he clucks over the array of blotches. "After a day like this, I'm allergic to doctors. And I still don't know why I fainted at the cabin."

"I'm sorry, honey. I suspected that might happen. Stuart picks up the roses and offers them to Claire. "I thought today might be a rough day." He smiles over the top of his reading glasses. Even the roses seem like an immediate demand on Claire's attention, a conciliatory statement that's a bit too glib. She carries them to the sink, removes a butcher board, takes a knife out of its block of wood and cuts their stems diagonally, then removes the lower leaves. The thorns glint like fishhooks. She sighs over the gurgling of the faucet and thrusts the bouquet into the vase.

"Stuart Foster, you know as well as I do that the experts never contest their theoretical infallibility." Claire turns to face Stuart and leans on the counter. "They can send me to specialist after specialist, attribute it to a new virus or environmental sensitivity. They may never come up with a definitive diagnosis, but they'll never say 'I don't know.' It must be a phrase that's removed from their vocabularies immediately after the Hippocratic Oath."

"Well, I know one thing for sure, Claire."

"And that is…, Stuart?"

"That you're a beautiful, sexy woman and I'll never stop loving you." Stuart rises from the table, shoving aside the documents with his right hand and reaching out to Claire with his left. He grasps her wrist and pulls her up, curling her into both arms and pulling her face down to his shoulder to kiss the nape of her neck. She can feel his breath on the short hairs there.

There is so much comfort and warmth compressed in a kiss, all the storms weathered and fights resolved are recapitulated each time they put lip to lip, whether lightly or with passionate intensity. This time is not so light. Stuart puts his arms around Claire's shoulder and leads her up the stairs.

Chapter XI

The Wedding Preparations

J ustine was sick of purple and she had a splinter in her finger. A drop of blood landed on the floor among the thousands of violets. The entire house was covered with violets: the carpeting, wallpaper, china, teapots, guest towels, bed linens. The soap was pressed in five-petaled molds and scented with violet-water. The doorknobs had elaborate wreaths of dainty blossoms cast into the brass. It was a wonder that the chamber pots were not of china resplendent with violets. It was impossible not to imagine Rene de la Violette wearing long woolen underwear covered with embroidered violets.

Justine smiled despite the hour and her duties as she conjured that image, then she knelt at the grate of the fireplace—no violets there—and arranged the kindling in a cone to light it. The sullen dawn cast shadows on the lilac walls of the parlor. Summer light had a way of alleviating Odile's purple scheme, inescapable and redundant, but the dawn was pallid and chilly. The sun barely cracked through purple-veined clouds, mottled like the eye of a brawler in the first waking hour after the night he cannot remember. The higher clouds skidded along, gathering the momentum that foretells a storm. The moon was loath to relinquish its time in the sky, and so loitered at the horizon, laughing at a day too weak to break through.

The inevitable bouquet of violets sat in the center of the table. The plain flower was incongruous in the cut crystal globe. Peonies seemed more appropriate, or perhaps some of Monsieur de la Violette's roses. God knows all he did was putter in the garden; they probably had one of every color. The breakfast china had pert yellow violets instead of the dark garlands on the dinner porcelain. Each egg cup had a little violet painted on the inside. If Justine had a schilling for every damned violet in the house she would never wait at table again.

If she were that rich, perhaps she would even be invited to parties like the ones she cleaned up after, or even buy herself a title and be a worthy prospect for Christoph de la Violette, the sniggering bastard. Justine set out the rolls, preserves, thin slices of ham, cooked gooseberry compote, oranges and coffee. The silverware had violets edging each piece. She went to the fire and knelt with her hands before it, rubbing her palms together for warmth. The flames needed to be fed with the bellows, their yellow tongues still tentative around the larger sticks of kindling.

The violets painted on the sides of the bellows were big and clumsy, more like pansies. Justine heard footsteps, hung up the bellows and stood at the mantel awaiting direction. Odile entered and Justine curtsied. Tante Sophia followed. Justine curtsied again, and paused as she tried to decide whether leaving the warmth of the fire was worth being in closer proximity to the women. She retreated to the corner and stood at attention, but shortly forgot and started warming her elbows with either hand.

"Good morning, Sophia." Odile gathered up her stiff skirts and arranged herself in the chair. She nodded at Justine to come and pour the coffee. "Good morning, Madame." Odile glanced over her shoulder to see Christoph enter the room. He gave the women cursory nods and plopped onto the plump chaise lounge before the fire. It was not yet a roaring blaze, so he prodded it with the tongs and inserted some more kindling.

"That should warm things up." Neither of the women responded. "Is it just me, or are things chilly in here?" He pointed at the side table and raised his eyebrows at Justine. She carried over a cup and saucer and the coffee pot, set the cup down, and poured.

"And where is my sugar?" he whispered at the crucifix nestled in the cave between her breasts. The tiny hairs there were not as dark as the mass of auburn curls that threatened to escape her cap. She smiled and leaned further forward, smothering the cross in cleavage as she pushed her breasts together with her upper arms.

"Monsieur?" She interrupted his focus. Christoph smiled and coughed. She turned to retrieve the sugar bowl from the service cart. Odile glanced at her with contempt; apparently this one thought she was special to him. Sophia just stared at the whorls on her glass. Justine returned with the sweetener and noticed he was doing his best to look like a sad puppy dog. His mock sorrow curled to a sardonic smile and he rolled his eyes toward the door to note the route of their imminent escape. He stood to leave, turning to the door without farewells.

"Christoph, my son, where do you think you are going?" Odile delivered the question without rising inflection, just a statement flat and cold. She pushed her coffee cup away, toward the table's center. He turned and bowed. "Mama, my chills were the warning sign of a terrible headache that has stricken me. I do not wish to burden you ladies with my aches and pains." Christoph caught the dagger gaze of Tante Sophia. If looks could kill and classify, he would be the most minute species of parasitic insect pinned to a naturalist's blank card. He offered the briefest of acknowledgments and walked through the door. Justine arranged a breakfast, one perhaps generous enough for two, onto a tray and was about to follow when Odile addressed her.

"Just where do you think you're going?" She evaluated the servant with her peripheral vision. Really! Christoph's tastes were too coarse sometimes, and they were far-ranging.

Justine put down the tray and curtsied. "I was going to take Monsieur de la Violette's breakfast to his chambers, Madame."

"No, I don't think so." Odile stirred her coffee. "Monsieur de la Violette's constitution is apparently disturbed. Go to the kitchen and tell Marta to prepare a soft-boiled egg, dry white toast and some weak tea. Have Hans take the tray to his quarters."

Odile held the teaspoon up to her face and noted the distorted reflection. The convex silver pulled her face to a sharp point. She put the spoon back in the coffee and sighed. "Marie-Ange and my husband appear to be similarly afflicted. You will take breakfast trays to them, and then go to the chapel and say twenty rosaries for the health of our beloved baroness." Justine turned to leave, shoulders down in a sulk. "You are not yet dismissed." Odile turned to Tante Sophia, leaned forward, and knit her fingers over one knee in a show of patronage.

"Is there anything we could send from the kitchen for Elysia?"

"Thank you, no." Sophia gazed out the window. The racing storm clouds were in the shape of a hunter on horseback pursuing a wolf. Then they melted into a pack of baying hounds, and then, a bonfire piled high.

"You are certain?" Odile tilted her head.

"Quite." Sophia whispered as Odile glanced at Justine in dismissal, flicking the fingers of her left hand back in the air. Madame de la Violette decided that the home turf advantage was hers, and that she may as well not lose momentum in negotiations. "Sophia, your gown is finished. Jean-Marc says it is a source of considerable pride in his craft to complete such a garment, and that the silk taffeta you selected has a beautiful drape."

"I have no use for this gown, no use for Jean-Marc Charbonneau, and no use for flattery. There will be no wedding." Sophia looked through Odile, with a stare that could have singed the design off of the lavender flower-flocked wallpaper. "As chaperone and guardian of my niece—and I need not remind you that I was appointed as such by the Baron Ignatz von Eschenbach—I hereby rescind the offer of marriage. I anticipate your cooperation in ending this arrangement." She returned her eyes to the window. "As soon as Elysia has recovered enough to travel to her home, we will depart." Sophia's index finger traced an imaginary road in the folds of the dress at her knee. "The surroundings here do not suit one of her background and temperament." Her fingernail negotiated a series of ridges. "Nor do the goings-on."

Odile sat up straight. "This is most extraordinary. The whole of Salzburg knows that Elysia and Christoph are deeply in love: they have been presented as engaged to everyone from the Duke to the Bishop. The bands have been published. To cancel so inexplicably, less than two weeks prior to the ceremony, would embarrass your family and mine. People know there are few conditions that can come on so suddenly and terminate so quickly. Rumors regarding her condition and the cause of her departure would be inevitable. Who knows where they might start."

Sophia shifted and smoothed her skirt. "Neither family benefits from such hearsay."

Odile smiled with only one side of her face; now she could speak from personal experience. "What is inappropriate in a young man is shocking for a well-chaperoned lady. He can deny his part in any condition: she cannot."

"You—and your most charming niece—have been the recipients of our generosity for weeks. She has been introduced to the finest of society at no small expense, and has herself described the entertainments as 'lavish.' More importantly, the arrangements that the baron signed, sealed, and sent to me do not appear to extend the power of your guardianship so far, although this guardianship may indeed be as effective as your chaperoning." Odile's nares flared and she shrugged. "The transfer of title, the arrangements for the marriage—all of these are documents that carry an obligation. Then again, I'm certain the baron would face no difficulty in meeting any remunerative demands that might arise through dissolving the engagement." At this suggestion, Odile could not contain her contempt. She unclenched her hands and lightly grasped the arms of her chair, leaning closer to Sophia.

"Elysia has suffered a collapse. She is a strong young woman and will recover, even if I must retain every physician in Salzburg. When she recovers, I will still hold the most magnificent wedding that this city has ever seen in order to celebrate the happiest day of her life."

"You do not understand the nature of our family." Sophia's voice was flat and her eyes were glued to the floor.

"What is there to understand about telling ghost stories to the peasants to keep them in line?" Odile flopped back in her chair with exasperation. "I understand your family all too well. You have nothing left to trade upon except ancient superstitions. The spirits of ancient von Eschenbachs cannot rattle their armored skeletons in the light of modern times. Not in Salzburg, not in my house. How much longer do you think you can peddle that rubbish?

"You!" Sophia hissed and leaped to her feet, leaning over the tabletop. "There is so much you do not know. First, you are incapable of understanding the affection I feel for the girl, how yesterday she reminded me of her own dead mother, Dorothea. You have no heart for anything other than your own ambitions. Secondly, you do not understand how this life is poisonous to her. I cannot allow her to stay here.

"Where she stays might be discussed after the wedding." Odile sniffed at Sophia's graceless display. "However, prior to the wedding, our only concern is making certain she is well enough to participate. You will fulfill your part in this bargain by going to her chambers, comforting her, cozening her with whatever tincture or ointment she might require, and then getting her to the church on time.

Odile stood up to give Sophia her final words. "You have no choice. The baron sold his daughter to recover the condition of his lands. You were merely along to transport the merchandise. When it is safely signed over, which it will be, in the presence of the finest society, your job is finished. Until then, mind the condition of your niece and prepare yourself to weep abundant tears of joy on the day of the wedding, welcoming me into your family as I will yours into ours.

Sophia covered her eyes with the back of her arm, shook, and collapsed in the chair. The fire had died down in the grate. After a minute, the woman uncovered her face, dabbed at her eyes with her hanging lace cuffs, and then sat up straight. "Perhaps I might finish my breakfast in solitude to consider how best to help Elysia recuperate." Odile nodded and rose to go. Next she would have to confront the groom.

Christoph sat in the bay window of his room looking out at the rain falling on the park. He frowned at the weather; it eliminated the maze as a convenient place for a collaboration with Justine. The breakfast tray was at his side, and he diffidently beat a hollow in the center of his toast with his spoon, keeping time to the buzzing, blubbering, trumpet-noises of his pouting lips. Odile knocked and entered simultaneously. He did not turn his gaze from the window.

"Christoph. Christoph, sulk all you like but hear what I say. It concerns what is dearest to you: your future, if you can conceive of it beyond harlot to harlot." Odile strode up to the window and planted her fists on the points of her pelvis.

"Your performance, or lack of one, this morning was entirely unacceptable. Your appetites do not concern me, but to arrange your little trysts with the help in front of your fiancée's chaperone is rude, coarse and stupid. Mon dieu! That the Creator would have given men enough blood to have their sex and their brains function at the same time. But this morning cannot be undone. What can be maintained is the appropriate devotion to the baroness."

Christoph dropped the spoon onto the plate with a rattle. "I thought that the engagement was off. Tante Sophia said so."

"Bah! You can't even eavesdrop well. Do you think I would concede to the demands of that mustachioed bumpkin, nobility or not?" Odile flung her hands in the air. "God help us! I have, with no thanks to you, saved your engagement. The wedding will proceed as planned."

The breakfast tray could have been balanced on Christoph's lower lip. He leaned against the window frame and folded his arms across his chest. Odile tapped her foot. "I await your expressions of gratitude and admiration of my consummate negotiating skills." Christoph stared at the park. Rene was out with an umbrella, examining his rose beds, prodding the base of each plant with a cane.

"Thank you, Mama." Christoph shrugged.

"'Thank you, Mama?' Is that all you have to say?" Odile flung her hands up again and started pacing back and forth. "I save your engagement to a baroness despite the unfortunate loss of our insurance, and all you do is slouch and mumble 'Thanks'? My dear boy, this is unacceptable. At least give her title the attention it deserves."

"So I should rub a tiara and a piece of paper with a coat of arms against my crotch at night? The woman moons on me constantly, a baleful cow. Elysia is *your* quarry—perhaps you should claim the spoils. It is not for me to return to the same prey, day after day after day." The boy slumped back, his fingertips grazing the carpet. He began to trace the scrolled pattern. "Such monotony is not an option."

"You flatter yourself to think that you have so many options." Odile sat in a chair before Christoph and folded her hands in her lap. Her demure posture was a warning of the significance of her words: they would be so serious that no extra dramatics were required. "Truly, Christoph, I did not know you had acquired independent wealth. Please explain to me how this occurred. Have you been saving winnings at the gaming tables for years? Did you secretly fund an expedition to one of the Spanish colonies, and did it return sinking with the weight of its golden spoils? Or perhaps you are an inventor, and unbeknownst to me have made some amazing device that a middleman sells for a portion of the profits? Or, perhaps, Christoph, you have decided to be a natural man, to be the prodigal son and wander the world in search of adventure, enlightenment...the Holy Grail? Are you considering signing up to be an apprentice to a craftsman? It will take ten years before you could be considered for a journeyman's guild, whether cooper, smith or *parfumier*. You may actually be a bit long in the tooth for such a scheme." She leaned back and drew her hands up to her chest, each fingertip pressing against its opposite. "So, I cannot wait to hear of your endeavors, Christoph. Do not keep me in suspense a moment longer."

Christoph removed his feet from the cushions before him and sat up straight. "What do you want me to do, Mama?"

"Only demonstrate the due concern of a betrothed for his bride-to-be after a tragic incident. Elysia needs to know that you love her in order to recover for the wedding. You will convince her of your undying devotion." Christoph snorted like a bull about to charge, before standing and turning toward the door.

"And Christoph?" Now Odile could afford to put her feet up on the window frame. "Your performance will be most persuasive. If you have to make believe she is a Venetian fishmonger in order to do so, that is no concern of mine, but you will make that girl believe she is wanted, desired, and adored. I have faith in your abilities. Just pretend she is a new chambermaid, and the rest should follow. Go now."

Christoph stood at the door of Elysia's quarters and tapped on the polished maple curls. Tante Sophia opened it, and then stepped back. "Is she asleep?" asked Christoph, entirely hoping that she was.

"No. Enter—you belong by her side." Tante Sophia took Christoph by the elbow and led him to a chair beside the bed. "The poor girl drifts from dream to dream, calling out the name of her dead brother, crying for her father, saying that the fire burns her. It is too sad to hear."

"When does her father arrive?" Christoph tried to feign appropriate gravity.

"No sooner than the wedding day." Sophia cursed his absence. Ignatz would be a pillar of strength and rectitude among these bumbling graspers. Any alliance with the la Violettes would be a disaster, but mostly for Elysia, the poor child. She must try to make this loin-led fool understand beyond his own vanity that he must care for his wife. She stood behind the chair and placed her hand on his shoulder. "Christoph, protect her and you will be safe."

"I beg your pardon?" *What could she mean?* He had expected Sophia to ignore him at best, or actively revile him—not offer him advice. Sophia took his hand in hers and withdrew Elysia's hand from beneath the covers. She pried Christoph's fingers apart and covered Elysia's hand with his. The hand of the baroness was cold beneath his palm. He recoiled but then remembered his mother's injunction for performance and grasped her hand again, intertwining his fingers with her cool, limp ones.

"I know how to care for her," Sophia continued. "She lost a great deal of blood, but can be healed. Her mother, Dorothea von Eschenbach, was the same: delicate, but dangerous; fragile, yet frightening." Christoph swallowed. The woman was not looking at him, but gazing at the face of the Baroness. Elysia was even more pale than usual. Her lips reflected a bluish cast, her eyelids imparted translucency.

"Christoph de la Violette, by marrying into this family you accept an obligation perhaps beyond your reckoning. The responsibilities of association with the von Eschenbachs are tremendous."

"The responsibilities are outlined in the nuptial agreement." Christoph let go of Elysia's hand and sat up, the better to examine this odd bird. His mother warned him that the nobility may be slightly inbred and eccentric, so this must be a manifestation of the same—some sort of delusion of grandeur. "I reviewed them with the Baron von Eschenbach before entering into the engagement. They are very clear. Beyond that, I have no idea what you mean."

"That much is apparent," Sophia snapped. "This is not some solicitor's scrawl on paper. This is an ancient tradition set in blood. As her husband, you will become party to it; you must know how to take care of her." She stepped back from the boy and sat on the bed. "Do you really think we would have entered into this marriage contract with nothing to gain other than monetary comfort? Dozens of other suitors could have provided for Elysia. I am beginning to understand why the baron may have accepted such an odd son-in-law. As your mother's son, you are used to following orders. Oh, don't stand up in protest of the obvious. I have no doubt that she sent you here herself moments ago." She put her hand on his shoulder and shoved him down into the chair, leaning into his face.

"Really!" Christoph turned his head to his left. The woman's nails were digging into his new waistcoat. He noticed that she wore a dragon ring. Perhaps the von Eschenbachs would make him wear one as well, ridiculous old insignia, as if they were knights or witches or something. Sophia grabbed his chin and steered his face up to hers.

"Elysia is not some lamb in your predatory games, not a trollop to decorate your mother's ambitions. She is the inheritor of a frightening strength, a dark river that flows through time. It is an ancient knowledge in the bones. It is not a thing that you—or your mother—could ever know. She and Dorothea flourish in a world of their own, creatures of..."

"So?" Odile stepped into the doorway. "How is our baroness? Well enough to be awakened by conversation?"

Sophia straightened and stiffened. "Perhaps her fiancé should inquire. He could try to wake her now."

Odile advanced into the room. The figures of her son and the von Eschenbachs were barely visible in the curtained gloom. Elysia stirred beneath the sheets and awoke, reaching out for Christoph's hand. "My love," she rasped.

"I am here," he announced, placing his free hand over their clasping ones. "How are you, my darling?"

Her eyes rolled back in her head and she panted with the effort of her exertions. "The baby is lost, Christoph. I am sorry." Her free arm tried to draw him closer but collapsed onto the coverlet.

"I know, Elysia." Christoph knelt by the edge of the bed and reached up to stroke her forehead. "All that matters is that you are well. We can make others." *This risqué intimacy should please all three members of his audience*, he thought. He traced Elysia's hairline with his index finger, and then combed her hair back with his hand, a gesture always popular under happier circumstances.

Elysia's hand flopped feebly under his. "Hold me, Christoph. I was so afraid—afraid that you wouldn't want to marry me anymore." Her eyes were half-open; her tongue lolled to the corner of her mouth. Her breath was a fetid stench. It reminded Christoph of walking past the kitchen scraps of fermenting potato peelings and mutton fat when seeking a new scullery-maid on a summer night. "How could you be so silly, Dearest? He moved his face down over her hand and kissed it repeatedly, three small ones, and then one long one, unmoving. Her knuckle felt like a chilled pig's foot. If he stayed with the hand, he could avoid the foul miasma emanating from her mouth. "I am truly counting the hours until we are wed." He raised his head and patted her hand, attempting to release it. Her free hand clamped down on them both. The speed and strength unnerved him, particularly seeing that she was so pale and weakened.

"Kiss me!" Elysia's voice was a near growl, echoing up from some cobweb-strewn cave inside her. He braced his elbows on the edge of the bed and attempted to plant a kiss on her cheek, but she turned her head and caught his lips with hers, prying his teeth apart with her tongue. It was all Christoph could do to keep from wretching. He turned his face away and gasped. "Save your strength, sweetness. You must recover." He regained his composure enough to kiss her hand but then stood up and fled the room. The girl's head flopped from side to side, mouth twitching, and then was still. Odile stared at Sophia and then trailed out after her son.

Elysia sighed through clenched teeth. Her eyes were closed but her face was not restful. One hundred demons streamed behind her curled lashes in some fevered dream that Sophia could only guess. Her hair was stark against the linen pillowcase, white embroidered violets peeping out from between the locks matted with the sweat of the previous day's trauma. The sleeping hand reached up and cupped the air twice, as if trying to catch an invisible apple thrown to her, and then fell back to the pillows. Her jaw unclenched and her breathing became smoother and less shallow, pulling into sleep as a rower leaves a pier for another shore. Her aunt leaned forward to kiss her forehead and then left the room. There was nothing to be done now except let the baroness rest.

The room was draped into darkness, sumptuous brocade covering the tall windows of the palace's guest quarters. The white roses Rene had sent to the baroness glowed blue on the bedside table, but their scent was too timid to venture into the gloom of the room. The traveling trunk was closed. The dress Elysia was to have worn to the next reception was still laid out, dancing shoes waiting beneath the hem of its skirt, a shawl folded demurely over the bodice. The sandpaper rhythm of the girl's breathing was interrupted by a rustle from a far corner, the scratching sound of fabric on fabric until the grating cloth stopped at the edge of the bedside. The intruder watched Elysia's chest rise and fall, a meadow design on the sheets shifting as she dreamt. The visitor spoke with familiarity: "You did not 'lose' your baby. God took it. He took it because you are a sinner. You are one of them. I know the signs and I recognize you. I know what you are."

The rustling retreated to the corner of the room. The wardrobe door creaked open to reveal a passageway, and the figure disappeared into it, closing the panel behind.

Chapter XII
Home Sweet Home

Trachilian he door bounces off the wall as their children enter. They catch Victoria's even, steady tread; Holly's sideways twists through the hallway; John's increasingly heavy steps. The door slams closed and they can hear rifling through cupboards, glass clinking against glass, then the refrigerator door opening, ice being knocked out of a tray, and the television coming on. Stuart sits up, puts both hands on the edge of the bed and lifts himself up to close the door. He calls down the steps: "Hey, kids: order pizza for dinner, will you? Your mother and I are indisposed."

"What does that mean?" Claire can hear John ask Victoria.

"It means that they are locked in acts of marital bliss," Victoria responds with prim certainty.

"Gross," Holly opines. "That's more than I needed to know."

Stuart clicks the door shut on an argument about whether green peppers are an acceptable topping. At dinner, everyone has a hearty appetite. John leads the way, a growing boy with his plate piled high. "I call dibs on the double sausage slice!" he yells, reaching for the greasiest of the lot.

"That's bad for your skin, you know." Victoria sniffs.

"Yeah," Holly adds, tucking a tendril of mozzarella into her mouth. "If you get more zits, Heather McAdams will never go out with you."

"Oh, who likes her, anyway?" John replies, a bit too quickly, speaking around a lump of doughy crust. The rest of the slice had already been inhaled. Incredible. "Goth chicks all look the same, anyway. Vampire wanna-bes."

"Well, you liked Elvira," Victoria teases.

"This sauce has enough garlic in it to keep away vampires," Claire adds.

"Spicy food is supposed to give you strange dreams," Victoria responds. "There's a theory that Goya's *Horrors of War* was first inspired by some questionable paella."

"Oh, really now." Claire puts some crust down on her plate. The sauce is a bit hot. "It seems silly to equate great works of art with someone's indigestion. But speaking of indigestion, I'd like to excuse myself early and just go to bed."

Stuart reaches out to stroke her hair. "You do that, honey. The kids and I will clean up. Hey, kids!"

"Awww," John complains as Claire climbs the stairs. "My show's on." Claire can hear Stuart reminding their son that he has no reason to be too proud to clean up after himself, that he's fortunate he works for his own entertainment money instead of having to contribute to the household, as she shuts the door behind her.

The nightmare returns to Claire. The dark coffin is moving. Her body slides from one side to the other within the stifling confines of the box. Some oaf jiggles his corner and her face slides to scratch against the acetate lining, bunching her cheek up into the corner of her eye. She can't even turn her head back; her neck is stiff with paralysis. Her fingers scrape at the sides, and she manages to get one fist over her chest to tap at the lid. She wants to pound with both hands, hammer her way out until the wood splits to admit air and light, not some gentle rap-tap-tapping at the padded wood above. She can hear the creak of pulleys as the box is lowered into the ground. When the clods shower down on the coffin lid in an escalating cascade, her mind screams, "Let me out! Let me out! Anybody! Somebody! Now!"

Her left hand fumbles against her side, finding a length of cord. This is the cord that had to be attached to some warning system, some way to alert loved ones that they had made the worst mistake of all. She somehow finds the strength to grasp the strand and yanks, pulling a rope encased in a length of tubing extending to the surface, a periscope attached to the top of a little silver bell suspended from a frame of wrought-iron spirals. The bell jumps, sending out its crying chime, but no one is there to hear it. Fog twists through the deserted cemetery, winding around the feet of the angel that tops Claire's monument, gazing down on its bouquet of new marble lilies. "Claire Foster" the inscription reads. "Devoted wife and mother". The mist obscures the date. But wait! The angel is smiling.

Although the angel wears Claire's visage, her clothing is out of the past. "I am Elysia. I will help you endure." Claire can see the spoken words written on the mist.

Chapter XIII

The Ceremony

.

Elysia was dreaming of the orchards of the von Eschenbach estate. One of the few cherished memories she had of her mother was being carried by her through the rows of trees at the turn of fall. Some early fruit rotted on the ground, soft brown and covered with the buzzing of yellow and black hornets, but most fruit was still on the trees, with its skin dappling into shades of red and thick stripes of gold. Her mother adjusted Elysia on one hip and then reached out to pick an apple for her. "Such simple food, child." Her mother flicked away a bit of white flesh from the corner of the girl's mouth. "Such simple food is the gift of the earth. Do not forget it—this is what should tempt your belly, not the rich and the seasoned." Then she lifted up the front of the child's frock and blew through her lips against the soft stomach, causing the girl to giggle, then scream.

"Mama! Mama! What are you doing?" The child held her palms up to her mouth, dropping the half-eaten apple in the grass behind them.

"Elysia! Elysia! What are you doing still in bed? It is your wedding day!" Elysia opened her eyes and saw her father standing before her. He reached down to shake her by the shoulder. "Time to get up, child. There are many preparations, and I have no doubt that Odile will want to inspect you ten times over once they're through trussing you up."

"Papa!" Elysia sat up and laughed, then yawned. "When did you get here?" He still had on his riding coat and was carrying his hat in his hand.

"Moments ago. We rode all night." He stepped back and leaned against the bedpost, looking at his daughter. "Have you recovered? Can you go through with the ceremony today?"

Elysia sat up and nodded, rubbing the corner of one eye with her little finger, then the other. "I do have a headache."

Ignatz leaned forward and felt her forehead. "Your temperature is fine. But what is that foul stench in your hair?"

"Oh, Papa, they will surely make you try it. The latest thing from Paris is to inhale this burning plant from the New World, something called tobacco. Jean-Marc Charbonneau, Christoph's friend, brought it along from France and now he cannot stand to have anyone see him without a pipe in his hand, morning, noon or night. It is the daring fashion, apparently."

"So did you try it?" The baron's forehead wrinkled with concern.

"Oh, no, Papa. Ladies do not smoke. There was just a small party last night, and all the men were smoking, and there were toasts to us." She trailed off, sat up, and pulled the covers up to her underarms. "It was quite festive, really."

The baron smiled a small, tired smile. "I'm certain it was. Did you drink to your happiness in married life together?"

"Why yes, Papa. It would have been rude of me to decline. Odile de la Violette stocks so many wines and liqueurs here, so many sugared extracts of fruit, and some even with flowers. And they are all served in these tiny etched glasses with violets on the side."

"And have all these toasts agreed with you?"

"I feel fine, Father." Elysia sat up straighter and bounced on the bed. "I feel wonderful! I *am* wonderful! Today I am to wed the man I love, and who loves me!"

The baron walked to the windows and parted the heavy velvet. The light in the east began to assert itself, pushing shoulders up against the mass of the darkness. "Very well, then." He turned his back to the panes. "I will go and retire to have some sleep before the ceremony." He winked at her and walked to the threshold, then turned and with loving concern asked her, "Elysia, you are certain that this wedding is what you want? The loss of your beautiful child no longer binds you."

"Papa! Of course it is!" Elysia turned toward the window and could see the outlines of their reflections in the dim glass. Her father's shoulders sloped toward the floor, as if someone had placed a weight upon them. He returned to the bedside, leaned forward and kissed the top of her head. His hands swept her hand to his lips, and with the planting of a kiss in the palm, he murmured, "Bless you, my child. I will be with you whatever you decide." Elysia closed her eyes as he leaned over her. They were still closed as his footfalls echoed down the hall. Once it was quiet, she sat up from the pillows and swung her legs over the edge of the bed. She wiggled her toes and threw her arms back, then pushed up the sleeves of her nightgown and stood. Elysia went to the window to examine the brightening view.

This park would be in her family soon, the lawns that Christoph had played on as a child. Families and memories coming together. She smiled at her own sentimentality about everything—"This sun! The sun that shines on my wedding day sheds its light every day, but today it glows for me." She turned back to the bed to pull the bell cord and start the day's preparations. All the women among the staff served as attendants, and even the ones who had no business in her quarters found some excuse to come upstairs and add to the hubbub. A pair of scissors may be necessary, or didn't the baroness call for some chamomile rinse for her hair? And what of her shoes? Might they be polished just in case she decides to wear them instead of the embroidered slippers? And extra stays might be needed for the corset. Breakfast trays appeared twice. The fireplace had never been so well stoked. A maid arrived to clean the windows, explaining to her superior with a hiss, "Well, you need the glass particularly clean for enough light to make certain the gown and everything is alright, don't you?"

One cough in the doorway, and the handmaidens cleared out. Madame de la Violette hovered forward to Elysia. "My daughter! Mon Cherie!" She kissed the girl on both cheeks, and then took both her hands in her own, squeezing them and bringing them up to her chest. "This is the happiest day of my life, so I know that it must be yours! Is there anything you require? Desire? Do not hesitate to let me know. Everything must be perfect for this wedding; not one detail can be left to chance. Everyone will be there to see me—you, you join the de la Violette family."

Odile smiled and released Elysia's fingers. The girl rubbed them to get some feeling back. Odile reached out and picked up tresses of Elysia's dark hair, holding them out and letting them curtain down on the right and left. "Look at you! Such a vision of subtle loveliness, and you've yet to complete your toilette, or don the gown." Odile gently clasped the baroness's shoulders. "Everything will be beautiful, my dear. You'll see."

Marie-Ange did not visit. Elysia would not have noticed, except that every other female on the compound had passed through on some pretext or another. Even the gardener's wife brought a bouquet of flowers for inspection with her daughter in tow. The child stayed behind her mother's skirts throughout, and then ran two quick steps forward and dropped a white rose bud at Elysia's feet before they turned to go. Elysia stooped to pick it up and walked to the door to call after them. "What is your name, child?" The mother stopped her daughter and turned her around to face the baroness, curtsying and trying to get the little girl to bow by tugging at her left arm.

"Her name is Lisle, Baroness." The gardener's wife looked at the floor.

"Thank you, Lisle, for the lovely rose. I will carry it in my dress. Come here." Elysia twisted a ring from the pinkie finger of her left hand. The childhood memento had a row of seed pearls on a thin band of rose gold. Elysia pulled the draw-ribbon out from the cuff of her peignoir and strung the ring on it, knotting the satin once around the gold. The girl tripped toward her, with her head bowed. Elysia bent over and cleared the braid from the child's neck to tie the ribbon over her nape, then stood up and turned her back to her mother.

"But, Madame Baroness, you shouldn't..."

Elysia smiled at the two. "Please permit me. It is good fortune to make a present on your wedding day. I was always told that this is a tradition of my mother's family." She added, "Thank you again for the rose, Lisle."

"She's right, you know." Marie-Ange suddenly appeared at Elysia's right elbow. "You shouldn't make presents to the help. They'll become spoiled, get a sense of entitlement, become truly insufferable, uppity, begin helping themselves to your jewelry when you're not around, and then will claim that it was 'borrowed' or a 'present.'" Elysia had not seen much of Marie-Ange lately. The girl had been avoiding her ever since their picnic and the subsequent miscarriage. And she was dressing like a nun—it was most bizarre. Once a whirlwind of color and noise, for the last week she had appeared quietly at one meal a day, dressed in somber shades, hair pulled back and covered. Elysia would not have recognized her.

Marie-Ange turned to Elysia and sniffed. "Speaking of help, I actually came upstairs to let you know that the gown has arrived." The women turned toward the noise on the stairs. The dress was carried up in a long box by Jean-Marc Charbonneau and his assistant, one on either side, as if they were handling the crystal goblet of the king himself. They cradled the bottom edge of the box in their hands. Odile clattered behind, and then ran ahead of Jean-Marc to the head of the stairs.

"Elysia! Elysia! The dress is here!" Her elbow bumped Marie-Ange but she neither turned nor slowed. "This will be the crowning glory of the house of la Violette—after your lovely self, of course. Now that I know it is here, I will attend to my own dressing." She clasped her hands together and the outside corners of her eyes showed accordions of delight. "Good-bye, girls."

Jean-Marc and the assistant bent their knees and their heads in greeting, careful not to tilt or relinquish any control over the box for a moment. They entered the room, and all the women began to trail in behind them. Jean-Marc set the box down on the bed and removed the lid so cautiously that it seemed he was afraid its contents might blind him. Then he reached down to part layers of delicate tissue, the side of his hand slicing from top to bottom. Once he saw that nothing had shifted during transport, he placed the lid to the side and addressed Elysia. "Voilà, Mademoiselle. C'est votre robe."

Elysia sucked in air with amazement, and every woman who could view the dress soon echoed her inhalation. The dressmaker clapped his hands and another assistant trotted in bearing a wire torso on a stand. He set it down next to the bed. All three men pulled white silk gloves from their jacket pockets and put them on. The second assistant held down the wrapping tissue as Jean-Marc and his aide lifted the dress from its crate. The wedding dress was not sewn as much as constructed, yet it possessed a weightlessness as if woven from ice and pearls and milk and petals and the wing feathers of swans. Once it was safely on display, Jean-Marc faced his audience as the assistants straightened the skirt, the overskirts, the bodice, the sleeves and the train.

"Madame Odile de la Violette was so generous as to grant me carte blanche in the design of this...the word 'dress' seems inadequate, don't you agree?...carte blanche in the construction of this creation for the event of your marriage, except that..." he removed one of his gloves and held a finger up in the air, "it was to be inspired by your beauty, Baroness." His fingertip wiggled in her direction. "That, and moonbeams, were my themes."

"The under skirt is of the palest aqua—it would be taken for white if it were placed next to a darker blue. This brocade..." His hand fanned over the first underskirt. "This brocade is embroidered with silver thread in a fern and fleur-de-lis motif." He leaned toward Elysia and conspiratorially whispered. "Not violets!"

He stepped behind the dress and replaced his glove to rotate the stand so that a sleeve faced Elysia. "These cuffs are made of the finest lace from Brussels. Only the virgin daughters of Belgian burghers are employed in its production." He paused before adding, "all two of them!" Once the giggling ceased, he continued. "This is abundance: there are five layers stitched together from elbow to wrist, increasing in length the nearer your hand. There is a thin strip of tulle beneath each layer to add volume. Your arms will look like angel wings, dear, and every gesture will be beautiful and dramatic." Jean-Marc sent the second assistant outside the room for another box. The dressmaker bowed to the second case, then to Elysia, and announced, "The accoutrements." The two men removed the lid and departed. Jean-Marc removed more tissue paper to reveal a pair of shoes. He lifted them out and shrugged at Elysia. "Well, some violets."

The silk shoes were covered with tiny flowers embroidered in lavender thread. Next he removed the underthings. The women giggled onto their sleeves and elbowed one another. The corset was a stiff skeleton covered with silk, spirals of rosebuds sewn up both sides, each button bearing a rose embroidered on its center. The corset was to be reinforced with a whalebone stomacher, the remains of some Greenland beast camouflaged beneath a panel of the sheerest muslin. The stockings were slices of clouds that had been woven in Spain, and the more intimate items were crocheted out of whispers of angels.

Everyone gathered around the box and the dress on its stand as Jean-Marc unpacked the final items. Jokes, whispered and aloud, alternated with giggles as he held the baroness's underwear aloft by two corners with grave seriousness, and then whirled around without embarrassment to have it dance a bit for the assembled crowd. He saw Odile noting the angle of the sun in the sky, and knew it was best to leave at the top of his game. Jean-Marc bowed to the assembled women and backed to the door, finally departing with kisses blown from his fingertips. "Au revoir, mes cheries!"

Odile clapped her hands. "Attention! That was charming fun, but it is now time for us to dress: time is of the essence. We have but a few hours. Everyone get busy!" The women trailed out with a final chorus of oohs and coos and compliments. Tante Sophia and her maid remained to help Elysia dress.

"Tighter, Tante Sophia," Elysia gasped, sucking in her stomach and exhaling a shuddering breath. "I want to look like those French court girls. I must look perfect for Christoph."

"Don't be a silly goose." Her aunt held a stay in each hand, kept her arms stiff, and leaned back. "You look one hundred times better than one of those trussed ducklings. Why gild the lily?"

"But I feel so bloated." Elysia held her hands up for a closer view and frowned at them, and then tried to put them behind her back for Tante Sophia's inspection. "These fingers are swollen to the size of knockwurst. My ankles are bad too, I know it."

"Don't be ridiculous, my dear." Her aunt pulled back on one lace with both hands and the maid intervened to fasten it. "You are merely a bit nervous, entirely understandable on this, your day."

"And these purple shoes," Elysia gestured to the pair on the bed. "They are entirely covered with little flowers. Is there no escaping violets?"

"Not after today." Tante Sophia leaned back with the second stay wrapped around her right hand. "The toes might blossom out beneath the skirt, but only on the stairs. After all this ado, I will commission Jean-Marc Charbonneau to sew me a set of violet-decorated pantaloons and think of your gracious mother-in-law-to-be whenever I sit down."

"Tante Sophia!" Elysia laughed. The maid and the aunt tied the petticoats around Elysia, two sets of ties at each of the five rings, each growing wider until the bottom ring extended past the range of Elysia's outstretched arms. Little silk ribbon violets festooned each ring.

Tante Sophia stood up from the last petticoat and its ring of violets, plucked at a loose one on the third ring, and frowned. "Are you feeling well, my dear? You look pale. Have you had anything to eat today? We can summon the kitchen maid for something, or perhaps even convince Odile de la Violette to prepare it with her own hands."

Elysia smiled. "Do not worry, Tante Sophia. I am too excited to eat. Also, I must maintain my fast from midnight until after communion."

"Such a ridiculous tradition." Tante Sophia faced Elysia toward the mirror and started to place a muslin underskirt over the hoops. "Your skin looks pale even by your delicate standards. I do not like to see it so sallow."

"Well, perhaps I'll look rosier in a white dress." The girl lifted her arms over her head. "Let's put it on me now, please! I can't stand to wait anymore!" Tante Sophia and the maid lifted the dress off the sturdy wire frame and held it above their heads. Elysia was obscured by the angles of its heavy folds, the yards of cloth, but once it was draped on her body, the seams hugged every limb and curve. Elysia hovered in a cloud of silver slivers, suspended above the frothy waves of the skirts.

Tante Sophia clasped her hands together. "Darling, you look beautiful! Let me get your father to admire you—he will be so proud." Her aunt left the room and the maid followed to find the emergency stockings to be carried in the carriage in case the first pair should run or snag.

There was a rapping at the door, and Marie-Ange stepped in. It was all Elysia could do to keep from throwing her own hands up to shield her eyes from the glare: Mademoiselle Marie-Ange was decked out in a gown of noxious orange, wide skirts reminiscent of a burning field, or of crackling embers.

"Is it me?" Marie-Ange gave Elysia a sideways smile. "Mother can't stand it, so it must be. A bit vivid, perhaps." The fabric rustled as she stepped beside Elysia and looked in the mirror. The effect was snow and fire. "This color has a life of its own. I had to scour our swatches and catalogs to find the most intense orange available to the house of Violette, and I did. Not saffron, or carrot, or topaz, or tangerine, or peach, but a true, fierce, proud orange. I have succeeded, don't you agree?" Elysia stood mute and the woman continued.

"You could not ignore this shade, am I correct?" She leaned toward the mirror, licked a finger, and tightened a curl hanging in front of her right ear.

"Impossible to ignore." Elysia wondered about what intentions Marie-Ange had up her sleeve.

"Now, you, on the other hand," Marie-Ange stood up straight to face the mirror with Elysia and squeezed her shoulder, "you have chosen this classic gown. Charming, the elegance of understatement." She patted the baroness on the shoulder. "I'm certain my brother will be pleased."

"I hope so! I want to be the most beautiful thing in the world to him. This day is the beginning of our life together. When he sees me, I want to be an absolute vision of loveliness to him. I want..." Elysia looked down at the bodice of her gown and traced a spiral of tiny pearls. "Well, I want him at least to be pleased with my appearance."

Marie-Ange clicked her tongue. "Yes, we can talk about pleasing

Christoph, if you'd like, but I really came here to discuss you, to share some confidences with you. But first, a toast!"

Elysia shook her head "no" and raised the palm of her hand to Marie-Ange. "No, thank you. There was quite enough toasting for me last night. Besides, I do not want to break my fast." The girl was removing a small flask from one side of her skirts and two small glasses from the other.

"Oh, please?" Marie-Ange frowned and stamped her foot. "You must be fortified to enter the church for so grand an occasion. The ban of the fast prohibits food and water. This is neither. Besides, this is our own communion, a moment remaining as maidens before you enter the covenant of marriage for the rest of your days. If we are not to toast to that, what will we toast to?" Marie-Ange held the two cordial glasses in her left hand and poured with the right. "This is a health tonic made by the monks of Alsace. The pope himself has a glass every morning and every evening to be ultimately sanctified with the good Lord's grace. It is also hours before communion."

"What do you mean? We leave for the ceremony in less than two hours." Elysia eyed the liquid in the miniature goblets. It was a brown syrup, looking very much like medicine.

"You do not know that the Bishop is officiating? His eminence, Slow Finzi of Salzburg?" Marie-Ange rolled her eyes. "Mother has not told you a thing. This will be a ceremony and mass in which one may consider every aspect of the divine, every creature herded onto the ark at the flood, the lineage of Abraham—and you might as well bolster yourself because you're going to have a long day. Look here." She handed the glasses to Elysia and lifted the blazing skirt to show that two small pillows were wrapped around her knees with gauze.

"Marie-Ange! To be so rude to a Bishop, a servant of God."

"God's servant should pad the pews if he's going to drone on like that." Marie-Ange rolled her eyes. "I will need some fortification. Cheers!" She took one of the glasses, clinked it against Elysia's, and downed it in a gulp. The baroness hesitated, and then raised her glass in the air.

"To married life," she said. The syrup tasted like roots, anise, smoke and burnt sugar. Her mouth puckered. The liquid unwound a hot ribbon down her throat and she could feel it reach the pit of her stomach. Marie-

Ange refilled their glasses. She lifted hers to Elysia and eyed her with the suggestion of a dare. "To the beauty of the bride!"

Elysia protested but followed Marie-Ange's lead once more. They toasted the handsomeness of the groom; the health of her father, the health of Tante Sophia, of each of her parents-in-law-to-be. The two women drank to the blessed union of the two families, to the city of Salzburg, to the handiwork of Jean-Marc Charbonneau. Elysia's stomach growled, so they drank a toast to the bride's entrails. Then one to Marie-Ange's freckles. The woman hooked her arm around the baroness's neck and pecked her on the cheek, and then poured the last drops into her own glass. "And, my dear, we must have a dram to the patience of the female heart, to understanding and to forgiveness."

Elysia hiccupped with discomfort, raised the glass, and emptied it. She held the empty crystal to the sunlight and spun it around. A slight stickiness coated the inside. "That's an odd toast for a wedding."

Marie-Ange laughed. "Oh, is it? Not if you are to marry Christoph de la Violette." She turned to Elysia and started. "What? Your eyes are so round, dear, I thought that you knew... of, never mind, you shouldn't trouble yourself on today of all days."

The baroness set her glass on the window ledge and turned to face Marie-Ange. She folded her arms over her silver bodice and leaned back. "What trouble? What should I know?"

"Well, a wife should always know how to forgive and forget, isn't that right? Book of Ruth: 'Whither thou goest, I shall go. Thy God shall be my God...'"

Elysia interrupted. "Oh, please, Marie-Ange, do not quote Scripture. Even I know you better than that." She tapped her foot. "Well, out with it. What do you expect of your brother?"

"Only that he will carry on in his usual manner." Marie-Ange threw her cordial glass in the grate and it shattered. "That he will act with typical grace, delicacy and gentlemanliness, attempting to get under the skirts of every new servant mother hires. He is rarely unsuccessful, but that is still not enough for him, so he also hires painted women."

Elysia sat on the bench before the window. "Do you mean...?"

"Yes, prostitutes. Whores, streetwalkers, red shoe ladies, what you will. He doesn't have to pay the household help. Mama generally pays them off. You would think he could be a little discerning, but no, he's ruled entirely by that snippet of flesh between his loins...Oh, I'm sorry, dear. I assumed that you knew of his habits." Marie-Ange bent before Elysia with a coy look.

"I cannot believe this." The baroness looked at the brash woman before her. She felt her eyes watering but wanted to maintain her composure before this creature. "He says he loves me."

"Mon chère, mon chère." Marie-Ange stayed lowered before the bride. "Any man can say any word to any woman any number of times. Did you think my brother exceptional? Well, his appetites are prodigious, I will grant you that, but his honesty is no better than delusion. Expediency is his poetry; the goal sparks whatever he says. It is all an act. He might as well say 'I love it...I mean, you.' It is all about his own pleasure, his own body." She stood up. "Pardon my bitterness. Too many such creatures crawl around Salzburg. Oh! Speaking of crawling creatures, here is my wedding gift to you."

"Whatever do you mean?" Elysia had collapsed against the window frame. The sun pulled beads of sweat from her forehead.

Marie-Ange pulled a little box from her skirts. "Here. You look like you may not have the energy to open this. Let me help you." She removed the violet-patterned wrapping paper to reveal a long, lovely leather box stamped with the name of the best jeweler in Salzburg. "I wanted to get you something valuable, personal, and useful." She cracked the box open with her thumb to reveal a flat silver comb, thin and fine-toothed. Violets were engraved on its side, along with the names 'Christoph & Elysia' and the date.

By now Elysia's eyes were dull. "What is it?" she asked, picking it up and turning it in the light. The silver matched the embroidered brocade of her gown.

"Oh, of course you would not know. Forgive me the liberty: it is a personal comb. My brother has been afflicted with lice there, so perhaps you might want to inspect yourself after the honeymoon." Marie-Ange sighed and shrugged. "I do not know. Perhaps we could have a physician inspect the servants: Marta, Justine, Louisette. I believe that Giselle just services him in the French manner, so there would be no need to check her down there."

Elysia leaned onto the wooden frame and closed her eyes as Marie-Ange continued. "Oh, I am so sorry, darling. I would have sworn that you knew. I just have your best interests at heart—my concern is for your health. And the strength of your bonds to my brother for the rest of your life, of course. Are you not feeling well?" Marie-Ange furrowed her forehead and puckered her lips outward. "I should really allow you a meditative moment before you enter the state of holy matrimony." She leaned forward and planted a kiss on Elysia's forehead, then turned to go. The baroness leaned her face against the glass, but it offered no cool relief.

"Baron von Eschenbach. Tante Sophia." Elysia cracked her eyes to see Marie-Ange bowing before her father and aunt. "Please allow me to express my joy at the honor of having your daughter join our family. I could not ask for a more delightful sister."

The baron bowed his head to acknowledge Marie-Ange. "This marriage is a blessing for both of our families."

"Oh, indeed." She curtsied to Tante Sophia again in deference. "I will see you at the church shortly." She turned to wave at Elysia. "Good-bye, sister!"

Both turned to see the orange mass bob away from them. Tante Sophia shook her head. "Ignatz, all that girl's taste is in her tongue. I cannot believe she is going to wear that atrocious dress to Elysia's wedding. Her attempts to outshine the bride will be fruitless. You must see how exquisitely beautiful Elysia looks in the gown."

Elysia stuffed the comb beneath a cushion and turned to greet her father. This was a time for the rectitude of nobility to be displayed; complaining about Marie-Ange would only serve to upset her father, and nothing could be done, anyway. Even if the woman was lying just to make her feel bad, there was no way to back out of the marriage at this point: it was too late. She was going to marry Christoph de la Violette.

Water welled up in the baron's eyes. He remembered her mother, Dorothea, their first child, Peter, and the wait before Elysia's birth. He bowed before his daughter. "My lady." But for all the displayed chivalry, all he could truly picture was a little girl riding on the saddle before him as he toured the nearer boundaries of the estate, a ring of daisies crowning her dark hair. He raised the dragon ring on her right hand to his mouth and kissed it, and then drew her to him. Elysia sobbed on his neck. "Blood of my heart." He smiled to see the same blue cast in her dark hair that had been in her mother's.

"Heart of my life." Elysia choked out the next phrase of their traditional exchange. No Violette would ever be greeted in this manner, and if one were, he would not know how to respond. "Life of my blood," the baron responded, easing her from his shoulder.

"Elysia," the baron now held her up straight, "what you do today you do for the good of the family. The von Eschenbachs, yes, but also the continuation of the bloodline. Now let us go show this gussied rabble true comportment." He wiped a tear from her cheek with the ball of his thumb as he tried to produce an authentic smile.

The von Eschenbachs stood in a row alongside their carriage. The Violettes' carriage drew up behind, purple bundles of violets affixed to the reins and bridles. The sun beat down on the family and the servants. The silk in the women's gowns was wilting. The baron was having difficulty keeping his temper. He strode up to the portico. "What is the meaning of this delay?"

Marie-Ange stepped out with a demure curtsy, and then leaned over to the footman. The servant bowed, and then approached the baron to bow again. The poor man cleared his throat. "Baron von Eschenbach, we beg your indulgence. Apparently the groom has been detained. He will be properly attired and arrive shortly. Some appointment held him up." Marie-Ange curtsied again and stood to the side to wait for the rest of the Violette party. *Why was this orange thing smirking at his daughter?* the baron wondered. *Did she really think that the dress flattered her at all? She looked like a ginger-glazed pudding sprinkled with ground cloves.* The baron turned back to look at Elysia and Sophia. His daughter was fading fast. He gestured for them to enter the shade of the transport and then stepped up to Rene de la Violette just as the man emerged.

The baron's reproach was terse: "We shall meet you at the church." Rene was wearing an elaborate hat that lofted feathers right in the baron's line of vision. The feathers bobbed as he responded.

"The wedding party is to arrive at the cathedral together. That is the plan. Christoph knows of this arrangement."

"That is so reassuring," the baron snapped, but then caught himself. He bowed toward Odile. "Did Madame inform the groom of this plan?"

Rene looked at his wife peripherally, and then looked out to the courtyard's dust and coughed. "Baron von Eschenbach, we beg your indulgence of this delay. After the months of preparation for the wedding, it would mean a great deal to us if the families about to be united as one departed as one." He gazed at the horizon and shrugged his shoulders. The baron grunted as he stormed to the carriage to wait with his family. Marie-Ange raised her fingers to her mouth to suppress laughter: her plan had unfolded too perfectly. She had given Justine gold nuggets to assault Christoph with a bachelor's last paroxysm of passion. Such an appeal to his vanity could not be denied.

At that very moment Christoph was buttoning his wedding finery as one servant attempted to finish his hair and another fished his boots out from beneath the bed. Perhaps Justine still sulked on top of the bed, batting her eyelashes at Marie-Ange's brother and smoothing the top of the coverlet. If Odile sacked her, Marie-Ange would provide her with references to work in another household. Perhaps she could retain the services of the wench as a new servant for Elysia. That would be too perfect! Almost as perfect as watching the rage and shame wrinkling her mother's face at that very moment.

"What's so funny?" Odile hissed at her daughter and then straightened herself. "This is nothing to laugh at!"

Marie-Ange bent her knees and turned her face away from her mother. "Nothing, Mama. I know."

Odile scrutinized Marie-Ange's profile. "Girl? What did you have to do with this?"

Marie-Ange lowered her eyes to the ground and tugged at her left sleeve's cuff. "Nothing, Mama."

Odile chewed the inside of her cheek and then spat out the words: "That dress is hideous! Whatever possessed you to order such a monstrosity? You look like a grotesque harlot, like you're with the carnival. Camp followers have more taste. Why, I..." The woman remembered the occasion and turned the other way.

Marie-Ange's voice shook as she replied. "It is my tribute to you, Mama. Don't you like it?" Christoph burst past her, interrupting any response, weaving between his sister and stepfather rather than risk looking at his mother directly. He turned and bowed to the von Eschenbach carriage and then ran to his own. A manservant then ran out bearing Christoph's hat, almost tripping on the hem of Odile's gown. The remaining Violettes filed to their carriage in a row: Odile, Marie-Ange, and the beleaguered Rene. The timing was most unfortunate. That morning he had noted some suspicious beetles on the base of his prized deep-red climber, 'Mary Magdalene.' All filled the carriage and embarked to St. Michael's cathedral.

Chapter XIV
The Trial

Claire awakens, drained and exhausted. After a day of medical prodding, being trapped in the elevator, and squabbling with Stuart, a nightmare on top of it seems quite unfair. And what a dream it was! Rising from the depths of her subconscious is this beautiful regal lady who is in trouble, but seems to be attempting to comfort Claire. Disquieting, but strangely reassuring as well. Claire stumbles to the master bathroom and looks in the mirror on the medicine cabinet. One would swear the mirror is dirty, her face looks so tired and sallow. But the day demands that she go to court with Stuart.

"Are you sure, sweetheart?" He places the back of his fingers to her forehead with concern. "After all the medical stress yesterday, perhaps you would be better off just staying at home. I'll let you know all the details. That Carlson character is such a slimeball, he'll be instantly transparent and this will be wrapped up in a day. Two days at the absolute most.

The case lasts five days, Claire insists on accompanying Stuart. The car wash is *their* project, and he already has so many responsibilities with the company. At lunch they discover that the nearest dining establishment is the 'Drop Inn,' the sort of smoky old local place with hunting trophy heads on the wall and a pool table at the back of the room.

Caricatures of regulars line the walls, alternating with mirrors painted over with beer label designs. The bartender gives up her glass-washing duties to saunter over to the table and wait on them. Stuart has a cheeseburger and Claire has the soup and salad special. The cigarette smoke makes Claire's stomach hurt. That afternoon the lawyers continue to review jurors. Carlson's counsel excuses every candidate who has any education, or who even seems half awake throughout the selection process.

The second day, the judge spends the morning in recess. At noon they trudge through the parking lot and down several blocks toward the Drop Inn. The sun makes the sidewalk ripple like a mirage; it looks as if they could wade through the concrete ahead of them. Stuart has a burger again and Claire tries the tuna salad sandwich. The walk back to the courthouse makes her dizzy. She has to lean far over to take a drink of water from the hallway fountain and rests her forehead against the cool porcelain before standing upright.

On the third day, the tavern offers a blue-plate special of fried fish and fried potatoes. They both try it but have to ask the bartender repeatedly for ketchup. She is engrossed in conversation with a young man who has a long ponytail tied back in a strip of leather with feathers hanging from it.

After lunch, their lawyer presents the case, pointing out all the relevant clauses and subpoints in the documentation. The list of conditions that the Fosters have upheld falls from his lips in a litany of letters and numbers individually pronounced. Uniform codes are cited, local ordinances acknowledged, and the competence of their contractor established. The parking lot is still steaming when they go to their car at the end of the day.

The fourth day, Carlson's lawyer performs histrionics for the jurors. He paces back and forth, waving a legal pad as if he's shipwrecked and using it to signal to the first rescue plane he's seen. The bar is serving roast beef sandwiches, open-faced, with thick rubbery gravy, an odd choice for such hot weather. Claire doesn't know which makes her feel more queasy as they hike the blocks back to the case in progress: the lunch, the sun, or the antics of these so-called representatives of justice.

Fifth and final day, the Drop Inn offers a fried chicken special, cole slaw and baked beans on the side. When they get back to the courtroom, Claire feels so exhausted that she sits in the hall throughout the remainder of the case, leaning against the wall and looking up at the humming fluorescent lights. The benches are covered in vinyl of institutional green.

Stuart's face is green as he emerges from the courtroom and Claire instantly knows that their case has been lost. "How?" she murmurs to Stuart as they walk to their car in the parking lot, squeezing his fingers in hers.

Carlson is leaning against the bumper of his Lexus. He has just lit a cigarette and grimaces at the Fosters before placing the lighter in his pocket. Then he reaches under his moustache to remove the cylinder of stench. "So, how does it feel?" He grins at Stuart and then leers at Claire, appraising her form before he takes another drag. "Why didn't you know better? I always get what I want—wouldn't do it if I didn't. Do you really think I'd be concerned with your enterprise or my reputation in this town? Life's too short to hang around. There are plenty of investment opportunities out there that need my special support." Ashes fell from his cigarette and he ground it in with the tip of his Cole Haans. "Anyway, you know the name of the game nowadays—adequate representation. My lawyer beat your lawyer. You get what you pay for. He knows how I do my job, so I make sure that he does his."

Stuart shades his eyes in the summer glare. "You'll never get away with this." He regrets the words instantly. Even if they are true, they threaten with cartoon melodrama, as if Brian's about to rob the bank or tie the heroine to the railroad tracks.

Carlson shakes his head. "No," he says with patient condescension. "You are slow. You just don't get it, do you? I've pulled this off countless times. Why should you be any different?" He snickers and reaches into his jacket pocket to fish out another cigarette.

"What goes around comes around, Carlson," says Claire. "You can't keep misleading people and expect permanent immunity!"

Brian leans forward to stare at her, but with his dark sunglasses she can't be sure. He tilts his head and says in deliberate tones, "Why not, Claire? Why ever not? And maybe I need to review that case from the car wash once more—perhaps there was something we missed." He sat down on the bumper of his car. "You can't be too careful in these cases, you know. Nothing is more important than establishing liability."

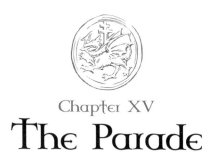

Chapter XV

The Parade

The circuitous route to St Michael's required by the meandering medieval streets remaining in the heart of Salzburg amounted to a journey of five miles, easily accomplished by a parade of carriages within a half hour. However, the most direct route was not the one planned by Madame Odile de la Violette. First, the carriages must pass by the park: the bride's, with the team of white Lipizzaners specially bleached for the occasion; then the groom's carriage, with the purple draperies on the windows and the chestnut team with their manes braided; and finally, the groom's family, with the golden Arabians decked out in violet-trimmed tack. Odile had instructed the coachmen to slow during the leg of the journey between the park and the church. Here the wedding party was to pass the summer homes of the city's gentry. Duke and duchess, count and contessa, lady and lord; all who cared to pause from their preparations as guests could glance out the window at the tableau.

Even an ostentatious upstart like Madame Odile de la Violette could remind them of their fortunate state. The scene provided by the carriages with their pretty horses, gilded door frames, liveried footmen, masterful drivers and fancy decorations did seem like something out of those charming nursery stories transcribed by the Frenchman, Perrault. Some wryly noted that while the wedding was of a baroness to Christoph de la Violette, it was as much a marriage of Odile to the aristocracy, and for the first time in her life she was a nervous, eager bride, swooning with delight and anticipation.

The baron anticipated nothing so eagerly as the end to this farce. He was red with anger. His poor daughter was becoming radish-skinned with a heat rash. He should have appealed to Odile's vanity and warned her not to present a sunburned daughter-in-law-to-be as her ticket to nobility. "What next?" he growled to Sophia. "Is she going to have wooden pedestals as they use at flesh markets to display the slaves for us to perch upon? Is she going to stand to the side and use us as models of landed gentry, gesturing to each relevant part in turn with a pointer? The woman is too much."

As the procession pulled in front of the cathedral, Odile could resist the temptation to stand up and wave only by sitting on her hands. She recalled her mother cursing the avarice of the wealthy as she left their back steps with mending jobs. Sometimes the woman would lose all composure and stand at the back gate, letting the wicker basket of piecework drop to her feet, and turn to curse a mute mansion. She'd mutter, or even cry out, "You think that you're better than everyone else, but you're not!" Odile collected the spilled clothing from the paving stones. For this day the paving stones in front of the cathedral had been strewn with white rose petals and violets, as per her instructions, to celebrate her induction—the induction of her family—into the uppermost classes. The bells rang and the crowd parted to make room for the carriages.

Christoph alit first and led the way up the steps, tipping his hat to a well-appointed young lady or two: the contessa from south of Limoges who always walked her little dog down Burgerstrasse on Saturdays; the blonde and cheerful widow of the Archduke of Friesland, resplendent in royal blue; and a suspicious, slow bow to the mayor's daughter.

The von Eschenbachs followed. Odile climbed out of her carriage, slipping on the rose petals and stumbling to catch the Baron's elbow. "There are some people here you simply must meet. Now the von Ducksteins…"

Ignatz von Eschenbach jerked his arm away. "Madame, the only thing that I must do today is see my daughter married. Is this a pageant for some patron saint of seamstresses of which I was not aware? There is to be a wedding today, not an advertisement for the house de la Violette!"

Odile stepped back and attempted her most imperial demeanor: shoulders squared, elbows back and angled toward her target, chin up, aiming a glare down the narrow barrel of her nose. "Indeed, Baron. It is exactly this blessed occasion that gives me the desire to introduce you and your delightful daughter to the finest of this city, who happen to be my friends and my guests."

"The pleasure is indeed all yours," the baron snarled. "Now, with your permission, Madame, I will escort my daughter inside." He bowed to Odile and turned his attention to Elysia. Her face was flushed and her eyes slightly swollen. He placed his arm around her shoulder to shepherd her to the relative coolness of the church's interior. Tante Sophia covered the left flank and they maneuvered up the church steps without further incident.

Not all the gawkers were invited, so the seating took longer than expected. The nouveau riche bumbled over one another to get a seat with the best view, while the established aristocrats lingered outside lest they appear too concerned with the pretensions of a commoner, even one such as Odile de la Violette who has the ability to negotiate herself a title.

All were united in quiet admiration as Elysia walked down the aisle. The organ bellowed somber tones as Baron von Eschenbach led his daughter between the dark pews up to the altar. At the head of the aisle he turned her to face the groom, taking her hand and kissing her curled fingers before he clasped them to his heart. He lowered her hand to her side and glared at Christoph in silent warning. The young man looked back at him with barely veiled impudence. *Well, what are you going to do now, Baron? Violette thought. No way to rescue the maiden back to your castle keep. I'm not the ogre who captured her; that was Mama. This dragon would rather roam the countryside than be shut up with any princess, but I'm afraid I don't have a choice in the matter. We're all like so many ebony and ivory chess pieces in some game strategized by that bitch who spawned me.*

As the Baron took his seat in the front pew next to Tante Sophia, Elysia concentrated on drawing deep, even breaths. With her steadiness still in question, she stiffened to keep from bursting into tears. Her cheeks still prickled with heat and shame at Marie-Ange's stories that afternoon. They had to be stories. Christoph couldn't lie to her with such contempt. Or could he? She looked at her groom and saw him surveying the crowd. She could not turn around to follow his gaze, and so rotated her eyes to the ceiling for prayer and distraction. The vault overhead buzzed with detail. Trompe l'oeil Apostles held scrolls unwinding through puffy clouds. They recorded the gospels with quill pens while cherubs held the inkwells. Saints gazed at the Apostles with glazed-eye admiration, and around the lower circumference of the ceiling holy martyrs were arrayed in a circle, each displaying his wounds, scars, or even a hacked-off body part on a silver tray.

One female saint gazed demurely away from the eyes she held before her, presented on a platter with a palm frond like two boiled-egg hors d'oeuvres. Apparently she had been granted a pair of replacement eyes upon her ascension. The thought of the gelatinous eyes made Elysia force a dry swallow. She averted her own eyes, looking down instead at the colored slices that the sun threw on her dress through the stained glass. A noise from behind the altar diverted her attention as the deacon entered, bearing the bishop's staff. The deep chorus of Gregorian chants rose up from the back of the sanctuary. The sound of two hundred rising bodies with their rustling clothes rattled beneath the choir's lament.

The people stood up when the priest entered bearing the leather-bound Bible with its gem-studded cover. Another deacon followed, swinging a smoking censer through the air. The twists of frankincense clouds disintegrated on the prow of Bishop Finzi's attire. The miter was the mere peak of his elaborate robes, stiff rectangles of brocade at every edge like armor plating, a carapace of luxury and authority. At the altar he blinked, and attendants came to remove the garments. First, the miter, laying it on a pillow to rest like the infant Christ. Two more priests appeared and lifted the wings of shimmering fabric away. The plain black shift beneath was quickly covered by a long, white blouse, the attendants expertly condensing it to a ring and slipping it about his head and shoulder so it appeared to cascade effortlessly over his bulging torso. The loose sleeves flapped as he stepped forward, and then his lips flapped open for the blessing.

The bishop apparently loved the sound of his own voice with an ardor that St. Theresa reserved for the ecstasy. He let each syllable rest on his tongue as if it were the host itself, better dissolved than chewed, and never spat out. His single eyebrow arced up and down in time with his rhythms of inflection, a bouncing line in time. Elysia became hypnotized as his voice braided with the ropes of smoke wafting from the incense burner the deacon swung around them. The plait of haze and dancing hair glittered with dark stars flickering in her vision. The bishop suddenly sounded as if he were speaking from the bottom of a coal mine. "Christoph de la Violette, wilt thou taketh Elysia von Eschenbach, here present, for thy lawful wife, according to the rites of our Holy Mother church?"

"I will," replied Christoph. His voice was a hollow echo off the vault of the watching saints above.

"And Elysia von Eschenbach, wilt thou taketh Christoph de la Violette, here present, for thy lawful husband according to the rite of our Holy Mother church?" The words flew past Elysia like swallows, scraps of noise that were supposed to alight in her ears but instead whipped against her senses on some mission of their own. She turned her head in confusion to try to follow their flight. She looked at Bishop Finzi to see if she could catch the words as she watched them launch from his lips.

Her own lips hung slack and her head shuddered from left to right. Her ears were stuffed with cobwebs. The bishop was looking at her expectantly, so she attempted a contribution. Her "I will" sounded more like "anthill" or "arrow," though, so she swallowed and tried again. The bishop was staring at her parched mouth waiting for the right answer to emerge. He felt insulted.

A parish priest deals with such indignities, but no one privileged to be married by a bishop, particularly the Bishop Enzo Finzi II, should muff their lines. He turned to the deacon for sympathy or direction, and the man scowled sharply. The bishop decided to incorporate a repetition into the ritual, gander and goose. Odile de la Violette would give him no end of grief if she felt it was a second-rate performance with this audience: no more dinner parties, no more fancy free frocks for his darling. He cleared his throat and turned to the groom, who was examining the stone floor at his feet with a raptness usually seen in the condemned at the gallows.

"Repeat after me: I, Christoph de la Violette..." The groom returned to attention, his peripheral vision catching his mother's feral glare. "I, Christoph de la Violette..."

"Take thou, Elysia von Eschenbach..." Christoph parroted his vows admirably, in deep, sonorous tones. The officiant whirled toward Elysia and began the parallel address in wheedling, honeyed tones. "Please repeat after me: I, Elysia von Eschenbach..." He nodded encouragingly as she tucked her chin down and concentrated, trying to force the sounds up past her arid larynx.

"Island sea fawn etching bought" would serve as the closest possible interpretation of the noises she made. The sanctuary twisted around her, the rainbow slabs of the stained glass slapping her sight. The stench of the incense became a vise closing around her rib cage. The syrup liqueur with which Marie-Ange had plied her fermented in the tight confines of her corsetry. Her tongue had swollen beyond the edges of her mouth and her eyes watered, overflowing as she nodded at Finzi to show her consent. He continued the script, deciding that any participation by the bride would be taken as a blessed affirmative.

"...to my wedded husband, to have and to hold, from this day forward."

Tears dripped from Elysia's cheeks to the silver embroidery of her dress. She was ruining her own wedding, and there was nothing she could do. She felt trapped, stuffed, mounted. Her jaw cracked as she tried to speak. "Tomb eye eddies hum sand, due apt end due old..." The last of her speech became a choking groan. Her eyes rolled up from Christoph's shoes. His face was curled with fear, the corners of his mouth drawn back in a tight line. The colors of the window swelled and burst over her, bleeding, pulsing fuchsia and gold, reflecting little scraps of stinging heat from every bit of metal shine in the crowd before her. She cried out and covered her eyes.

Damn this bride! She was ruining Finzi's show. If he could not walk off stage at the top of his game, he would have to change the lines, the entire scene. The bizarre tongues this woman was speaking, the twitching, the guttural cries—all qualified as evidence of demonic possession. He hit her with holy water and chanted Latin in equal measures. The assembly rose and gasped. The bride fell to her knees, the stiff pale arcs of silk crumpling to an accordion.

For the first time since his father bought him the bishopric, Finzi rattled off phrase after phrase with speed, eliding the words to a steady hum. Elysia's head rolled to her shoulder and her blistering tongue protruded obscenely. He held a holy wafer in front of her face in reproach. "Salvation!" he thundered.

Elysia was floating above the noise, watching the bishop continue his gesticulations over her prostrate form. She saw Christoph stepping back with terror, her father running up to take her head in his lap and plead with her not to die. Tante Sophia screamed and dug her fingers into her own scalp. Odile stood and shrieked, turning to face the pews with her arms outstretched, as if she could hide the debacle from the assembled mass.

Their figures became smaller as Elysia's spirit rose up to join the frescoes. A miniature physician knelt at her chest, lifted his head slowly and moved it from side to side. Her father leapt up and dashed at a stunned groom, trying to put his hands around his neck to shake him. "Murderer!" echoed up into the vaulting. A deacon and two guests pried the baron from Christoph de la Violette. The soreness that had abraded Elysia's skin was fading. It was cool up among the painted saints. St. Martin was cutting his cloak in two for a beggar—he gave her half and she wrapped herself in the comforting dark of its velvet nap. She gathered it around herself in a protective shawl, clutching the fabric at her chest just as her father clutched at his chest and fell over, dead, on the stone floor beside her body.

Chapter XVI
Attack

The air in the casket gets drier and heavier; her lungs fill with sawdust and earth. "Out!" she cries, scratching at the lid of the coffin until a nail breaks off. "Get me out of here!" The dust settles on her skin, burning and prickling, each mote a sandpaper drill bit burrowing into a pore. The pain wakes Claire but she does not want to waken Stuart. What could he do? Her skin is too irritated for one of his usual sweet back rubs, gently kneading her shoulders at first, pulling her arms back, then playing her spine like a xylophone with his fingers. The mere thought of any extended touching makes her itch and recoil. Her joints creak as she props herself up on her elbows, squinting at the time on the digital alarm. It is past 1 a.m. Stuart rises and lowers with each breath of sleep, safely escaping from the day's disappointments.

Claire sits up with effort: her hands coil into the edge of the mattress to push herself. Her slippers are in the closet. She opens the door carefully so that no untoward squeaking will wake Stuart. She puts them on, not able to bend down, but just half-sticking her toes into each tiny cloth cave. They won't stay on. She has to leave them behind, bracing herself on the door frame as she gets to the hall. The hinges in her knees and elbows scream for oil as she clutches the banister. The stairs take a decade to descend and she nearly trips on the last one. Her skin is still burning. The pavement is cold beneath her bare soles as she limps to the car. The car is clean, but their dream of clean cars for the entire community has been stolen by a charlatan and a thug. Brian Carlson had duped so many and fooled the judges, and it's up to Claire to set things straight.

The evening air has cooled and Claire is startled by the drops of condensation that have formed on the door handle. She struggles to get the key in the lock—her fingers are dowels, unmoving and wooden. It's a relief to hear the bolt click in the door. Still in a trance, Claire uses all her weight to pull it open. The car has become an aircraft carrier, heavier than a thousand tons of steel. Settling into the seat, she moves like a sloth, banging her elbow on the door frame as her arm flails out with a twitch. Claire is a marionette beneath an inept hand operating the strings. It takes all of her concentration to find the ignition in the steering column, start, shift to reverse, and leave the driveway. In the rearview mirror she can see her eyes, shocking red; her cheeks, shiny with tear trails. The twin yellow lines in the center of the road snake as her face spasms. Why did she jerk her head like that? There had been no bright light, nothing to startle her.

The trimmed evergreens on the sides of the road loom over her, columns appearing to totter as she passes. To the right, south on McAllister, past the strip mall with the dry cleaners and the florist, there's the police station. Claire does not attempt to navigate into the parking lot but just pulls up to the front door. Her head snaps back as she angles the car to a stop, and in the mirror she catches her reflection. The soreness in her face is not inert, but a shuddering contortion. Her cheekbones climb past her ear and her jaw wants to be anywhere but its usual place. No matter, the police station is not a place for a beauty contest.

As she climbs out of the car and the cool air soothes her skin, she does not notice the car door is left open. She takes a breath to concentrate on the walk up to the entrance. A burning mercury vapor light illuminates the path, its blinding eye overhead affixed to a steel goose-neck tube. As she leans on the door, she notes that it says 'push' instead of 'pull' and is instantly grateful: pulling would require far more coordination than she currently possesses. To push the door in, all she needs do is lean against it, and she does, falling into the warmer light of the police station, sliding to a fall on the linoleum. She lies unseen, unable to move.

Chapter XVII
The Burial

Odile de la Violette was crushed and tormented, destroyed in a way only possible for an ambitious woman to be ruined, that her completely publicized moment of glory became her most abject humiliation. She surely would never recover. All of Salzburg would be laughing behind their fans at her for decades to come. Hot saltwater stung her cheeks as she collapsed across the violet-strewn upholstery of her parlor's chaise lounge. "The scandal!" she moaned. "All is ruined, all is for naught. Those hours of research, the hunt for a suitable prospect, the finely tuned ear for rumor and innuendo…all my talents and efforts wasted." She gnawed at the knuckle of her index finger to suppress a sob.

"At least we are still a family," Marie-Ange piped up from the carpet. She knelt by Odile's side. The girl's eyes were puffy and red-rimmed. "We still have each other."

Odile looked at her daughter in her flaming orange taffeta gown, glanced up to see her son sprawled out in an armchair paring his nails with an ivory-handled pocketknife, closed her eyes and groaned. Marie-Ange reached up to grasp her mother's hand. She wanted to have her confession heard, but there was no way she would tell her tale to slow Bishop Finzi. She wanted her mother's blessing and forgiveness, but to tell one-tenth of her plotting would have meant death on the spot. Odile would club her with the violet-traced enamel handle of the fireplace poker, or strangle her with the help of the blossom-embroidered swag that held back the parlor curtains. *Mama, Marie-Ange wanted to say, please forgive me. I was just sick of the baroness getting all the attention—the baroness this, the baroness that, the moon-drenched alabaster and marble soaked in milk, and the palest petal, fine skin of the baroness, her blue sheen, her impeccable calm and reserve. Every compliment paid to her made me rounder and spottier and more stained in my garish color, my fly-away hair, my thick limbs. Mama, the daughter would continue, it was all a little prank gone horribly wrong. The lark was inspired by childish petty vanity, jealousy, and spite. With you drooling over her nobleness, it was Christoph all over again. Even the in-laws are more favored than myself. What did I ever do that you reject me so? Am I not your daughter, but a foundling? Did Rene find me in the rose bed beneath the thorns of a fiery tapered apricot blossom?* Now Marie-Ange blushed shame upon shame to realize the selfish origins of these needless deaths: the baby, the baroness, and perhaps even the baron. No mea culpa could appease the mark of such base manipulation for such low reasons. She shuddered and swallowed to think of her future as a penitent, decades in a cell with bread, water, and a Bible for study. She would only have a cross to meditate upon, a sign of the suffering of God's son for all, even those as crass and twisted as herself. Marie-Ange pouted as she sat at the edge of the chaise. "Mama," the girl placed her head on her mother's hand. "Let me rest up against you. Please, let us embrace to find comfort in the face of this tragedy."

Odile recoiled. "Marie-Ange! You are crushing my hand!" The woman pulled her hand out from beneath the supplicant's head, scratching the side of her face with a ring and tangling her fingers in the disordered orange coif. She rolled upright from the other side of the lounge and shook herself, standing up to pace. The purple and gold of her skirts seemed obscene, spirals of color washing down the stiff fabric of the dress. Marie-Ange stayed on the floor. She folded her hands on the furniture and flung her face down upon them. Odile did not look at her.

"The bodies of the von Eschenbachs are in the rectory with Tante Sophia in attendance. She is inconsolable." Rene had appeared in the doorway. His face was lined and he held his hat in his hand. "The doctor has left me a tincture of opium for her, if I can persuade her to take it. I want to return to her in case she decides to hurt herself in her grief. We must make decisions regarding the funeral."

"Funeral?" Odile snarled. "Today was to be a wedding day, not a funeral! Damn and blast these lily-complected wilting noble folk. They ruined everything. I need time to think, and not about how to bury them, but the debacle that they created." Her pacing picked up speed and her hands scissored the air.

Rene stopped and drew his shoulders back. He tilted his head forward and moved his hat to his other hand. "I thought you might like to prepare..."

"I will prepare everything—tomorrow! Today has been more than enough for anyone. I am in a panic. It is a wonder I have not disintegrated completely." She spun around and mashed her foot into a hapless violet in the rug.

"Odile, you do not understand." Her husband looked at her with a solemn stare. He clasped the rim of his hat in both hands and drew it up to his waistcoat.

"Understand?" She almost spat. "You are the one incapable of all understanding! Do you have any idea how many hours of preparation this marriage represented? Never mind the expense of this day. The coordination was monstrous—the clothing, the refurbished carriages, the additional servants, the invitations, the flowers, the feast, the champagne, the requisite price of the blessing of our Holy Mother the Church? Not to mention all the parties introducing our aristocrat to everyone and his brother. All wasted!" Now Odile stood motionless, infuriated. Her fists hung plumb to the ground, dragging her arms straight along her sides. "And you come whimpering in here with your ludicrous concern for that hairy spinster. Have you no respect for the magnitude of today's losses? All my dreams have been shot, Rene de la Violette."

Rene strode forward three steps, shoved his wife aside and headed straight for the crystal decanter on the sideboard. Odile stretched out her hands in case she had to catch herself but only scraped the dress over her shins on the polished cherry of the lounge. Marie-Ange watched the proceedings, absorbed with the tentative curiosity of a mouse watching two cats in a fight. Christoph was amused. He had stopped cleaning his nails and contemplated like a gambler about to place a bet on who the winner would be. Rene poured himself a goblet of red wine, drained half of it in one swallow, and filled it again.

"Odile de la Violette! Shame!" Rene slammed the glass down on the tabletop and wine sloshed to the wood. "Has it occurred to you that two people died today? Your ruined party is not a tragedy. In fact, your entire pretentious scheme was a farce for which this could be considered divinely ordained poetic justice and retribution had it not entailed the deaths of two innocent people. You have a smaller, meaner heart than I thought possible. You might as well have a petrified horse-pie soaked in violet cologne in your chest. These are the remains of real people in the rectory, not stolen pawns in some chess game that you play against your own fears." He leaned on the table's edge in a state of deep exasperation. The light outside was almost gone entirely.

"Elysia was a girl embarking on a marriage, the ultimate rite of womanhood." Rene's voice rose in a crescendo. "And instead of beginning a new life she collapses on the altar. Her father was a truly noble man; may he be forgiven the devil's bargain he drove with us. Tante Sophia has lost her entire family, is completely alone on this earth, and you mock her? You are a monster with no soul!" He roared the last sentence, punctuating it with a slammed fist on the sideboard that sent the wineglass flying.

He paused to take a breath and then turned to Marie-Ange. "Not knowing how Elysia died, I have no doubt what killed Ignatz von Eschenbach. He died of a broken heart. I can imagine the pain of losing one's only and adored daughter." Christoph's eyes ferried from Rene to Marie-Ange and back. His half-sister had buried her face in her hands again. Rene faced Odile and continued. "You have no vision beyond your greed, woman. The baron should have grown old with us, dandled grandchildren on his knee before the fireplace, peeled Christmas chestnuts for them and told them stories of the wolves that used to plague the estate and how they were hunted down. I would have enjoyed hunting with him, drinking with him, showing him the latest additions to my garden, decrying the latest follies of the Pope or the emperor over a private glass of brandy in the wee hours of a visit. Instead of becoming the acquaintance, and perhaps even the friend, of such a fine man, I am burying him. And what I was rushing here to tell you was," a long pause emphasized his irritation, "that the good Bishop Enzo Finzi II has decided, in his most divinely ordained judgement, that the von Eschenbachs were struck down in a fit of demonic possession and therefore cannot be buried in hallowed ground." He didn't hide his revulsion. "Perhaps this is more of an embarrassment than your spoiled party, Madame?"

Rene's boot spun on its heel, crushing his hat on the floor where he had dropped it. All three heads of the others twisted to see this seeming stranger storm away. Once he reached the garden his breathing lost its ragged edge. Rene stopped and surveyed his refuge. He traversed the green lawn to the square entrance of the maze that Klaus so meticulously trimmed. Perhaps if he walked in far enough he would get lost to emerge from the shiny green leaves into a different labyrinth, one in another country with a family that loved one another, aspired to love their neighbors, and worshiped God instead of their own vanity.

Odile could see Rene striding across the lawn toward the maze. She turned from the window and collapsed on the lounge, narrowly missing Marie-Ange's head. "How dare he!" she snarled. "That subsidized drone, that useless bud-sniffer. How dare he presume that I do not mourn the von Eschenbachs? Of course their passing grieves me—people grieve in their own manner. Even the Savior said, 'Let the dead bury the dead.' I just get right back to business and work over sorrows. Your father never did understand me, you know." She lifted her rump to remove a shank of Marie-Ange's hair from beneath. Her daughter sat on the floor and administered to her running nose with a lace cuff. Christoph stood up, strolled to the window, and moved aside the vase on the sill. Last week's violets had yet to be replaced, and the decay rendered their usually delicate scent putrid and over-sweet. He leaned forward to exhale on the glass, and then with a flourish signed his own name in the fog. "He is here." The young man offered his mother the same gaze that falcons reserve for rabbits. Odile was startled into sitting upright. She straightened her skirts about her knees.

"Who is here?" She licked her fingertips and began rearranging the disarrayed ringlets that framed her face.

Christoph picked up the tassled cord that tied back the lavender drapery, and swung it in a circle. "Slow Finzi," he replied with quiet glee, whispering at his mother with narrowed eyes and dancing brows.

Odile sniffed. "Show the appropriate respect to the bishop."

"To do that I would have to break wind when I speak his name."

"Christoph! No more childishness. He is a very important man, regardless of what you think of his sermons. I have never asked that you listen to them, just attend services." Odile walked to the window and stood at Christoph's side. "Ring Laurent and Guillame. Tell them to decant some of the best brandy and prepare a fire in the first floor parlor. We will receive him there." She rubbed her hands together as if trying to remove a stain. "I do not look forward to this interview. You two will join me. And remember, everyone: *grief-stricken*; I want to see grief-stricken. Sob, rub your eyes red before you enter the room. Rumple your clothes. Christoph, perhaps you should rend something."

"But I just got this waistcoat yesterday!" Sarcasm reigned in his voice as he ran his palms down the tailored fabric.

"Oh, Lord in heaven, I exaggerate, you simpleton! Just do something other than whistle and pick your teeth. You are a tragically widowed young man in love who has a deep and abiding respect for the Holy Mother Church. Remember that. Your beloved was stolen from you at the altar on the very day you were to wed. Now, sackcloth and ashes my darlings, let's go!" She held her hands before her face and clapped them twice, leading the procession out of the room.

The trio arrived just as the servants finished setting out the brandy, snifters, and an elaborate tray of sliced melons, quartered figs, and chilled sugared grapes. Odile stepped to the center of the window so she would be backlit. She motioned Marie-Ange into the corner next to the marble fireplace, and then snapped her fingers and pointed to a spot on the carpet for Christoph to stand upon. He had already flung himself down in an overstuffed settee covered with little purple flowers, but he sighed and heaved himself up from his quilted patch of meadow to take his place at Odile's side.

The footman appeared at the door. "His Holiness the Bishop Enzo Finzi II." Two deacons, like bookends, filed in, each inspecting a separate corner of the room and then converging upon the circle of well-appointed chairs and settees arranged in front of the fireplace. They grasped two and moved them to the center of the room. The beads hanging from their waists rattled against the scrollwork of the chairs' legs. The older of the two made eye contact with Odile, and then glanced at the seat of the chair before him. The presumptuousness of these skirted choirboys! Well, at least he did not snap his fingers. That remained Finzi's prerogative, but she felt within her rights to negotiate whatever bizarre charge or demand he might be bringing to her.

The Bishop had been chosen for his multiple advantages as an officiant. He was available for the ceremony on short notice. He was a satisfied customer of the house of Violette, having procured many fine peignoir sets for his amply endowed Tyrolean singer-friend, Renatta Pozzobano. She had the ability to move her breasts in time to the music, individually, a charming folk tradition that was taken into consideration when bodices and corsets were constructed. The bishop's business was handled with utmost discretion and received Odile's personal attention.

Such arrangements for clergy were almost commonplace, but Finzi's account wasn't nearly as intriguing as the Bishop of Strasbourg who ordered a gown for himself with embroidered lambs bearing crosses appliquéd along the bottom hem, or the cardinal who requested an elaborately constructed suede vest that was decorated with half-arrows stitched upon it at intervals that made the wearer appear to be as pierced as St. Sebastian. Odile, being an astute businesswomen, realized such intimate acquaintance with the local clergy was not an entirely useless thing.

Even the most superficial knowledge of Finzi would reveal that he was a vain man. His pride was evident in the way that he stood frozen, listening to the call of the herald whenever he was announced. Once the full title was trumpeted, he would lower his attentive ear, close his eyes, and concur in satisfaction. Then his nose would rise in the air and lead him, like the prow of some ostentatious barge cutting through the mists of officiousness and hierarchy that clung to him like a miasma. This pompous show, and his particular fondness for Renatta, were the sole individual traits the man ever revealed. He staked his tent of overweening pride on a bedrock of meticulous dedication to rule and routine. He shuddered to think of a life without regulation and precedent, a horrifying, shifting realm where he would actually be required to innovate and interpret. No, no, no: he was saved from such by canonical law, by ritual, by the established Latin rhythms of each rite and benediction.

Odile wondered whether he followed biblical injunctions with his singer-friend: if there was a Vatican-endorsed length of time mandated to admire each breast, an apostle-sanctified ratio of strokes per minute, a Pauline doctrine of proper thrust. Perhaps his mistress dozed through his ministrations as the masses dozed through his Masses.

When planning the wedding, Odile had considered Finzi's slow thoroughness an advantage: there would be no doubt that the couple was officially and completely wed, and the ritual elevating Odile de la Violette to the ranks of the nobility would be long enough that even the densest aristocrat in attendance could not deny its occurrence. Now she cursed her choice. A speedier service and there would have been no grounds to dispute her son's inheritance of the von Eschenbach title and estate. Now she was resigned to quibbling over Elysia's final moans and gargles. *Well, mother always said that if wishes were horses, beggars would ride.*

A cough interrupted her reverie. Odile saw a third deacon standing in the doorway. Aha—all seated, all rise. It must have been stated in some dust-covered ledger of thirteenth century protocol that a bishop could not enter the presence of a mere noble who was not seated, and could only confer with secular leaders ranking duke and higher if they were not seated higher than he. Exceptions for kings, emperors, and officials higher in the church, of course.

Finzi moved into the room at a glacial pace, like someone moving a statue of a large man covered with dark fur wearing red vestments across her parquet floor by shoving it an inch every ten-seconds. "Your Eminence." She lowered herself to the floor, doing the best to array her skirts in such a way that they would not be too creased or get trod upon by this sedated bull of the Vatican. She counted to ten and finally felt a hand upon her crown. If she had looked up, she would have seen him marking the air in routine blessing. Then a hand appeared beneath her face, its large gold ring waiting to be kissed. She obliged, and then it continued its orbit back to the side of the bishop. He sighed and lowered himself into the chair. It creaked.

"Your Eminence does us a great honor with your visit during our mourning. It has been a tremendous shock, I'm sure you will agree." Bishop Finzi agreed that it was too tragic, but did not agree to have any refreshments, and even declined the rare vintage. Odile shifted in her chair, concerned that Finzi was going to pretend he did not know her. After expressions of consolation for the la Violette's new family so quickly lost, the bishop cleared his throat—apparently the traditional method consisted of one deep harsh rattle followed by a slurring roughness increasing a quarter-octave in pitch—and addressed the disposal of the deceased.

"Madame de la Violette, I come to you today out of consideration for our years of friendship," said Enzo Finzi. Odile was so relieved that she wanted to loosen her stays and put her feet up on the back of a deacon. One of them would get on all fours if instructed to by Enzo, if he thought it would increase his rank in the church hierarchy. So, Enzo acknowledged that she knew him, and each hoped they could reach an arrangement that satisfied them both. "We are faced with a dilemma." He gently shoved the long cuffs of his gloves to his wrists, removed his ring and stored it in his right palm, and then began to individually tug at each fingertip. The gloves lay in his left hand like two bright fish skins. One deacon appeared at his elbow to collect them, and another stepped up and knelt at his side to replace the ring on his right hand. "The von Eschenbachs died while I was embarked upon an exorcism, in the church, at the altar. Their souls were stolen from beneath my nose with the entire city of Salzburg in attendance. It was an embarrassing and well-witnessed defeat." He examined his bare fingers splayed on each of his knees.

"Considering the circumstances of their deaths, it would not be proper to proceed with a funeral Mass and service for them before assuring ourselves of their piety. Since they died without the benefit of grace, even burial in hallowed ground presents a difficulty." Odile exhaled with relief: *difficult, yes, but not impossible. They may find a way to give the von Eschenbachs an appropriate burial yet.*

She immediately assumed her most innocent smile, a grimace that still could not redeem Odile de la Violette from a decidedly wheedling appearance. "Your Eminence, words cannot express my gratitude at your addressing this complex situation. The issues involved obviously exceed the knowledge and rational capacities of a layman, let alone a woman like myself. I have no doubt that your abilities and experience will lead us to the divinely ordained resolution."

"May I speak, your Eminence?" Christoph interrupted, catching both Odile and the bishop by surprise. Finzi nodded at Christoph to proceed.

"I have just lost my bride, Elysia." He paused, looked to the floor, and proceeded with a quaver. "As lovely as she was, her piety exceeded her beauty. My mother, your friend, would not have approved of the marriage under any other circumstances. I beg you, your Eminence, to give them absolution postmortem. Forgive them their transgression. There could be no doubt that your exorcism was most efficacious, and that it was the abrupt force with which the demons departed that brought about their seizures. They lost their lives here but may still know the infinite mercy of God. Forgive them, grant them the blessing of a brief ceremony for their intimates, and allow them to be interred in holy ground." He dropped to his knee and wiped his eye with the back of his hand. He counted one, two, three, four, five petals on the flower embossed on the carpeting to measure the pause. "Your merciful Eminence, show to Salzburg that God and the Bishop Finzi welcome the fragile Elysia von Eschenbach and her noble father into the heavenly realm of the Lord Christ our savior, amen."

Finzi's eyebrows interlaced in contemplation. The young man made an excellent point. To bury the two in unhallowed ground would be the ultimate confirmation of his own ineptitude, and what sort of protection would the souls of Salzburg be assured if he could not be counted upon to save two individuals? On the other hand, if the two were buried in the churchyard, it would be irrefutable proof that their last anguished cries were merely the screams of vanquished demons. He put his hands together and rested his full lips on the tips of his index fingers.

Odile put aside her astonishment and continued the charge. "Your Eminence, our family accepted a parcel of neighboring property as payment for an old account. There is a small but suitable crypt on the land. I could send men to prepare it at once. The von Eschenbachs could be interred by sundown. Their one relative to grieve, good Tante Sophia, is already in attendance. If you have a previous engagement, perhaps one of your entourage could officiate." She curtsied toward the deacons. One shifted from one foot to another and his cassock rustled.

Finzi cocked his ear to the grating of fabric against fabric. All could hear the quiet ticks of the clock on the mantel, a golden device framed with a wreath of enamel violets. "I would send Brother Adalberto." His confirmation was typically slow and oblique. Christoph began his pleas once more. Odile was shocked at his display of acting. Perhaps being the audience for all those exaggerated claims of ecstasy had taught him some skills. "Bishop Finzi, will you anoint my bride with your own hand? Please introduce her to her Maker, her redeemer, in the name of He who loved her. It shall maintain my devotion to the church for the rest of my days on earth to know that my wife waits for me to join her in the hereafter." With this he looked to the ceiling and a thin stream trickled down each cheek. Odile turned away to hide her amazement. She appreciated her son's acumen. If the bishop himself performed the rites and interred the bodies in consecrated soil, there would be no grounds on which to repudiate Christoph's status as heir. She looked at Finzi. He gazed at the wainscoting above the fireplace, ardently wishing that someone else could make this decision. It would be too much for him to do, to become personally involved in this suspect burial. He would be deviating far enough from strict interpretation to permit their blessed burial at all, never mind standing over the bodies, dabbing them with small puddles of oil, intoning his words into their still, blue faces. He frowned, the corners of his mouth crawling away from one another and beginning to sag toward his chin.

"Enzo, my dearest friend." Odile was not about to let him say no, particularly in front of subordinates. Now it would be irrevocable. Her voice dropped to a husky whisper. "Please forgive the boy. He is grief stricken; he knows not what he asks. I have no doubt that a holy man of your stature could perform these rites, could grant this mourner's request without a second thought."

Blunt but effective. "I am God's servant," the bishop said, "and as such, it is my sacred duty to anoint both Elysia and the Baron von Eschenbach. Preparations are necessary for this evening's service. We must leave now." Deacon ring-remover preceded deacon glove-bearer, and they performed their appointed tasks with a speed that their master would never achieve. The cuffs were delicately tugged back to the elbows, and the gold ring was replaced over the glove.

Odile knelt to receive his blessing. "I am in your debt, Enzo." He coughed to acknowledge his agreement, then traced crosses in the air above the bowed heads of Christoph and Marie-Ange with a deliberateness and precision that suggested he was measuring a model for the true crucifixion. Marie-Ange noted the self-absorbed relief of her mother and half-brother, and followed the bishop to the door with soundless steps.

"Your Eminence," she started, speaking in a quiet, girlish voice, "'you must hear my confession. No lesser cleric could absolve me of the heinous sins I have committed..."

"Now, now, my child. At least it is obvious that your grief is genuine." His glance threw spikes at Christoph and Odile. "Elysia would have been a new sister to you."

"But what I have done is unforgivable, Father." Marie-Ange was sobbing, so her freckles took on a sharpness like island archipelagos drawn on a map.

"Nonsense. The Lord gave his loveliest creations gentle hearts." Odile thought of the gentle, striped, fiery orange tigress, or perhaps the lovely screeching peacock. The bishop reached out to Marie-Ange and continued, "Those who grieve will magnify their every transgression against the deceased in their loneliness and loss." He tucked a strand of hair behind her ear and bid her rise by bending over and lifting beneath her elbow. Marie-Ange could smell the bleu cheese he had eaten for lunch.

The Bishop patted her shoulder, entangling his ring in a fall of curls.

"You are a very charming young woman. When I saw you in the congregation this morning I thought, 'Now, such a vision renews even my faith in providence. No doubt I shall be performing her wedding soon. So exquisite, she looks like a peach—no, more like a delicacy from the South, perhaps a tangerine, ripe and fragrant.' Your gift of beauty is better shared by smiling, my child."

His gloved hand squeezed her shoulder, a cooler streak of red upon the field of shining orange. Marie-Ange gasped, collected herself, and continued. "Your Eminence, I must clear my conscience. I have sinned most terribly." She looked down at her feet and her nose quivered.

"Very well, my child, if you are in turmoil, come to my apartments in the city to receive private counsel." He raised a gloved finger. "Such specific theological consideration is a rare privilege. And if the errors are as grave as you suggest, it may take many meetings to resolve them, find the appropriate penance, and grant absolution." The back of his fingers caressed the edge of her bowed jaw. The attendant deacons stood in a row, like monuments consigned to gaze into nothing for eternity. Finzi turned from Marie-Ange and the trio filed out in his wake.

"Splendid addition. Marie-Ange." Odile couldn't suppress a cackle. I believe that the Bishop fancies you."

"Mama!" The girl shrieked. "You are too cruel!" She grabbed huge knots of her skirts and ran up the stairs to her room, orange flaring out behind her. Odile smiled to think that the child may redeem herself yet.

"Mama," Christoph said more musically, leaning forward to kiss her on the cheek, "I must go change into black. I hear that's the color that's all the rage for burying wives this year. If you see Justine, send her along upstairs, will you? She must be chastised. Her behavior this morning was really out of line. Such presumptuousness is not acceptable in a servant."

Odile sat in one of the chairs that had been displaced for the conference with Finzi and motioned for Christoph to be seated across from her. "My son, in theory you were just deprived the consummation of a love that was to span time. Perhaps you could tolerate a day or two of celibacy in your sadness."

Christoph leaned on the arm of the unoccupied chair and drummed his fingers in thought. "Why should I?"

"Christoph, your attitude is inappropriate. We must keep up appearances until the von Eschenbachs are in the ground, at least. People have enough to talk about already."

"And how will these people know if I dally with one little servant in the privacy of my own home? For God's sake, Mother, it's not as if I asked you to hand-pick nine virgins for me to deflower in front of town hall at high noon on market day."

"Christoph! Shame!" Odile hissed at her son and gripped the ends of the armrests, smothering the roars of sculpted lions' heads. "After all I've done for you!"

"Shame? Please, Mother, do you know the meaning of the word? And I have done nothing for you? I have merely played the puppet-suitor in your quest for nobility. Well, Madame, you appear to have achieved it. The estate without the strings of in-laws attached is a pleasant surprise, mind you, but if anything I have done quite a bit for you as well. Or would you have killed Rene and attempted to marry a noble yourself if I was not available for such vicarious ventures? Sometimes it does not seem beyond you."

"My own son!" Odile's eyes watered. Rene and now Christoph in one day? The shock of this revolting turn of events really was too much.

"That is correct. Your son, the *baron*." Christoph leaned forward and placed his hands on the arms of his mother's chair, pinning her right hand. "And you would do well to know a baron, particularly if Rene is no longer content to spread manure in his flower garden, eh?" He leapt back, spun around, clapped his hands, and then half-squatted with his hands on his thighs, presenting Odile with a clownish grin.

"What an incredible day! A barony without the burden of a bride or a father-in-law. Estates, vineyards, a castle, prestige, power, pomp, circumstance, stables, fields, forests—all mine. Mine!" He brought his fisted hand up beneath his chin and cocked his head in contemplation. "Also, I believe there is a charming tradition called 'the rite of the first night' still recognized among the peasantry in the hinterlands. Now, there's a reason to aspire to aristocracy. When I decorate my palace— when I, the Baron Christoph, design my coat-of-arms, I can assure you of one thing." He sprang up and threw his hands in the air. "There will not be a single damned violet anywhere among the lot! Nor a scrap of purple, lavender, mauve, you name it."

"Now, Madame de la Violette, if you could send Justine to my chambers immediately, I may be more well-disposed to considering your petitions in the future. Good day." He flounced out his coattails and danced to the door.

"Bastard!" Odile spat behind him. Her son stopped, turned to her, and bowed.

"If I am a whore's son, for that is the common meaning of bastard," he spoke in the cool and measured tones of pure rage strapped down with great will, "what manner of woman are you?" The door swung shut behind him and Odile glared at the flowered doorknob staring back at her. Very well, let the boy have his amusements. She had birthed a fool indeed if he thought that she was so easily vanquished. As she pulled the bell rope to summon Justine, she recalled the jest—that the Creator had given men organs and brains, but not enough sanguineous humor to use both at once. Let Christoph expend himself in bed all he likes; he'd be less prepared to take her on. Giselle appeared in the door. "Madame?"

"Send Justine to the chambers of the Baron Christoph at once, and have the carriage brought round immediately." Odile straightened her cuffs. "I must attend to the burial of Elysia and the Baron von Eschenbach."

All are lambs of God, but whenever Bishop Finzi blessed the dead he could not help but shudder with the knowledge that the Lord took the blessed home to heaven like so much chilled mutton. He traced small crosses upon the late Baron von Eschenbach's forehead, home of the intellect; mouth, recipient of the holy host, and heart, fortress of the spirit. The baron's skin had become gray, a dull blue from beneath chalk-dusted skin. His eyes had already sunken. His daughter's younger, firmer eyes had yet to so recede. The bishop began to administer to the corpse of Elysia von Eschenbach.

Enzo Finzi paused in shame. As a man of the world, and a divinely ordained son of the Church of Rome, he had seen many things. Things that a lesser soul, one not capable of complex theological interpretation, might find decadent or corrupt. The given companions of those in the Vatican hierarchy, the sculptures of Priapus saved from the friezes of Greek temples, the instructive watercolor paintings made by infidels before Mohammed and brought back in saddlebags from the crusades, and the sketches of hermaphroditic malformations among the royal families of ancient Egypt documented on papyrus scrolls, for example. However, the one thing that he could not abide, that made his worldly brow rise and his lips curl with distaste, was a violation of the dead. Some scholars condoned attempts at coitus with a recently deceased husband as a final attempt to procure progeny, but with a female there could be no such excuse.

In all his years of these final rituals, from placing holy oil on the merchant's wife who had died in childbirth, to making the cross over the remains of a dusty duchess a week previous (the bodies that had received his rituals, male and female, could be stacked like cordwood all the way to Bologna and back), no corpse had ever given him the living stirring as much as the remains of Elysia von Eschenbach. Her eyes had not fallen back in their sockets at all. While somewhat open, her jaw was not entirely slack. Her black hair framed her white face in a delicate balance of ravens and doves, the wisdom and the love. There was no sign of stiffness—the girl looked as if she might be awakened by the tender ministrations of a lover, laughing as she passed from dream to waking, reaching up to caress the cheek of the man before her, an angel on earth.

Once again, the honored rite: he drew a small cross on her forehead, then over her mouth. Her lips could not have moved. It had to be the perverse streak that had been placed in his imagination, the desire to have this girl awaken, to tease the end of his finger with her puckered lips. What a day of bedevilment; the exorcism was only the beginning. The woman was obviously bearing some Satanic taint to inspire such thoughts. He would have to consult with the specialists in Madrid, the keepers of the Malleus Malefactorum, to determine the proper procedure for handling such an event if it should occur again. He must bury these forsaken aristocrats as quickly as possible and let them be damned or not. Bishop Finzi crossed himself, paired fingers grazing forehead, heart, and shoulders, and then he flicked some oil in the direction of Elysia's heart. "Amen," he announced, basso profundo.

Finzi rushed from the chapel, knocking over a rack of candles in his wake. One of his deacons ran over and stamped out the flames of the flickering wicks and sprinkled their ends with holy water. The entire day should be doused in holy water: the heavens should burst and it should come down in torrents to wash Salzburg clean of all the unholy things visited upon it that day. The bishop crossed himself again and took deep, regular breaths to compose himself. "Brother Adalberto will complete the interment," he announced to no one in particular, and then whirled around and retreated to his chambers.

All gaped at his departing backside: none had ever seen slow Finzi move so fast. Brother Adalberto stepped forward and beckoned Odile's servants, Laurent and Guillame. He lowered his voice and the heads of the three men entered a small circle as the transportation of the bodies was arranged. Tante Sophia stepped around the three for a final visit with the baron and Elysia. First she placed an open palm on Ignatz's chest and recited a blessing of her own, words of remembrance unsanctified by any Mediterranean church, but written in the dark catacombs of Carpathian caves at sunset.

Tante Sophia recalled all the joy that had come from knowing Ignatz von Eschenbach: his marriage to her sister, Dorothea, a festival that brought the entire estate together to feast. The bride was crowned with white roses and the peasants put on the most amusing pageant about the wedding of the King and Queen of the fairies. Their children played the parts of the tiniest fey spirits, lamb's wool beards glued to the chins of those supposed to be dwarves and gnomes. Her sister had been toasted again and again, but never touched liquor herself. Then there was the joy of Peter's birth and the tragedy of his death. And now this. The Baron's chest was still under her hand and she knew he would not stir again. She leaned down and kissed the side of his neck, the bristles of his beard brushing over her nose.

Tante Sophia stepped to the bier that held Elysia's body. The baron had lived a full life, and although his death was still too early and unjust, to see Elysia stricken down on the cusp of womanhood was a true tragedy. Sophia reached down to wipe the oil from her face. Her skin was still soft. There was no cooling or stiffness. "Heart of my life," whispered Tante Sophia. "She is only sleeping. My child..." She held her breath and her hand crept over Elysia's heart. The aunt stood bolt-upright. "Not dead!" she shouted. She grabbed Elysia's hand and kissed it, letting the arm fall over the table's edge as she ran out of the room.

"She's not dead!" the woman yelled at Brother Adalberto. "Elysia is not dead!" She grabbed his sleeve and spun him around to face her. His rough cassock sleeves gathered in her fingers: she shook him. "Do you hear me, man?"

Brother Adalberto wrested himself from her grip and stepped back, steadying himself on a pew. "Madame?"

"Elysia von Eschenbach is not dead. She is alive." Tante Sophia lunged forward and addressed the cleric nose to nose. "Are you deaf? The baroness is living." Tante Sophia grabbed his chicken-bone wrist and drug him into the room. Elysia was still upon the bier. Brother Adalberto shook his head, twisted his wrist from the aunt's grasp, and placed his hands on her shoulders, attempting to steer her outside.

"Unhand me! What are you doing?" Tante Sophia strained to escape the cleric's grasp. "You ignorant wretch! The ancient tales are true: the blood of the Dragon Clan can sleep and reawaken. She will awaken and will need my help. I must be with her!" Her cries echoed against the stone walls. She could hear the footsteps of the other deacons approaching the doorway.

Brother Adalberto shook her once, and then tried to hold her in place. "Madame! Calm yourself! The grieving often question the judgment of our Lord, but it is not ours to decide when we depart this veil of tears. Your sadness is a stove in which the desire for her return is sparked by your imagination, by the sight of the body. Elysia von Eschenbach is dead. She died in front of hundreds of witnesses, the assembled community of Salzburg. The most accomplished and respected physician of the city examined her. Bishop Finzi has consecrated the body for burial."

"No! Not if I am still alive!" Tante Sophia stopped twisting under his grip and panted. "If I have a single breath left in my body it will be used to keep that girl out of a mausoleum and tend to her until she wakes up. She is only sleeping. There are things you do not know, man of God."

Four nuns arrived, rather brawny specimens of brides of Christ from the adjacent St. Anne's convent. Sister Judea was the largest of the lot, half a head taller than Brother Adalberto. To hear a dulcimer-sweet voice chime from beneath her moustache was a surprise, indeed.

"Come with us, sister. We will share your mourning. We are saying novenas for the soul of Elysia von Eschenbach at this very moment. Surely it will be soothing for you to see the candles lit in remembrance of her soul, to hear the many voices lifted in one prayer." Brother Adalberto lifted his hand from Tante Sophia and the nun reached out in sympathy to console her. "Let us share your suffering."

"I suffer only from being surrounded by ignorance!" Tante Sophia stood as still as a marble statue. Perhaps now they would unhand her.

"Your barbaric rituals will guarantee my niece nothing other than the hellish trap of being buried alive! I am not your sister. I am the sister of Dorothea von Eschenbach, the late wife of the Baron von Eschenbach, and Elysia's mother. And I will not leave my niece here to be interred while still breathing."

Odile de la Violette had arrived at the rectory. She could hear the echoes of the struggle as she walked up the aisle of the small sanctuary. A huge nun and one of Bishop Finzi's deacons were trying to pull Tante Sophia from the inner chamber. She clutched onto the inside of the door frame with both hands. "Who would have thought the old girl had the strength in her?" mused Odile. "This day will be the end of me yet."

"What is the problem here?" she demanded. Silence filled the room. She could hear the ragged breaths of Tante Sophia. "You!" She pointed at Brother Adalberto. "Explain this scene immediately!"

"It's this one," replied Brother Adalberto, moving his head sideways toward Tante Sophia. "She refuses to believe that the girl is dead. She denies the rites of Our Holy Mother the Church."

"Perhaps a demon has afflicted the entire family," whispered Sister Judea, as she crossed herself. Odile rolled her eyes. She must put an end to this possession prattle immediately, or they might delay the burial and throw the transfer of the title into question.

"Nonsense!" she shouted, and then softer, "Have you no compassion for a poor woman who has lost so much in one day? She is plainly disturbed, so grief-stricken that she has lost her reason, but that can hardly be a shock to anyone here. Why, last year when the Duke of Burstadt lost his bride, did he not sleep outside her tomb for weeks? It is the same here."

"No!" Tante Sophia shouted in return. "You do not understand, you French tart! I will not leave Elysia. I must protect her. She must not be buried. Where is Christoph? I tried to explain things to him earlier. Where is her husband?" Tante Sophia sought any ally but had no hopes of anything other than the merest delay.

"My son, so cruelly widowed on his wedding day, is disposed with a damaged heart. Sophia, you must let us bury the dead." Odile clasped her hands together in front of her waist and tried to keep her most sympathetic face, despite the hot blush stinging her cheeks from the woman's insult. This was no place for a brawl.

Tante Sophia's hands shook and she grasped either elbow. "Elysia is only sleeping. She will awaken. I must take care of her."

"You must be taken care of, Tante Sophia," replied Odile, trying her best to keep her voice sugar-sweet. "You will rest at Ste. Anne's until you recover." She nodded at Sister Judea and the formidable nun clamped her hand down onto Tante Sophia. The largest deacon appeared behind her, looped her arms together behind her back, and then flipped her over his shoulder, clamping her legs to his chest with his right arm, skirts bundling up to expose her ankles. Tante Sophia tried to kick her captured legs and flailed her fists against the man's lower back as he carried her from the room. Her dignity being damaged was nothing compared to her loss. She screamed, "She sleeps! She sleeps!" as they carried her from the rectory and across the courtyard.

Brother Adalberto turned to Odile. "It is too sad to see someone so deranged. It may take her quite awhile to recover."

Odile responded almost too swiftly. "Yes. It will take at least a month for such an extreme case. Bishop Finzi would agree. If he has any questions, please tell him that I am, as always, his humble servant, and that he may send for me at once." She reached into a fold in her skirt and produced three gold coins. Brother Adalberto's upturned palm briefly appeared before her and the transfer was complete.

"I trust you will relay my message to the bishop, and please be sure that Tante Sophia receives the most comfortable, secure quarters. The woman might do harm to herself, and the noises of the street would only serve to disturb her further. Let us proceed with the burial."

"Do you not wish to check the body?"

"Did you check the body, Brother Adalberto?"

"The raving woman insisted that I examine her, and she seemed quite dead to me." Brother Adalberto remembered his job that day and glanced upward. "I am certain she sleeps at the right hand of Christ."

"With yourself and Bishop Finzi performing the rituals, I am confident she will rest in peace." Odile de la Violette bowed almost imperceptibly in the face of such sagacity and holiness. "The workmen are here. Let us delay no more." She left the rectory and Brother Adalberto followed behind.

The crypt had fallen into disrepair. Guillame peeled away vines from the eroded limestone as the coffins were unloaded from the cart. "They look like crates," Odile mused, leaning against the side of the carriage. "We are all so much cargo on our final journey." The scent of pitch stung her nostrils as the attendants lit the torches.

"Madame de la Violette, all is ready." The older of the two laborers bowed to Odile. "The bodies are placed for their eternal heavenly rest. Please know that I and my son are men of honor. They still wear their jewelry."

Ho ho—Odile had not heard of this. "Jewelry?" she questioned, her ears perking up and her palms becoming moist. Well, she deserved some sort of memento for all the trouble these godforsaken blue bloods had brought her. A ring, bracelet, or charm would do very nicely, thank you, some token of appreciation from beyond the grave. Elysia von Eschenbach wouldn't need it where she was going, that much was for certain. Perhaps a ring with a large stone, or a brooch. What had Elysia been wearing? Of course, an amethyst would correspond perfectly to her violet palette.

The crumpled brown bag of muscle bent at the waist again, as if someone had just pushed him from behind. "Yes, Madame. The baroness wore a ring, as did her father. Seeing that it bore a family crest, I thought you were following some tradition to bury them with the things on."

"No," Odile shuddered to consider such waste, "that is not our way. It was an oversight in our grief. In the tragedy and chaos of the day I forgot that the von Eschenbachs were wearing jewelry."

"Shall I reopen the casket, Madame?" offered the man, half-turning toward his son. The younger man held his hat in front of his belt with both hands and raised his eyebrows.

"If you please," she answered.

The father worked his way around the casket prying the nails with the claw of a hammer, and the son followed, inserting an iron bar to pry wood away from wood. She could see the glimmer of the cloth lining reflecting torchlight through the crack. Brother Adalberto stepped forward and coughed. "Madame de la Violette, it is past vespers. I will miss services. It is necessary that a man of God such as myself maintain a consistent schedule of prayer and meditation in considering the nature of the divine." His eyes skated over the cracks in the ceiling of the crypt. The cobwebs wafted like layers of lace. His fingertips drummed one another in the air in front of his chest. "Also, it is past dinnertime."

Odile inclined her head in the direction of the cleric. "I am certain that you can be patient in the face of a matter of such sentiment. My son will request her wedding ring as a reminder of the beauty of Elysia von Eschenbach as soon as he recovers from this attack of grief that has stricken him. Quite understandably, I might add." She tugged at the cuffs of her dress. Had the temperature plunged?

Brother Adalberto glanced at her with disbelief and retrieved his missal. The spine was dented and the book fell open at this rite: it appeared that Finzi always sent Adalberto off on burial duty. "Child of God," he intoned the passage by rote like a student trapped with a tutor on a sunny day reciting the alphabet.

As he picked up speed, the workman's son pried the last nail and the men picked up the angled lid and put it on top of the baron's coffin. Odile leaned over the body of Elysia von Eschenbach. The torchlight made it seem as if someone had painted dark hair and eyebrows on a Greek statue, some softer marble used to sculpt a new race on moonlit nights far from the eyes of humans. Odile ran her finger along the ridge of a pleat in the wedding gown. It glimmered with the sudden streaks of silver seen when a shoal of fish are frightened beneath the calm surface of a lake. *Amazing, isn't it?* she puzzled to herself. *How is she so beautiful even in death? Her skin has none of that ashen shadow.*

"Repeat after me," Brother Adalberto announced. "Our Father, who art in Heaven, hallowed be thy name…" The workmen and her servant Guillame followed the prayer. Odile heard comfort in the rhythm of the familiar cant and reached for Elysia's hand.

"Thy kingdom come. Thy will be done. On earth…" Brother Adalberto saw Odile de la Violette cradle the bride's hand in hers and reach for the ring as carefully as if she were trying to remove a wasp from the cheek of an infant it was preparing to sting. Odile held Elysia's hand tighter—she might have to put a little muscle into the removal of a ring on a finger so swollen.

Once, her father had come home with a ring that had somehow escaped the pockets of an executioner. While stumbling past the paupers' graves, he saw the man left alone by a ditch, a glint on his finger. The ring wouldn't come off the fat, cold finger, so he sawed the finger off with his knife. Odile remembered him waving it in front of her, laughing, and then bracing it between the first two fingers of his right hand and waggling it as if it were a part of him. Then he removed the ring and tossed the grisly digit out the window to the swine. The sliver of topaz had probably been good for only one bender.

How strange—Elysia's ring slid off without any difficulty whatsoever. Odile held the ring between the thumb and forefinger of her right hand and splayed out the fingers of Elysia's left hand with her own. The fingers moved easily, not as a set of wooden bolts. The hand was cool, but not stone cold and hardened. Odile tasted bile in the back of her throat as she considered the possibility that Tante Sophia was right: what if Elysia von Eschenbach was not dead? What if the young woman was merely in some deep sleep? Odile's eyes widened and she stepped back from the coffin's edge.

The men stood in a cluster to the right of the torches. "...And forgive us our trespasses."

Odile closed the ring in her palm and returned to the body for the brooch. She picked up the girl's left hand and prepared to place it back on top of the right one that had remained on the silver-filigreed bodice of her dress. *But deliver us from evil, indeed!* the woman thought. Elysia's fingers spasmed just before they came to rest.

"Mon Dieu!" Odile dropped the hand and jumped back, stumbling as she tilted and reached to support herself against the wall. The ring made an echoing clink upon the stone floor of the crypt.

"Amen." said the men as one. The younger workman untwisted his hat like a dishrag that he was going to lay out to dry and clamped it on top of his head. Brother Adalberto closed the missal. "If you are finished, Madame?" he asked, one eyebrow arched in inquiry.

Odile lowered herself sideways to pick up the ring with as much dignity as possible. Ordinarily she would just point to it and have Guillame collect it and present it to her, but speed was much more important than appearances in this instance. "Yes. Let us go now," answered Odile as she backed farther away from the box, keeping her back to the crypt wall and feeling its reassuring solidity each time she took a sliding step. Brother Adalberto tucked his book under his arm and marched outside.

The two laborers lifted the lid of Elysia's coffin and realigned it over the box. The older bobbed his head. "With your permission, Madame," stated the older man as he and his son lowered it, "we will nail the coffin—again."

"No, you do not have my permission. Leave it." said Odile. Her voice quavered like a clavier with a dead mouse stuck between the strings. She could hear her heart beating as the hammers. She stood in the threshold with the key in her hand. "We have kept them from their rest long enough. We will go now."

"The torches?" he asked with surprise as he backed away from the coffin.

"What of them?" Odile pointed to the exit as if the workmen would have difficulty seeing it. "It is a family tradition for the von Eschenbachs to have a light on the first steps of their final journey. Besides, they will burn out soon enough. It's not as if anyone will be harmed if something accidentally catches on fire." The men bent to and fro, collecting the hammer, pry bar and a lantern.

Odile stepped up behind the departing workmen and turned to close the gate. Her hands came away with rust stains striping her palms. The gate was still cracked open. She grasped the bars again and leaned back without success. Then she placed her feet on the bottom crossbar and leaned forward and back again. "Just as a child tries to get a fast rhythm on the backyard gate on a sunny spring day," she panted, frowning at the contrast. Would this infernal errand never end?

Finally, the latch rasped into its home and she wound the chain around the bars, once, twice, and a third time, and if there was a particular knot that she could use for luck, she would have tied it thus. The padlock bit shut with a firm 'click,' and the clamp of dread in her stomach began to loosen. If only she had a blacksmith with her, she would have him forge a whole new gate: sturdy bars of iron heated to red hot and then pounded free of dross on the anvil, the hammer clanging, the sparks landing on his leather apron, the heat of the fire upon them. He would take the orange strips of ore, as flexible as saplings, and bind this gate shut, hammering the ends together like an alchemist's snake swallowing its tail. Odile looked at the crypt door and shuddered.

Madame de la Violette moved with the same precise automation possessed by the china figurines that danced from the interior of her precious clock each time the hour struck in her parlor. She could almost hear the tinny chimes in her ears as she instructed herself through each action, trying to keep down the trembling bag of bile inside her, the demands screaming "Run! Run now!" First, the workmen must be paid:

she motioned to Guillame to hurry the removal of coins from a leather pouch in the pocket of his vest. He would likely exaggerate the expense when he reported it to the household accounts. The laborer and his sons bowed, touched the brims of their hats in syncopation, stepped backward, bowed again, and then turned their backs on the crypt, happy to disappear from the commands of this strange Frenchwoman who forgot jewelry and left coffins unnailed.

Their cart was already well down the road as she climbed into the carriage and sat frozen as one of the praying crypt angels, blank eyes staring forward at the empty seat opposite her. As they pulled away, she stuck her head out the window. *Lot's wife*—she thought. *What do I gain in this looking back?* The tomb became smaller and smaller, finally reduced to a tiny speck.

Her mind turned over the unspeakable. *What if?* she argued silently with herself. *What if she is not dead? What if we have just buried two people alive? Or just one? Or what if it is two; what if the whole von Eschenbach family has a tendency to false dying? The nerve. But no: I saw the Baron fall in the cathedral. He seemed quite dead. Elysia, I saw repeatedly and I touched.* She slumped against the cushion of the carriage bench. Her teeth bit into her lower lip and she tore at the cuticle of her thumb. No, this nattering was foolishness, just a sign of the strain upon her own nerves. It was merely a spasm, a reflex contraction of the flesh as she removed the ring from Elysia's finger. The girl was officially, entirely, and completely dead: dead in the eyes of the church and with the entire city of Salzburg as a witness. Who was she, Odile de la Violette, to consider disputing such evidence?

Odile put the loose ring on her own finger and spun it. Her throat became dry and her hands became damp as she remembered the stories she would hear at the fireplace the rare times her mother would take her along on bundle runs and let her linger in the kitchen, perhaps being given a scrap of pastry left over from the lady's breakfast table or a leg of chicken from the night before. Young Odile would gnaw her surprise bounty and prick up her ears as the women wove stories of aristocrats who hunted girls down like foxes, grave robbers, the ancient traditions of All Souls' Eve, men who changed into wolves with the full moon, and cursed souls who were not dead. The ruins of the Castle de Argnac, they claimed, were still haunted.

The Duke of Argnac, of a family known when the first missionaries brought the word of Christ to the Franks (at this, all around the kitchen fireplace would cross themselves), went on the Crusades and returned to find his wife with child. He waited until she birthed the child, and then had both nailed into a barrel that he raised on a post and set on fire. Soon afterwards, the duke's own dogs turned on him during a hunt for a boar and tore him apart until nothing remained but a leather glove and some scraps of mail. If you enter the ruins you can hear the screams of the mother and child in the courtyard.

Her mother had been awakened by Odile's nightmares after one day of such tales but merely cuffed her and rolled back over to sleep. "You cry over foolishness," her mother snarled at her. "There is no need for ghost stories. We have more than enough to fear from the living."

If no dogs turned on her, who would haunt Odile de la Violette? Her mother, for having been left behind? Her first spouse, and father of her current husband, old George de la Violette, cut down in his golden years by the presumption of too much vigor in taking on a young and lovely bride? Then there would be the beautiful ghost of Elysia von Eschenbach, already so pale, coming to smother her as a live burial smothers. No, the girl had not been buried, but put in a crypt. She would not suffocate, at least not now, seeing that Odile had had the workmen leave the lid off the coffin, but her screams would draw no rescuers and she would linger for days without food or water. Perhaps she could last a week, if she had the insight to drink her own urine. Her death would be on Odile's head, and would not have been a merciful one. If spirits have memories and know vengeance, the ghost of Elysia von Eschenbach would be the one to haunt Odile de la Violette for every moment of the woman's life, and would appear to her in dreams.

Two wishes wrestled in the heart of Odile. The child who woke from her own screams in the dark prayed the lock of the crypt would not hold, that it was as old and broken as all things on the abandoned property and would break if battered by a young, strong girl. The conniving woman who had grown more callous since childhood scratched her nails on the thick nap of her skirts and gave the curse of a hope that the lock was as solid as a new one smelted of steel or zinc, and that there was no way Elysia von Eschenbach, if buried alive, could escape.

As Elysia stirred from her paralysis, she knew she was still bundled in the half cloak the saint had given her in the cathedral. It was warm—

spread over her like a wing, twisted over her completely. If she struggled out of it, she would sit up in the center of a circle of generous beatific smiles, all the martyrs in a ring to welcome her, laughing politely with her in her warm encumbrance. She knew there were stars on the other side of the darkness. Her fingers splayed into the air in an attempt to move the velvet cloak aside. If she could only reach up and shove away the darkness, she would be able to breathe with comfort: she knew this.

She opened her eyes but saw only blackness in the warm, close air. This was some heavy shawl she could not push away. Elysia lifted her hand, wanting to touch her eyes, to rub them and see if they would then perceive anything other than the unbroken dark. There was a tremor at the end of her wrist, but she could not make her hand move. She was no longer the mistress of her own body; she was directing a recalcitrant servant who was pretending not to hear her. Elysia concentrated to visualize the message as a scroll being borne by a courier riding horseback down the length of her arm. He would dismount at her wrist and use a trumpet to herald her palm and fingers. She knew these parts were still attached: she had a sense of some warm weight. Relief! Her hand received the message. Her fingers curled into her palm to form a fist. Success! Now she ordered them to disband, and the fist slowly flattened out. Elysia tried to lift her hand to her eyes and discovered that she still could not. There was something over her, some obstacle. It smelled like a carpenter's workshop, of planed and varnished wood.

Her mind began to clear. She tried to turn her head from side to side, to see if light was leaking in from any direction. Fabric rustled beneath her ears. Her head was on a satin pillow. She moved her hands to the side and the backs of them grazed satin, also. Three clues in the riddle: the smell of newly varnished wood, a satin pillow and walls, no room to move at all. Elysia's mouth hinged open to scream as the answer fell into her consciousness.

"No!" she shrieked. "No, God, no!" She arched her back and twisted. Her elbows tried to dig caves in the walls of the box. One of her nails tore backward as she scratched the inside of the lid, for now she knew she was trapped inside a coffin. Her feet pounded without result. She did not have room to draw up her knees and use all the strength of her legs to push the lid away. Or did she? Her knees thumped up against the top of the box and she tried to wrest up a shoulder in the same moment.

There was a single drumbeat thud above her as the unnailed lid popped open and fell back down. Never had a sound carried a greater message of hope. Elysia pushed again and a crack appeared to her right, an unstable yellow line of light. Her fingers went into the seam and served as a wedge. Her whole hand had escaped. Now, to brace it against the edge of the lid. The crack expanded—a sun was rising over Elysia von Eschenbach. She beheld the sputtering torchlight like a thousand dawns. She shoved against the lid and it clattered to the floor in a twisting fall. Her fingers curled over the sides of the death boat, and she pulled herself up instead of pulling on oars into the afterlife. Three torches burned low, but there was light enough for Elysia to see there was another coffin beside her. Christoph! Her legs were stiff, but she lifted one and then the other—she had to use the same concentration as she had used with her hands: send a phalanx of messengers out to her knees and then to her feet. She rocked on her hips to heave herself out of the coffin, but her legs crumpled and she fell heavily to the stone floor.

"My husband, my love, my betrothed," she panted as she tried to pull herself up. "My Christoph." All of Christoph's faults were hearsay; she could hear his explanations later. All that mattered now was rescuing her husband so they could escape the tomb together. If they survived this, and if those terrible stories were true, perhaps he would be so grateful that he would see the error of his ways and mend. She limped to the coffin and tried to raise the lid. Nailed shut. "No!" she pounded on the lid with her fist and then stopped to look at the floor. A loose stone had caught beneath her foot. She fell to her knees and shoved her skirts aside to pry up the rock.

She pulled herself up, leaning against the polished box. Then she stood up, took a gasping breath, and hit the corner of the coffin with the stone. The wood splintered and she lifted the triangle of stone again. More naked wood grain appeared from beneath the varnish. A third blow suggested some large creature had chewed off the corner of the box. Another hammering and the dent tore into a splinter.

"Christoph!" If he had air, he could talk to her, they could reassure one another as she tried to figure out how to pry the lid off of this damned thing. But had she hurt him? Elysia dropped the stone and reached into the hole she just made. A cold face was beneath her hand. A sweet smell like ham in the sun leaked out from the chasm.

"Christoph?" she called. She spread her hand over the face and felt the fur of a beard at her fingertips. This was not her lover. The jaw was covered with bristles and the hair started higher on his forehead. Whoever he was, he was dead. No rush to get the lid off now, bless and keep him. She withdrew her hand from the coffin and leaned on it to catch her breath and collect her thoughts. If it was not Christoph, who was it?

Elysia chose another target on the coffin's plane and hit again, causing parallel cracks. She tore at each with the stone and her hands and the wood came away in long, thin slivers. The torch flames bowed and recoiled. The stone crashed to the floor like the hammer of judgment when she recognized the face framed by the ragged wood.

She put her hand inside the coffin again, pressing on her father's shoulder and shaking him slightly in the vain hope that he would open his eyes. She pulled out planks from the coffin's lid and made room for her arm. Stepping to the other side of the box, she ran her hand down his arm. Her fingers closed over her father's fingers, and she felt the ring on his smallest finger. Elysia twisted it over his knuckle until it arrived in her palm.

Her hand weighed the jewelry as it crept back out of the coffin. She had not held the ring recently, and it was heavier than she recalled. The band was thick. She remembered her mother showing it to her, squeezing the curve between her thumb and forefinger as the heirloom was backlit by candles at an evening chat. "This is no thin bauble, Elysia! Pay attention: this not a trinket that you wear to match a dress for one dance, but a treasure that has been in our family for centuries. It was made from a single nugget of pure gold. It has not been touched by fire since God's first smelting in the core of the earth." Elysia was hypnotized by a full stomach and the candle flame reflected in the ring's sparkling center. Peter rested his head on the table, making a pillow of his forearms. "The ruby is a treasure from the Holy Lands, brought back from the Crusades. The dragon is our crest."

After her mother died, her father wore the ring. He never took it off. Peter was to inherit it, but after his early death, Elysia was the only one left. Without her father to protect it, the ring was hers. What had fit her father's little finger needed the girth of her middle finger to stay on her hand. She held her hand up to the torchlight to see the glorious dragon on the red stone.

She lowered her hand to her father's face. "My heart—" she choked with wet eyes. The torch flames melted as she sobbed. The fire had eaten the last of the pitch and small flames cast her shadow on the stone wall for a final moment and then plunged her into darkness. Elysia put out her arms and felt the rough surface. Her fingertips led the way as she stepped sideways to the passage. Her limbs were loosening as she stumbled down toward the gate of the crypt where the dark of the overcast night was framed instead of the black of the tomb. She grasped the bars in her hands and called for help. There was no reply. Elysia pulled at the bars and tried to rattle them. They were rusted but solid. It was time to use the tools available.

Elysia's hand skidded down the wall back into the crypt's darkness to search again for the loose stone. Moonlight reflected off the corner of her father's coffin. Kneeling on the floor, her hands patted the paving stones. There: the stone she had used to open her father's coffin. Elysia felt her way back to the gate. Her hand reached around the chain and found the padlock. Now, how to best attack it? She braced the rings of chains against her belly and curled her arms through the bars to the lock. Her hand rose to hammer it. As she lowered her fist, the impact swung the door into her stomach. Again. And again. She heard a crack. Elysia hit the lock repeatedly. The front of her fine skirts tore. Another blow and the lock separated. Elysia twisted off the broken square of metal and unwound the chain from the gate. It clattered on the floor behind her as she flung it back and then shoved the gate open. She was free.

She took a few deep breaths of night air and looked about to get her bearings. Where was she? If the mountains were to the south, that meant that the la Violette estate was…. She took a deep shuddering breath and closed her eyes, slumping against the wall of the crypt. Married, died, orphaned and risen all in one day. This was no time for tears: she could mourn later. She must tell Christoph she was alright. She aligned her path by the peaks and stumbled toward them. Glowing with the triumph of the accomplishment of walking, she felt brilliant, racing, but her body was still stiff and slow. Why was it so difficult for her to move? Her stubborn joints no longer required independent direction, but they would not cooperate.

Like a marionette, she thought, *except the strings are cut now*. Her left leg would not respond at all. She was reduced to dragging it most of the way.

Elysia hobbled through the gate onto the grounds of the gardens that Rene de la Violette so lovingly tended. She leaned against an oak at the end of the drive. The leaves rustled overhead as her mind churned with questions. How did they mistake her for dead? How did her father die? Where was Christoph? Was he alright? Elysia panted from her exertions and gathered her wits about her for the final yards to shelter and safety.

There was a rasping snort in the bushes behind her. Tired and stiff, Elysia pushed herself away from the tree, and, braced against it with her elbow locked, looked over her shoulder. Surely a wild boar would have rushed at her by now? And what would one be doing so far into the interior of Salzburg where there are so many dogs? The snort reverberated again: the leaves on the shrubbery rattled. A wheezing exhalation followed, and then the sound of twigs breaking. Elysia took small steps toward the source of these blatting honks.

Grumbling came from the bushes in front of her. She bent forward and parted the lower branches. Rene de la Violette was drunk. He was not drunk in a companionable, hail-good-fellow-well-met way. He had tried to drown his sorrows but the damned things learned how to swim. He was out cold. Elysia's nose wrinkled at the smell of wine and mouth-rot wafting from him as he wheezed and snored, slack-jawed. He threw his head from left to right and leaves stuck in his beard. His arms flailed out in some sodden dream as the stone of his ring fell with a clink on the green glass of one of three empty wine bottles by his side.

Elysia gathered up the circle of her skirts and squatted down to try to wake him. His vest was damp from lingering on the leaves. She tried to say his name but all that emerged was a growl no more articulate than the man's snores: the same affliction of the tongue and throat that kept her from her wedding vows was still upon her. "Rrrmay," she gasped. Rene de la Violette flubbered his lips and then opened his mouth and belched. Elysia dropped his shoulder.

She shook her head and rose to leave the man, thinking, *No use. He cannot be awakened, and even if he could, who knows how he could help me.* The stone steps loomed on the other side of the lawn. It stretched in front of Elysia like a plain. Her legs were stiff like logs and her elbows creaked like rusty hinges. The grass might be too slick for her to navigate; she would have to concentrate.

She looked up and saw the leaking yellow light emanating from the rectangles of half-shuttered windows. The steps were on the other side of the lawn, the doors were at the top of the steps, and her beloved was on the other side of the doors. With resolve, she made fists of her hands and took the first stride toward the house. When she reached the stone balustrade at the base of the steps, she leaned upon the curl of the column.

Her breath rasped sore inside of her; perhaps her breathing sounded as labored as that of Rene de la Violette right now. She shook her head as she panted, her tongue brushed by the cooling night air. The tiny, pebbled roughness of the stone beneath her hand reminded her of the crypt and her grip tightened. What had happened? She must discover what had gone wrong, how her father had died, and whether Christoph was healthy and intact. She had to show him that she had survived and had returned to his arms. The torn lace of her dress's cuff snagged on the handle as she opened the door, and the light frame of the tall French door parted from its twin and swung into the parlor.

Her eyes adjusted to the loss of moon and starlight to the particular internal darkness of an unlit house. She stretched her hands before her. If this was the parlor and she had her back to the balcony, the door to the hall would be past the couch to the right of the fireplace. Her hand went out on an exploratory foray and discovered the edge of a table. There—a guide to the couch. Once she was in the hall, she knew that Christoph's room was up the flight of stairs and then a left turn to the east. There would be no secret passages or hidden doors in this new and shiny city house.

He would be so relieved when she arrived. If he had managed to fall asleep, she could soothe his sorrow and wake him from his troubled dreams, sitting on the side of the bed and placing her head upon his chest. His eyes would flutter open and the look of surprise would soon pass into a glow of delight. He would smile and reach up to her, stroking her cheek and then drawing her mouth to his, his thumb on her chin, for a kiss. Top of the stairs, now she was there. The door squeaked as she leaned on it. She almost fell into the dark space. Her attempt to say his name was mangled, the bite of a consonant impossible from her stiff jaws. "Christoph," she wanted to announce in jeweled bell-tones. "My love, I am here, I have returned." She took a deep breath and the sound fell from her lips like chewed-up boiled potatoes. "Thrist off," the sounds fell, "Thrist off eye hab...."

Her voice trailed as she took in the sights of the room. Though lighter than the night hall, the single candle flame at the bedside illuminated little but showed too much. Christoph was not alone. The mound huddled under the thin cotton sheet had a twin: two forms made parallel mountain ranges. One of them rolled over and a pale arm crept out from beneath the coverlet. Its finger curled around the handle on the metal saucer that held the candle and poured away the puddled wax.

The flame shot up from the tallow tube and revealed the features of a woman. Justine lifted the light and stared at Elysia. Her eyes opened wider, ready to fly out of her skull in their desire to deny the thing before them. Then her mouth opened and she screamed like a rabbit when lifted from the field by a falcon: a high-pitched keening that tears the ear and lasts for a sickening, long wail. Elysia could see the nugget of flesh that hung from the roof of her throat, the girl's mouth was open so wide.

Christoph bolted upright, both hands pulling the covers away from Justine into his own naked lap. He saw his bride and his back slammed against the bed railing behind him. "No, mon dieu! Impossible!" exclaimed the startled man. He started to scoot further back in the bed, his spine now completely aligned with the bedstead. His arm reached out blindly for something, anything, some object of defense, but his fingers grabbed empty air. Justine gasped and panted, but only for a fraction of a second. Then she resumed screaming.

Elysia could hear the slamming of doors and thudding of footsteps in the hall behind her. They drew nearer, one pair of feet, then another. Elysia faced the doorway at the exact moment Odile scudded up with a candle. The Frenchwoman tilted sideways for a moment, drawing her taper close to her.

"Hell spawn!" shrieked Odile, then she spat on the floor in front of Elysia. "Bride of Satan! Demoness!" Odile's hand flew over her chest, making the sign of the cross again and again, lost on a repeated migratory route. "Monster! Creature of darkness—Return to your grave! You heard me! Back! Back!"

Elysia maneuvered to escape and bumped against the bedpost. Justine renewed her screaming and tried to pull the covers back from Christoph. The mother tigress advanced on the threat to her cub. Elysia was no longer a beautiful corpse, a figure prepared for a crystal coffin display in a wax museum, but a frightening peril returned from the crypt and standing in the middle of Odile's child's bedroom. Elysia von Eschenbach did look monstrous: her sore limbs convulsed, arms drawn up and fingers extended, claw-like. Her delicate pale features had twisted to a snarl, and whenever she tried to speak, her tongue protruded from her mouth before the half-intelligible sounds emerged. Her heart boomed in her chest like a drum. She must make them understand. She had returned to take her rightful place at the side of her spouse. "Christoph, I have..." With great effort she could force a coarse whisper from her throat, each syllable arriving separately and wrapped in sandpaper.

Justine stopped screaming and flung herself on the shoulder of her cringing bed-mate. "She has come for Christoph! She wants to drag him to her grave!"

"Not...deahd." Elysia garbled with difficulty. It was obvious to her the grave should not be hers. Why had they put her in it? How long had she been away? Why weren't they ecstatic to see her?

"Yes! The not-dead. The Undead!" Justine raised herself up from the questionable shelter of Christoph's side and stood up on the mattress, showing them her bare buttocks. She braced herself on the headboard and then reached up to wrest the crucifix from the wall. "Undead! Nosferatu! Vampire!" Justine hissed at Elysia as she squatted to lift the candle from the nightstand, and then, brandishing the flame and Christ, leapt from the bed and waved both at the apparition. The light stung Elysia's eyes and she winced.

"Our father who art in heaven!" Justine shouted and swung the cross at Elysia von Eschenbach by way of punctuation. "Hallowed be thy name!" The servant took a sideways swipe. Elysia backed away, looking to her husband. He was as pale as a sheet and he sat shaking on the corner of the bed, clutching the sheets over his most prized possession. The young lord of the manor was defended by his mama and his mistress. He wasn't about to risk any part of his anatomy.

"Merciful Christ!" Another female voice joined the melee. Marie-Ange was framed in the doorway behind Odile, adding the light of a third candle to the room, and grasping a robe closed over her nightclothes. The candlelight threw Elysia's profile into focus. "Please, please, I meant no harm," Marie-Ange whimpered and fell on her knees. The candle fell beside her and the wick sputtered out in a pool of its own wax. "It was only to be a joke, a joke gone wrong, terribly wrong." Marie-Ange sniffled. "I never meant to harm your father—I only wanted to ruin mother's party. That is all—just punish her for showing off you instead of me."

Odile stepped in front of the weeping Marie-Ange and continued cursing Elysia. "You hell-bitch! You big white phantom! I used to say that you were pale like marble—it is more like maggots. Return to your grave!" Justine crouched and swung the crucifix out toward Elysia, and then leapt back, gained courage, and swung again. Elysia could not walk between them and seek protection from Christoph, obvious that he was unwilling to help her in any way. If she turned to leave she would trip over his cringing, crying sister.

"I am damned!" Marie-Ange babbled. "I will not spend a moment in purgatory but will go straight to hell and burn—burn in the fifth circle and devils will cut out my tongue and feed it to flaming sparrows for all eternity!" She bawled and hit the carpeting with clenched fists. Elysia stepped around the girl and leaned against the door frame for a moment, then pushed against it and propelled herself into the hall, panting.

Elysia sought an escape route and headed for the stairway. A six-inch Christ clipped her on the shoulder and she turned to face the naked Justine brandishing the representation of their hand-painted martyred savior. Odile snarled at the servant, candle aloft. Elysia grasped the railing with both hands, trying to navigate the stairs, but having to duck and weave from the swipes of Justine's attacks with cries of complaint from her sore, stiff limbs at every second.

"What is this?" shouted Rene. "Let her go! Enough!" He stood at the base of the stairs with his legs rooted far apart, but the trunk on top of these branches leaned from side to side like a willow in a storm, ready to test gravity. The shocked women held their curses, prayers and invective, and Elysia clattered down the remaining steps.

Rene walked to the entry and held the door open for her. As she approached across the foyer he extended his hand to take hers. Elysia reached out to clasp it, overcome that there would be one human being who would not flee from her. Just as her fingertips curled around Rene's, his hand fell from her grasp and the rest of his inebriated body toppled to the parquet flooring.

"Rene! My husband is dead!" shrieked Odile de la Violette. "You make me a widow seeing that you could not drag my child back to your tomb! Vengeful beast!" If called a beast, she would behave like one: Elysia abandoned all hope of explanation, understanding, and reunion with Christoph, and fled across the grounds, gasping in the damp darkness and striving toward the goal of her own survival.

Answers to questions were no longer important. She gave no more thought to Christoph. One message beat in her mind: "SURVIVE!"

Chapter XVIII
A Purposeful Trance

Officer Hurley was used to tranquility at his post. That was the advantage of the night shift. Sure, it messed up the sleep cycle, you saw less of people, but things tended to be nice and quiet. An occasional burglary, kids getting too rowdy in the church parking lot, a drunk brought in for driving home under the influence and caged to sober up until his wife picked him up. The woman dragging one foot and staggering toward him was not there to collect a soused spouse, at the very least, those ladies had the decency to arrive in bathrobes. This one was in her nightgown. She didn't act drunk. There was no tell-tale tang of gin wafting his direction, no warm breeze of hops-vapors that beer-drunks carry like a cloud. Also, drunks are loose, sloppy. This woman moves like a zombie, stiff and uncoordinated instead of liquid-limbed. Her hands are clutching at nothing with a violent iron grip. Her face twists in twinges and rivulets flow from every facial feature. Low growling emits from her throat.

Hurley's coffee runs from the Styrofoam cup over the desk log as he presses the silent alarm under the counter. His hand trips back along his belt to the butt of his gun. Where is everybody? At that moment, several amazed officers rush into the bullet-proof enclave to assist Officer Hurley in defending himself against this astounding vision.

Claire feels like she's on display in a zoo. All these policemen have rushed into the glass-enclosed office and are gazing out at her. Some have cups of coffee, others do not. *Why aren't they rushing to her aid?* She opens her mouth to speak, but spasms rob her larynx of noise. The muscles of her face stretch and snap and no words can be formed. It is the same helplessness as being trapped alive in the nightmare coffin. Make all the noise she wants, but no one will help her. The officers look at her uneasily. A cluster of navy uniforms shuffles back. A couple of cops have their hands on their guns. "You fools!" she wants to shout. "Help me! What am I going to do to you? You are armed men and I am a woman in a floral nightgown who can't even talk to you. Someone, please, help me...." Instead, all that comes out of her mouth is, "Ghlargh...ahh" and then a series of choking noises. She reaches the window and leans forward to press her forehead on the glass. Emerging from his stupor, an officer steps up.

"Mrs. Foster? Claire Foster? It's Claire and Stuart, right?" He nods over his shoulder to a colleague. They emerge from the office, the second carrying a blanket which he drapes over her shoulders. It smells slightly dusty instead of like detergent and sun. The first policeman arranges the folds around her and begins to inquire:

"Mrs. Foster, I'm Doug Parvanski. We met at the widows and orphans charity fundraiser. Are you all right? What can we do to help you? Do you need me to call an ambulance?"

He and the other cop steer her toward a hallway. They open a metal door with a small, wire-hatched window. "You sit right here, Mrs. Foster, and we'll figure out what's wrong with you. Would you like some coffee?" He gestures at the second cop who walks out. As she sits, Claire's breathing becomes more regular. The fluorescent bulb hums over her head. She slumps in the chair and lets her head hang to the side, concentrating on keeping her breath even and her face still. The muscles around her mouth and eyes are sore. Officer Parvanski sits at her side, looking on with concern. "Now, Mrs. Foster, can you tell me what's wrong? Is there a crime in process? Was there something stolen from your home? Is there something you'd like to report?"

"The judge was wrong."

"I beg your pardon?" The policeman leans forward, elbow on his right knee, attentive.

Claire takes a deep breath. "Today. The judge. He believed Carlson. There's a lien on the lot where we're going to put the car wash. He can't do that to us. It's not right..."

Officer Parvanski is silent, so she takes a deep breath to continue. "I need to call the judge and tell him what is going on. He needs to understand. Carlson's the one who's at fault, not us. It's illegal to place a lien on property where you've not yet turned a spade of dirt." Her jaw clenched shut and her face quivered. Officer Parvanski put his hand on hers.

"Mrs. Foster, I understand how you feel, but it's not a good idea to wake a judge at home at this hour. We're used to taking complaints and dealing with all sorts of people here at night, but those jurists need their beauty sleep. How about if I call your husband and we meet at the hospital? Pardon me for saying so, but it looks as if you're not feeling too well."

Claire gives up. "Fine." She shifts her head to the other side, feeling the scrape of the cotton against her still-sensitive skin. "Let's go now."

Chapter XIX

The Vampire
of Salzburg

Elysia von Eschenbach pulled her cloak tight to her neck and cowered into a dark corner. The once-privileged heiress of a barony was reduced to a bewildered outcast. Her home, her family, her lover and her future were all denied to her because of some dark curse which caused her to die on her wedding day.

"How has this happened to me? Where do I go now?" she wondered. *The church—that was where the nightmare began.* She moved with stealth from shadow to shadow, keeping off the streets to avoid notice.

Small clouds sailed across the sky; moonlight flickered off the copper roof tiles of the church. She carefully picked her way through an overgrown thicket and emerged on the edge of the cemetery of Saint Michael's. An audience of stone angels witnessed her approach. As she passed each one, she reached out to touch the sculpted marble. How gentle they looked. The winged statues were dressed in flowing robes of satiny stone. Eyes unflinching, hands outstretched but unfeeling, their garments draped over unyielding breasts. Their open arms offered comfort.

The delicate breezes of the cool summer night whispered in her hair and Elysia was drawn to the comfort of the seraphim's beckoning. She lingered in front of a life-sized angel. His glittering wings were of a powerful cut. Silver light slipped over his polished surface and lit his face with holy magic.

She grasped his smooth fingers with the desperation of a lost child. Her losses flooded over her. No more reason for polite composure or noble bearing. She had never known such loneliness, such absolute helplessness. Elysia's knees collapsed at the feet of her angel. Instead of her mother's velvet skirts, she clung to cold, carved marble. Despair overtook her as she sobbed for release from her unnatural misery. "God, please finish your work. How could you let me die in Your house only to reject me, trapped between life and death? Michael, Archangel, lift me up, carry me to Heaven, to my father and mother!" Her head fell hard against the rocky effigy.

"Why am I punished? What have I done?" cried Elysia.

A soft voice answered, "I hear you, Child. Confess and be free."

Startled, Elysia looked up to the face of her angel but his blank eyes stared past her, into the darkness. She pressed closer to the statue. The edges of his robes bruised her arms. Was this the chance for which she prayed? Would the angel carry her message to Heaven? Her voice was small and high-pitched through tears. Elysia recounted her story of her love for Christoph, the miscarriage, the wedding, and the agony and confusion of her death. She poured out her heart hoping it would satisfy the angel. She spoke of Christoph's rejection and his servant's curses. "I want to be dead. Truly, completely dead."

Elysia watched the angel's face for a reaction. She waited for him to break his pose, to gather her up in his arms the way her father used to when she was a little girl.

Silence. Stillness. Her angel ignored her.

"How much longer must I endure this existence? I belong nowhere. I am shunned. Michael, Michael, is there no love, no place left for me?"

"I am here, whispered the voice, but the stone lips did not move.

She peered through the dark, scanning the cemetery. Standing behind her, leaning casually against a grave marker, was a man dressed in elegant dark clothing. His cape fluttered as he moved toward her. Elysia saw his face more clearly as he drew closer. It was thin, angular and as white as her frozen angel. His sparkling dark eyes contrasted with his pallor. His long black hair was pulled back, oiled and fastened with a clasp. He held his hands out to his sides. "I mean you no harm," he said as Elysia shrank against her angel's arms.

She held the statue to steady her trembling hands. She was frightened by the intruder, angered by his ruse but fascinated by his attitude. Like a bird before a snake, she was locked in a terrified trance.

Keeping his distance, he rested his hands on his hips, looking deep in thought. Elysia stood motionless to watch him pace back and forth. He would stop, look at her, and smile, then return to his pacing. Seconds stretched into minutes. Interminable! But when he was ready, he pointed his finger at her and spoke.

"I know of you. I know everything that happens here. You are the girl who died on her wedding day. Heartbreaking tragedy! Dead, dead, dead at the high altar of this very church. Poor child, so sad." He shook his head with gentle mockery.

"How did you like being buried? Quite an experience to wake among the dead. All dressed in your finery, showered with little wilted blossoms. So sublimely alone. Were you sealed in? Did you scream?" With closed eyes and clenched fists, he growled to push his own memory back. His eyes snapped open. He was smiling again.

Elysia hung her head and folded her arms tightly. She remembered the crypt, straining her eyes in the total darkness, wondering if she had gone blind, then feeling her way around until she realized where she was. She thought of how the sputtering torchlight revealed the body of her father, his skin turned hard and colorless.

The man moved closer to her. "Corpses will not answer, no matter how loud you yell. They are no help at all. Terrible conversationalists but fabulous listeners!" He slapped his thigh but caught himself before he laughed at his joke. Elysia did not respond.

"Now, now. No need to be so glum," he teased. He stepped forward and bowed. "When the student is ready, the teacher appears. Permit me to introduce myself. I am Herr Acksten Otto Hensel. My friends used to call me Acky (Ah'cky), but like you, Liebling, I am dead. Or, more precisely, undead."

Elysia gasped and stumbled backward. Herr Hensel chuckled at her surprise.

He pressed his hands to the sides of his cheeks in an impression of exaggerated amazement. "Darling! What shocks you so? That I am a vampire, or—that YOU are?" His chuckling subsided. "Oh, no. You have nothing to fear from me. I can take no sustenance from you. We are the same."

"Our kind," he leaned close to her face and whispered, "always know each other. It is instinct. You know I am right...I can see it in your eyes. Let me tell you what else I see."

He grasped her by the shoulders, rotated her toward the moonlight, and peered into her eyes. He sighed and touched her astonished face with his fingertips, gently wiping her tears.

"So beautiful, so pale," he whispered, " Your skin is like silver." He gave her arms a reassuring squeeze and spoke with confidence, " I see that you do not yet understand your true nature. I will be your protector and teacher. You have much to learn, my dear. Lesson number one is very simple but very important. Everthing else rests on this. Accept your nature. Do not deny that you are a vampire. A splendid gift has been settled on you and now you must embrace it."

Elysia was stunned. Her mouth hung open. Who was this very odd man?

She had wandered to the church in sorrow, crushed by loneliness, hoping somehow that her wedding had been a dream or a mistake. Maybe the angels looked away too soon. Or perhaps she was experiencing some terrible wrinkle of madness. She imagined that she would be able to return to the start of the day. But the nightmare held firm.

Instead of escape, she was intercepted by a strange man who seemed all too familiar with her dilemma. He was not repelled by her. He claimed to be like her. He did not wave crucifixes in her face or scream at her or chase her away. Monster or no, this peculiar man promised her safety. Not only did he understand her pain, he offered her protection and companionship.

He slipped his arm around her and with a little push on the small of her back, guided Elysia across the graveyard. Acky waved his other hand in the air while he spoke as if he were conducting a performance of his own songs.

"Lesson number two. The night belongs to us. This is the tapestry of our existence, embroidered with the moon and the stars. This is our territory. I shall teach you how to master the shadows."

Acky's voice was mesmerizing to Elysia. She hung on every word. He continued nonstop in the same undulating whisper with dramatic emphasis interspersed. "The price for this dark kingdom is our exile from the daytime. Remember this. Sunlight is poison to us. We must seek shelter to hide from the sun and from mortals who fear us. Look behind you. Dawn cracks the sky and melts our night. Those nauseating little birds are starting to chirp. It is time to rest, Liebling. Come with me. I have a safe place."

Elysia interrupted with a more mundane need. "Herr Hensel, my stomach aches. I am hungry."

"Please, call me Acky. You and I are a rare breed. We have special cravings. I have a little food in my chamber. It will quiet your hunger for now. Tonight, when we wake, I will teach you lesson number three. Hurry now and follow me."

When they reached the entrance to the catacombs at the far end of the cemetery, he removed a section of iron grating. His voice labored as he set the heavy bars to the side of the fencing.

"The priests keep a chain and lock on the gate. I allow them their illusion by using my own door. See, once replaced, it looks like the grating is unbroken. What do you suppose these iron bars are designed to do? Keep the mortals out or the dead inside?" He chuckled, took her hand and led Elysia deep into the ancient catacombs of St. Michael's.

She strained to see but there was no light. Her only senses were of the slow descent of the uneven steps, the smell of the long dead, and the pressure of Acky's hand around hers. She reached out to steady herself and felt dry bones covered in rotting cloth. Elysia was again afraid. She halted out of instinct.

The crumbling odors of burial pressed her memory. Her chest tightened. This was too much like the hell she had just escaped. How could safety be waiting down this macabre path?

"I cannot continue," she pleaded. He tugged her hand. "Take me back."

"Impossible."

"Please!" she sobbed.

"There is no going back for you, Liebling," insisted the vampire. She felt his hand stroke her hair. He drew her closer and gave her a reassuring kiss on the forehead. Under normal circumstances, familiar gestures from a stranger would have been intolerable but normality had dissolved from Elysia's existence. She allowed the touch and accepted the comfort he intended. "The way behind you is as dark as the way in front of you. I will lead you. You must trust me." He squeezed her arm firmly and she allowed him to pull her along the narrow passage.

"Wait here." his voice echoed softly in the blackness. She heard wood scraping over stone. A crack of light opened to a chamber before her. Acky waved her forward.

"Come, come Liebling. This is my home. The lair of the Vampire of Salzburg! Let me show you around. I have all of the modern conveniences. Light." He lit candles as he spoke. "The finest furnishings. Chairs, a table, even a settee. It was a challenge hauling that brocaded beast down here, let me assure you. I even have potable, running water."

An ancient drain dripped a steady rhythm into a large copper basin. The overflow continued on its path down a gutter that disappeared underneath a wall. Carved into the walls of the chamber were crypts. These were filled not with bodies, but with personal possessions of books, clothing, small chests and a variety of jars and bottles.

"In the beginning, I tried to live with them, to respect the dead, as they say." He picked up a broken skull, poked his fingers out the orbital sockets and wiggled them at Elysia. "I could not tolerate the constant chorus of empty eyes. They stared at me." He juggled the skull from hand to hand as he continued.

"Well, I simply had to change things to make my existence comfortable. I stacked them and packed them. Sealed all the bones into a single crypt. Not a single complaint. Now they can stare at each other for all eternity.

"The odor in this chamber improved immediately. It is rather pleasant, do you not agree? All that horrid mustiness is gone. And...when I relocated my companions, I was rewarded for my great care. I found all manner of bangles, trinkets and treasure tucked here and there."

"You plundered the graves of Christian martyrs?" demanded Elysia.

"Not exactly," he countered. "They are still here. Their booty is still here and I am still here. It is a minor issue of redistribution. Of stewardship. I have relieved the saints of their burden of ownership." He stopped tossing the skull for a moment and clasped it to his heart. "I can feel their gratitude."

Elysia recoiled.

"Ah, I see. M'Lady does not approve." He cleared his throat and placed the skull on a crypt shelf. Acky pointed toward the ceiling. "Have you noticed the magnificent fresco which decorates my dwelling?" Elysia turned her attention to the vaulted ceiling. The painting was ancient, but well preserved. She moved closer and tilted her face to see the face of Jesus. A backlit halo illuminated the simple lines of his Byzantine likeness. His wide, almond-shaped eyes offered serenity back to her. One of his hands was outstretched as if in invitation. The other hand held a golden chalice beneath his open heart. Blood poured into the cup.

"The inscription is unclear. What does it say? Acky stepped behind her and answered in a hushed tone. "Drink of my blood and you will have life eternal."

"My prayers have been answered. The power of Heaven will protect me in this place," she sighed.

"Heaven?" Acky smirked.

Elysia turned away from the mural to face him. "Thank you for bringing me here, Herr Hensel. For the first time in many hours, I feel safe."

"That pleases me, but I insist you call me Acky."

"It seems improper to address you by your familiar name."

"Vampires have a different code of manners from that of your former life." Elysia's smile faded but Acky continued. "We are a breed apart. An intimate clan."

She looked at the face of Jesus then back to Acky. Her tone was superior. "I am not some evil ghoul."

"Oh, pardon me. I forgot." Acky's voice was snide. "You died on the altar as the bishop raised the Holy Host before you. You were buried. You came back to life stinking of the grave. You ran from crucifixes. Sunlight is intolerable to you. But most importantly, you have a pain that grinds your belly. Nothing you have eaten quite satisfies you, does it? Well, tonight you will have your final proof.

He threw open his arms and raised his voice. "Look around you! We are at home in a crypt! Familiar among the dead!" He thrust the skull into her hands and forced her to hold it. "Woman, accept this. The dead are dead. The living are the living. You and I...our kind...make up the middle ground." He could see that she was withdrawing again into her confusion and despair. As he took the skull from her, she covered her eyes and started to weep.

"I apologize. Please, no crying. You need time to adjust to your new identity. Here. Sit down. I will prepare a calming drink for you." He faced a shelf lined with apothecary jars and bottles. As he worked, he jabbered on about his life as an orphan. A monastery had taken him in to their care. They educated him. One of the brothers was a chemist who was kind enough to teach the boy how to prepare medicinal tinctures from roots and plantstuffs. He rattled on about the bitter taste of valerian root. Mostly he talked to calm his own nerves, to hear a sound other than Elysia's crying. He sniffed the potion and wrinkled his nose. "Here we are, Liebling. This will relax you. Drink it all at once."

"Why?"

"So you do not taste it." He handed the cup to her.

"What is it?" she asked in a suspicious tone as she smelled the liquid.

"It is good for you."

"It smells disgusting." she objected. "I will not drink this." She held the cup out to him but he refused.

"When you are finished with the potion, quickly take this bread and honey."

"Why?"

'To change the taste in your mouth. Now drink your medicine."

"Is there wine in it? Wine and spirits make me ill."

"No wine, Liebling. We do not drink wine. Come now." He nudged her elbow. She stared at the cup as if it were filled with live spiders.

"I appreciate your efforts but..." Acky drew a heavy breath and let out a disappointed sigh. "Oh, very well, if it is that important to you..." She held her nose and gulped the entire contents of the cup. "Saints protect me!" she winced. "That is the foulest potion I have ever ingested!" He passed the food to her.

"Soon you will be very sleepy."

"Where is my bed?"

"I rest in that sarcophagus. It is large enough for two."

"How convenient that vampires are an intimate clan." She yawned. "Tell me, should I trust you?"

"Do you have a choice?" He cradled Elysia in his arms and carried her to the edge of the stone coffin. Acky lowered her onto a thick featherbed.

"Ohhh, clean linen," she purred. Acky drifted to the far side of the room and began snuffing out the candles. Elysia, in her stupor, gazed at the mural above her. The eyes of Jesus, lit by a solitary flame, looked at her with compassion. Darkness filled the chamber. She could hear the rustle of clothing being removed but Acky's voice sounded as if it were underwater. She slipped into her own blackness as the last candle went out. Acky Otto Hensel was not tired. He felt elated. *At last! A companion. Someone with whom he could share his unique existence.* His touch was tender as he loosened the stays at her bodice.

Something was keeping her neckline closed. He investigated with his fingertips. It was the golden brooch he had noticed earlier.

"Liebling. Can you hear me? Ah, perhaps not. Well, I think it is best to remove this trifling piece of jewelry. It might be uncomfortable for you. There." He slipped the brooch into his pocket. "Better? Sleep well, my precious. Sunset brings new experiences for you."

Tempting as it was to extend his exploration of Elysia's body, he stopped. He decided to content himself with the sublime pleasure of holding her. Acky nuzzled his head next to hers. "How exquisite," he mused, "to sleep next to another creature who is just like me.

"Elysia? Elysia, wake up, darling." Elysia von Eschenbach awoke from her slumbers after a night of troubling dreams and realized she was near the bank of a pond on the von Eschenbach estate with her mother. They were sitting in the tall dried grass between the pond and the apple orchard.

"Mother, am I dreaming?" She rubbed at the interior corners of her eyes, knocking away little dried commas of sleep. Dorothea reached out to take Elysia's hand and gave it a little squeeze.

"Why, of course you are, dear." Dorothea's smile was beatific. It was so wonderful to see her mother again. Elysia's insides warmed and her limbs relaxed. She saw the red stone of the dragon ring glinting on her mother's finger, the very ring she had put on her own hand earlier that day, so she had no doubt it was indeed a dream. "I just wanted to tell you how proud I am of you, and how happy it makes me to see what a beautiful, strong young woman you've become."

Elysia's eyes skated over the pond and then rotated up to the lapis blue of the sky above her. A quick breeze skidded clouds along like plates and rustled the grass at their sides. She looked over her shoulder and saw apples just beginning to blush with red streaks of ripeness, and her father riding a horse along the pasture fence on the slope beyond the neat rows of trees. Two swans were gliding overhead and began to circle down. They landed on the pond's surface, two parallel white boats tucking in the wings of their sails, then paddling toward the rushes of the further shore. Tiny bits of down floated in their shallow wakes. Her mother picked a flower from amidst the grass and began pulling off the petals one by one.

"Because you know, Elysia," another petal fell away, "you are going to need every bit of that strength, fortitude, and courage in the months to come. You are going to be tested even beyond the trials of the last day. That is why I wanted to give you my blessing before you wake up in earnest. Remember, my darling: the dragon is the blood..."

Chapter XX

Progress at Last?

Things are quiet at the hospital. Potted plastic palms separate groups of orange vinyl chairs. A young man sits alone, holding an icepack to his eye. A woman with a face as blank and blameless as a cabbage sits rocking a child, staring at the hand she's placed on its forehead. An older gentleman dozes in a wheelchair near the elevator bank, plaid blanket tucked over his knees despite the summer warmth. Claire pulls the blanket serving as a coat closer to her body. When will Stuart arrive?

"Mrs. Foster? You can come this way." The man with a clipboard is smiling at her. 'Dr. John Tynan' reads his nametag. She rises, bracing a hand on each arm of the chair to gain leverage. Dr. Tynan and the policeman lead her down the hall past empty wheelchairs and stretchers into an examination room. There is the usual geometric arrangement: a rectangular table with a gooseneck lamp at one end, a small counter with a square steel sink and clear Pyrex cylinders full of cotton balls, swabs, and tongue depressors. They help her lie down on the table. The officer describes her arrival at the station and then leaves, assuring Claire he will call Stuart to make sure he is on his way.

Dr. Tynan addresses Claire. "Now, Mrs. Foster," he says, looking at her from a cocked head. "Could you describe what happened tonight? Have you ever experienced similar symptoms?" Claire tells him of the lake, her aversion to alcohol, her apparent allergy to the cabin and as much history as she can muster, considering her weak condition. He nods throughout, pen cap braced in the cleft of his chin, but actually wandering south on occasion to take notes on his clipboard. They go through the routine examination: on the scale, off the scale, back to the wall, height measured, black arm band pumped for blood pressure, cool circle stethoscope to the chest and back. "Breathe…breathe…and again. And again."

Dr. Tynan sets aside the cuff, and with a seer's depth of understanding, looks directly into Claire's eyes. "I believe I remember your case. You've come here to the ER a number of times, haven't you, Mrs. Foster?"

"Why yes, very often. You remember me?" Claire is reviving and feels more relaxed because of Dr. Tynan's compassionate bedside manner.

"Yes, I do," he replies, "primarily because of the unusual symptoms.

Dr. Land is your primary physician, is he not?"

"Yes he is." Hope is rising in Claire as she responds to the doctor's interest in her case. "And how would you know all of this?"

Dr. Tynan becomes serious. "There's not a whole lot that happens here without my knowledge. I'm not here very often because I'm in charge of several Lake County ERs, but we're short on docs at the moment, so I guess you're forced to work with the "boss" this evening. I think Dr. Land is on the premises with another patient. If I can track him down, it will give us an opportunity to talk about your case. I'm sure he'll allow me to send for your file, so just relax, and I'll return soon. In the meantime, my techs will be coming in to run some tests. I want you to make certain that the arrhythmia, tachycardia, or atrial fibrillation I detected in you is not something we need to worry about right away."

Noticing Claire's discomfort at such scary prospects, he continues, "No, no, no...don't worry. We'll know soon enough if there is anything to be concerned about." With that, he hurries away and Claire takes a deep breath without being told.

After the review of her body is inventoried and all tests are completed, Dr. Tynan returns to the examining room. "Mrs. Foster," he says; his smile is winsome. He taps his clipboard with the pen that had previously been lodged at his chin. "Dr. Land and I have conferred and I've read your past files. It was decided you should be admitted to the hospital for a twenty-four hour fluid collection. These specimens will be sent to the Mayo Clinic, since they are one of the few labs that can test for a suspected rare disorder. Are you OK with that?"

"You bet!" Claire responds with unexpected energy. "But—would you tell me exactly what it is you're looking for?"

"Well, Mrs. Foster," the physician's face grows more somber, "it will take six weeks for conclusive, finalized results and their cross-verification. First we'll test for Pheochromocytoma, just to rule it out. And then we'll test for one other thing. I feel confident the lab results will return confirming a genetic condition known as 'porphyria.'"

"Poor-*what*?" Stuart rushes into the room, moccasin soles flapping on the floor. The pale blue and white cotton stripes of his pajama top show beneath the collar of his overcoat. "Claire? Are you all right? When I heard from the police station I didn't know what to think. I wondered if you'd had a car accident, that you might have broken bones or a head injury, to be so disoriented. What happened?"

"What happened, Stuart, was possibly an attack of porphyria. Exactly what that entails, Dr. Tynan was about to explain to me. Dr. Tynan—my husband, Stuart Foster. Stuart, Dr. Tynan is the chief of emergency rooms for several Lake County hospitals, and imagine my good luck: he just happens to be on duty tonight. He is the first physician who may be getting us somewhere. Please continue, Dr. Tynan."

Stuart wrings his hands, looks for a place to sit, decides against it, and steps over to the table next to Claire. They clasp hands with one another. Doctor Tynan coughs and stands up straighter. "Porphyria," he announces, and takes a deep breath, "is a metabolic condition that is difficult to diagnose due to the nature of its manifestation. Although a genetic disorder, there is not a single definitive syndrome, because it causes a wide range of symptoms in varying combinations, and most of them are temporary. A porphyric episode is easily dismissed as a bout of flu, food poisoning or any one of a variety of common low-grade diseases, all short-lasting." Dr. Tynan sits down at the small desk in the corner and starts drawing Xs in the border of Claire's chart. "If all that was involved was a lifetime of uncomfortable episodes, the condition would be just that: uncomfortable. An inconvenience—not to diminish the discomfort and pain of attacks—but something that would be dealt with occasionally and then forgotten. Unfortunately, it's not that simple: each attack damages the body a little more. The effects are cumulative, so that each subsequent attack may be more life-threatening and degenerative than the one before it. So, not only is more damage done due to attack upon attack, but if left untreated, each subsequent incident is stronger and has the potential to do additional damage to the nervous system throughout the body. This is what we call 'chronic damage.' An acute reaction to an attack can be life-threatening. Very dangerous. A porphyriac can experience respiratory failure and die in an instant. Many 'faint' and are considered clinically dead but revive if their hearts are strong. I'll tell you a secret—My own family is plagued with this disorder and my sister has had episodes since childhood. She has literally died dozens of times over the years, but fortunately her heart is very strong and she pops back when oxygen reaches her lungs and heart again.

"A typical attack includes, but is not limited to, symptoms such as stomachache, migraine headaches, vomiting, impaired speech, motor difficulty, facial spasms and even paralysis.

"The definitive characteristic is a positive urine sample. The urine of a porphyriac is often sort of plum-colored. Or, a reddish-purplish brown. Or even plain dark brown." He waves his fingers in the air to the right as if reaching along a spectrum. "Hence the name of the condition. The term 'porphyria' means purple. Trajan's column in Rome is made out of a purple marble also called porphyria, if you've heard of it."

"Interesting." Stuart interjects. "Compelling, even. But tell me, Dr. Tynan, how is it that we've paraded poor Claire through an army of doctors, and not one has suspected or known of this condition?"

"Mr. Foster, I appreciate your skepticism. Informed patients never take a speculative diagnosis for granted. This would fall under the category 'happy accident' as much as a porphyric attack could ever provide a cause for celebration. In medical school I prepared a report on rare conditions, and this one fascinated me beyond all others. I even traveled to Europe in pursuit of information because this disease is associated with vampirism."

"Mr. And Mrs. Foster, let me get something from my office that may put your mind at ease. Please wait one moment." The young physician rises to attention and opens the swinging door with a straightened arm, marching out into the hall. Claire and Stuart sit in stunned silence.

Dr. Tynan returns brandishing a bound sheaf of papers. "What you'll find is," the doctor leans against the wall, "that the symptoms of porphyria are similar to the identifying traits of the undead in the vampire legends."

"Please. Dr. Tynan! Oh, my heaven! "I can assure you that I am not, nor have I ever been, a v-v-vampire. Ridiculous to even suggest that such creatures exist. And, I am not even a mythical vampire. Really! A vampire?" Claire almost swallows the word.

"Mrs. Foster," Dr. Tynan inclines his head toward her, "I would never suggest that you are Nosferatu. What I do posit for your consideration, however, is that centuries ago, victims of porphyria were accused of being vampires. Monstrosity was the explanation of the symptoms. In case you think I'm demonstrating a lack of appropriate faith in science or religion, hear me out. Medicine was in its infancy— whatever knowledge accumulated during the classical period was destroyed by the rise of the medieval church. Scraps of information were saved through the Arabs, but Europeans were virtual savages. And, the church was corrupt.

"Charlemagne was perceived as a madman because he liked to swim. Up until the colonial period of the United States it was commonly believed that bathing was bad for you. Until the last century, physicians refused to wash their hands before examinations. Semelweiss became a pariah after documenting that doctors were actually spreading illness at a lying-in hospital." Tynan's cheeks are flushing with indignation. "Given this all-over wretched atmosphere of ignorance, hearsay and superstition, is it any surprise that a rare disease would be given monstrous attributes and be associated with legend?"

Dr. Tynan continues, "You know, Vlad Dracul, the Romanian whose son was 'Dracula,' had a rare disease in his household. He would call all alchemists to his castle every year for a study in a vain attempt to discover the illness. Dracul is still revered as a hero in Romania. He was not a vampire. He was a cruel man against his enemies, but so were all the other leaders. They were all animals. The Church had something to do with it, too. Actually, the Church had a lot to do with it. The Crusades were battles from which many aberrations developed. There is the suggestion that the Church used the myth to frighten the masses into believing royalty were demons and not to be trusted.

"But I digress. The symptoms of porphyria that would contribute to the myth of the vampire are many. In addition to the symptoms I have already mentioned, there's the sensitivity to light. Not all porphyriacs are photosensitive, but most would be well-advised to stay out of the full sun at all times, and avoid even partial sun exposure if possible. Sunlight exacerbates the skewed enzymatic processing that brings on attacks. Also, sufferers do well not to drink alcohol for the same reason.

"What was that line in the last Dracula movie? The Count says, 'I never drink—wine.'" Tynan scowls and continues. "Nor should a porphyriac be in the presence of smoke. Oh, there are so many no-no's. But, the nail in the coffin—oops, no pun intended…I beg your pardon—the final damning characteristic would be an accidental live burial. Porphyric attacks often bring on a coma of sorts, so with the low medical standards of the time, and no embalming practices to speak of, victims would be wrongfully buried. If a sufferer arose during his funeral ceremony or escaped from a mausoleum, the people would not consider a misdiagnosis on the part of the barber-surgeon, but rather would shout 'vampire!' And out of the roar of the mob, innocents were slaughtered. Think of it! Falling into a dead faint, coming to only to discover that you've been buried alive, and if you do manage to somehow miraculously escape, having a stake driven through your heart. A sharpened piece of wood between the fifth and sixth ribs on the left side was counseled by the Church itself."

Claire's hand flies to her chest in an automatic, protective gesture. The doctor pauses, looks at the floor, and shakes his head. "I'm sorry, Mrs. Foster. The news that you have an inherited metabolic disorder could explain any mysterious illness in your family. You may want to ask if any relatives have suffered from seizures, or spells of delirium, or died in a mysterious coma. Another symptom would be extreme sensitivity to sunlight. Did anyone acquire unusual blisters or rashes? If you looked far enough back in your family tree, perhaps you could find unexplained illnesses."

Stuart sighs with exhaustion. "Tell us when we'll get the results and what course of treatment we should follow until then."

"Of course, Mr. Foster, pardon me once more. I just get reminded of my old school research interests and get on my soapbox. Honestly, I'm just shocked at discovering another person who displays symptoms of this rare disorder. Providence intervened tonight, because I can help you a lot—in tandem with Dr. Land, of course. It is so distressing to think of all the people who were tormented, tortured, exorcized and abused for illnesses beyond their control due to the crassest ignorance. Epileptics were assumed to suffer from demonic possession; any disfigured woman was a witch, and porphyriacs were condemned as vampires. History is full of such injustice, but its frequency doesn't make it any more palatable. Until the results are returned from Mayo, I suggest that you avoid sunlight, alcohol, tobacco, sulfa drugs, and barbiturates."

"Is that all?" Stuart leans forward and smiles at Tynan with a hint of mischief. "How about garlic? Crosses? Holy water?"

"Well, actually, Mr. Foster, if you do hold something holy, now is a good time to trust in your faith." Tynan turns to Claire and stoops as his exultant display of knowledge grows somber. He remembers that she is an individual, not a specimen with a rare and historically rich condition. "Mrs. Foster, you are under strict orders to take good care of yourself. Porphyria can be a life-threatening condition."

"And, actually, Mr. Foster," Tynan stands upright again, "garlic contains a sulfurous compound. I mentioned sulfa drugs are to be avoided; sulfur is a no-no, so perhaps people noted the porphyriacs' reaction to garlic and it became an aspect of the legend."

"But aren't you supposed to take garlic for a healthy heart and enhanced digestive system?" Claire recalls a display at the local health food store, a pyramid of little boxes holding plastic bottles filled with capsules of garlic. 'All the health!' a banner declared, 'None of the odor!'

"In your case, Mrs. Foster, no." Tynan says. "Pizza is definitely out, and you will want to avoid marinara."

"Really, now, Dr. Tynan," Claire is fatigued and this all overwhelms her. "How far does this legend play out? Do I have to sleep all day in a coffin? Do I have to have a nice fresh glass of type O+ every morning?"

"No, I don't need to write you a prescription for supplies from the Red Cross, but with sunlight having such potential for havoc, it's no surprise that porphyriacs became nocturnal. But actually..." Tynan gazes at the lights in the ceiling as he drifts back to the scientific abstract. "Whether or not to drink blood is an excellent consideration. It could function as an iron supplement. Many pastoral people, the Masai of Africa, for example, drink blood on a regular basis. However, there is a risk of transferring pathogens—all sorts of blood-borne diseases."

Stuart is weary. He slumps against the wall with his hands in his coat pockets. "So, you'd have my wife drink blood except for the risk of AIDS? You'd have her practice safe vampirism?"

"Well, given the possibilities of contracting diseases, that wouldn't be bad advice. Hepatitis is a nasty bug."

"Well, that's all I can do for you tonight, I'm afraid." Dr. Tynan's warm, dry hand grips each of theirs in turn in farewell. "Please call me if you have any other questions. Six weeks will go very quickly, I assure you. We'll get the results from Mayo and Dr. Land will call you to discuss them." He nods in closing, and the door swings shut behind him.

Claire and Stuart look at one another in disbelief. He leans forward and rearranges the donated blanket still draped on her like a toga. The pale folds remind him of a shroud and he shudders. What a tragedy to think that so many in their prime were buried alive, doomed to a horrifying end after a lifetime of inexplicable attacks. "Take me home, sweetheart," Claire says leaning back against his chest. "I'll need to sleep all day."

Stuart feels his body stiffen despite himself. Already, she becomes a nocturnal creature. What next? A bed in a box of earth in the basement? Faithful guardians in long dark cloaks? Angry peasants brandishing torches near their mailbox? It was all too bizarre. It sounded like a bad situation comedy: "I Married a Vampire." He shouldn't be so ridiculous—his thoughts are only straying this way because he is so fatigued. *But couldn't fatigue be caused by blood loss?*

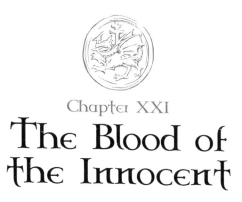

Chapter XXI

The Blood of
the Innocent

"Remember, my darling, the dragon is the blood...the blood is the dragon," thought Elysia as she awoke, climbing gradually from a deep and peaceful sleep to the realization that she was resting in the arms of this stranger in some dark, mysterious confines. This was no meadow of soothing breezes and maternal comfort. She was in a box again, her second in two nights. As the events of the previous night refocused, she remembered that not only was the man next to her a stranger but he was a particularly bizarre fellow." Who is this man with whom I am sharing my bed?" she asked herself. "*My bed?* Not mine. Not a bed. His coffin. His place. What did he call his place? The lair of the Vampire of Salzburg. Oh, God, help me! What have I done?"

Dread cut into the peace of the night, giving way to her apprehensions. Was she truly what he had said she was? Could it be possible that she really was a vampire like Herr Hensel? Thoughts whirled through her mind. If he really was a creature of the undead but she was not, then he would have attacked her. But he recognized her and welcomed her. He knew about the church, about the ceremony and her death. He knew everything.

What manner of being slept in coffins? She tensed beneath the limb that held her. She was in a vampire's bed. Any doubt of the memory was cast aside when she noted that the dark blanket which covered them was wrapped around the man's neck: a cape. How had she arrived to this place and this company? How was she to know that he was indeed a vampire, and not just some madman trying to draw her into his own surreal lunacy? Odile de la Violette was crazy enough, but at least her cravings were those of manipulation for status, prestige, and wealth, not the animal bloodlust that this vagrant had boasted of in the churchyard the night before.

His presumption was even more extreme than his possible delusion, he had told Elysia that she, too, was a vampire. It was really far too much. She tried to scoot out from under his grasp but her back promptly hit upon the interior wall. In one day, to be married, buried, self-resurrected, and then find oneself sleeping on stone with a lunatic? Her mother's words wafted back to her from the dream. Her survival was her responsibility now—no Dorothea, no Ignatz, no Peter—Elysia was the last of the line.

"Christoph." Elysia was chagrinned and saddened to realize that the man lying next to her was the first man she had ever slept with. Christoph had come to her in the night through passageways leading to doors in the backs of closets, but their liasons had been illicit and it never occurred to her to put them both at risk by asking him to stay. Instead of a nuptial bed garlanded with roses—and, inevitably, there would have been violets—she spent what was to have been her first night as a married woman trapped in a crypt with a loon. She shuddered, knowing she was deriding Hensel to make him seem safe. The nap of the fabric beneath her cheek carried a whiff of dust and mildew. Acky stirred and turned his head down. Elysia leaned backwards and his face came to rest in the hollow of her neck. She felt the rhythmic breeze of his breath above her bodice. She felt weighed down by him: uninvited head on chest, his narrow forearm under her head, his leg thrown over her two legs. Not only was she caught in the box, she was pinned by this unwieldy man.

Keeping her mouth open in an attempt to breathe as quietly as possible, she tried to twist out from under him, right shoulder back, left elbow pushing up from the floor of the coffin, but found that there was no room to escape. Slender as a scarecrow, his dead weight felt heavy, like a bag of wet sand. He slumped his head back again and paused in his snoring to open and close his mouth like a fish, making a series of smacking noises. His breath smelled like a scrap of old steak that the baron's hunting dogs would have savored. The break revitalized his snoring: it started again, with increased tempo and volume.

Well, perhaps it was better to stop delaying the inevitable. She would have to face the Vampire of Salzburg eventually, but she did not relish the thought of a continued interview. And there were considerations of hospitality, he had welcomed her into his home and provided her shelter, whatever shelter that may be. The de la Violettes had kicked her out of their home like a toothless dog—like a reviled, possessed, toothless dog, actually.

The mouth of the Vampire of Salzburg gaped before her. Elysia examined it in the dim light, seeking extra-long canine teeth or coagulated clumps of blood amidst the molars. "Blood of the saints!" she exclaimed to herself, picturing St. Edwina of Cutorno, the martyr who had been bled to death by Roman soldiers on a slow afternoon at the Coliseum and was always depicted carrying her blood in a jar on her hip like peasant wine, spilling just a bit upon the ground for illustrative purposes. She sighed heavily, drawing all the muscles of her stomach and releasing the air like a bellows. If only it were so simple. The idea of her vampirism was repulsive enough, but to become a murderer of innocents? If Herr Hensel had a pantry where he had pots of blood he was going to share with her, then joining him among the night-dwelling 'undead' would not be so frightening. Drinking blood from a jar would appeal more than sucking it from a human.

What *was* frightening was the kernel of knowledge that this shelter in a grave may be the only shelter she could have. He who had been rejected by ordinary, common, decent folk was the only one who accepted her. The lands of the von Eschenbachs' were in the claw-like talons of the la Violettes. Her father was dead. Her aunt was even less propertied than she was, and all the material things in the world Elysia was certain of were upon her body: a wedding gown, a cloak, a brooch, and a ring. This tomb may be the only chance of a home for her.

The vampire's arm stretched out above the cover of the cape, fingers spread wide, landing on her breast. Elysia cried out, startled, and then attempted some composure. It was time to wake him, apparently. "Herr Hensel!" She took a breath to deepen her voice, "Remove yourself this instant!"

"Huh? Oh, I beg a thousand pardons. He pulled his arm out from under her head and stretched both arms straight back, arching his back and then flopping onto his side to scoot off the platform. His cape tangled her in the bedding, and Elysia had to roll over directly behind him. She tried to scoot down to emerge from the bottom edge of the coffin,and her skirts rode up past her waist. Finally, she threw one foot over the edge of the box, followed it with a calf, and gripped the side of the sarcophagus with her leg to pull herself down and swing the other one over. Herr Hensel finished a yawn and reached over to help her, hitting her other breast this time. "My mistake, Madam," he mumbled and chuckled with the same breath, and then stepped over to pull her out. He trod on the hem of her skirt: Elysia heard the sound of tearing lace. She braced herself with her elbows and then swung up, her left elbow hitting him in the face. "Uhnff," he made a noise not usually associated with night-stalking predators, and slipped on her dress to land on his backside with a thud.

"Did I tell you that vampires are the ultimate embodiment of grace and smooth movement?" he laughed, stretching all four limbs out and then scratching the nape of his neck with his right hand.

"Not just grace, but the ability to glide through the night sky and break through the barred windows of their victims," Elysia sniffed, "or so the legends proclaim."

"Well, you cannot believe everything you hear, mein Schatz." His long nails scratched his cheeks in a waterless pantomime of a morning toilette, and then he folded his fingers around a raised knee and spoke from a pose of contemplation. "But these legends may have been formed for a reason. Already beings of power, if only in a willingness to defy convention and take what is rightfully theirs, vampires accumulate power over time and practice, an event or process that I like to call 'Becoming.'"

He turned his head in the direction of his guest. She sat motionless and silent, not in the mood for a philosophical discussion of her newfound state. He folded his legs in front of himself and sat up straight, inclining his head. "And how is our Baroness this morning, Hmmm?"

"Herr Hensel, I am famished." Elysia was delighted to return to the comparatively straightforward subject matter of breakfast. She reached up to the edge of the coffin's platform and pulled herself up.

"All my friends call me Acky. You must call me Acky." His voice carried a smile through the dark.

"As you wish." Elysia tried to imagine this man's motley crew of friends.

"How hungry are you?" The strange man's tone had become softer, wheedling, inquisitive.

"Very. Quite hungry," she insisted, drawing the tips of her fingers to her stomach.

"Is this the first time you have known hunger in your life? I would wager that it is, indeed."

"There are cramps in my stomach, Acky." Her settled hand contracted on her belly to counter the squeezing and grumbles on the inside.

"Perfect!" She heard his hands clap from the other side of the stone box. "Most excellent!"

"You would wish these pains upon me? This is amusing to you?" Elysia's estimation of her host fell lower yet.

"Not amusing in a comical way, darling, no…no, not at all. Rather, it is encouraging. It means many things, all of them good signs. Where there is appetite, there is a will to survive. If you were depressed and defeated then you would not want to eat. Any creature that will not rise to feed is universally recognized as sick, broken, and not long for this world. And, in consideration of your newly discovered condition…" she heard rustling and he stepped up to bow before her. "When one vampire tells another that it is hungry, they both know what must ensue."

Elysia could not believe what she was hearing. The strange events of the previous evening had not been conjecture: her host actually believed that she, like he, was a creature destined to feed upon human blood. "Surely you are not suggesting..."

"And what else would I suggest?" His fingertip grazed her cheek.

Elysia straightened herself and drew back. "Perhaps you could offer me a crust of bread? If you are willing to go to the trouble to stalk and kill, picking up a burned half-loaf from behind the baker's does not seem too great an imposition."

Acky shook his head. "This is what you say now. Deny your true nature and the pains will only increase." She heard a scraping of metal on stone and then the striking of a match. A flame flared and she saw that he held a candle on a metal plate. The light danced upon the right side of his face as he stepped toward her. She could see the dark stain of shadow on the hollow of his cheek and under his eyes.

"Elysia von Eschenbach, this is your destiny. You were sent here to me as an apprentice." She opened her mouth to protest but found his finger firmly planted over her lips. His voice lowered to shush her and then continued with as much deep sincerity as he could muster. "You shall not hesitate any longer. Such wavering is a sign of weakness, and that is not the baroness I have so admired. I must leave but will return shortly. This interlude will grant you the opportunity to consider all I have said."

He bit off the last word and set the candleholder on the coffin's ledge, then stepped back and flung the black expanse of his cape over his shoulder. As the dark of the doorway swallowed him, Elysia realized she did not recall where the passageway led, or more importantly, how to navigate between here and there to the surface. Considering what waited for her on the surface, this ignorance might not be as daunting as one would suppose.

Elysia slumped against the wall. She pictured Christoph not too many hours ago, curled in the bed's corner behind the cursing Odile and the flailing, naked Justine. She remembered the awful verification of her father's beard beneath her fingers, her hand creeping down his arm in the narrow space of the coffin to remove the family ring from his smallest finger. All of this loss after losing her child, losing her sugar-coated dream of life in a castle with the man she thought was her true love. An entire warm, safe and familiar life was snatched from her. Were these pains inside of her from the injuries that came from lack of food—or loss of love?

There was nothing to be done. Even if she were to feed upon blood, she could not squeeze a glassful from the rocks around her. Elysia drug her feet as she returned to the coffin. Asleep, at least she would not be expending more energy. She recalled the story of Job: she, too, had been abandoned and afflicted. Elysia curled into a ball and wept to herself. Her cheeks flushed and she dabbed at the liquid from her nose with the cuff of her dress. No amenities here. Eventually, the labored rhythm of her sobs transformed to the smooth and even breaths of sleep. She dreamt of her father.

The Baron von Eschenbach stood in the garden and beckoned her. The flowers and hedges would have brought pride to the heart of Rene de la Violette, but this garden was all white, and the blossoms were all open in the night darkness. The bottom of Elysia's wedding gown licked the dew from the lawn as she approached her father. Once she stood directly in front of him, he spoke. "The path in front of you is not broad and smooth, my child." He smiled as he lifted her bridal veil. The deep comfort of his voice warmed Elysia even as she slept on the stone. "This road may be narrow, twisted, steep, strewn with sharp boulders, split by a hidden crevasse, but you must persevere. You are the last of the line. Our future depends upon it. You will bear a child." His hands became as transparent as the veil they held and his face also began to fade.

Elysia reached out her hands to try to grasp his disappearing image. Her fingers closed around air as her veil drifted back down in front of her. "Do not leave me, Father!" she cried. "I need you now more than ever!"

"Do what you must to survive." His voice still echoed in front of her, deepening and darkening. Elysia saw the blooms of the garden quickly switch from white to pale pink, and then, in half a blink, to a mottled rose that was followed by bright red and then concentrated itself to red-black, staining only the urn-shaped buds of roses watered with the tears of lovers. "Things are sometimes not as simple as they seem. You will make great personal sacrifices and do things you may not understand."

The sound of footsteps overlaid the pulse of her heartbeat and Elysia opened her eyes. Acky came in from the passageway, the bent bundle of a child asleep in his arms. His eyes were short knives of wicked glee.

"Herr Hensel, I refuse! I cannot 'become' whatever it is that you insist I am if it requires spilling the blood of an innocent!" She swung her legs out of the coffin, leaping to the floor. Her lips and voice quavered. "I will not be party to the murder of a child!"

"Well, perhaps the Baroness Elysia von Eschenbach will find something else to dine upon, hmmm?" Acky gave the body of the boy a half-toss, as if he were checking that he had not been cheated in buying a sack of potatoes. "I offer you sustenance, I offer you life, and this is the gratitude I receive? If you are concerned about preserving innocence, perhaps you should go above ground and harvest a few urchins yourself. I have no doubt that they survive principally by robbery, and in addition delight in influencing the offspring of wealthy burghers to enjoy the same form of corruption."

"His personal guilt or innocence is immaterial. You have no business ..." Elysia sputtered like the flame dancing above the last inch of the candle.

"Business doing what? You don't even inquire how he was injured: you hardly know me and you instantly assume the worst." Acky took two steps to the coffin and placed the body of the boy in it. The child appeared to be around eight, red-headed, and not terribly clean. His pants had been patched a long time ago.

"What happened, then?" Elysia's hands were on her hips in a gesture that already said, 'likely story.'

Acky opened the collar of the boy's shirt and shrugged. "He fell."

Elysia's eyebrows climbed halfway to her hairline. "Into your arms?"

Acky nodded his head and stepped back to contemplate this manna from heaven. "A gruesome coincidence, I agree." He continued without a change in inflection. "The events unfolded as follows: shortly after leaving here I was turning the corner—quite cautiously; you will have to learn how—from a side street into an alley. I happened to glance overhead and saw this little mongrel scampering among the eaves. 'Careful!' I hissed at him. 'You might fall! Get down from there this instant!' Unfortunately, he must have taken my warning too literally, because he slipped from the ledge and plummeted to the ground at my feet. The crunching thud of his small body on the cobblestones was indeed sickening. I believe it was his back. If only he had been more cautious—but his error is our providence, my Baroness. Who knows what mischief he was up to up there? Spying on some good wife? Possibly on the verge of breaking through the window and stealing her jewels?" Acky turned his analytical mien to her and his expression conveyed a request for consideration.

"That is how it happened?"

Acky raised his hands to his chest and placed them together as if in prayer, then rolled his eyes to the ceiling of the catacombs. "I swear it. Now he may know peace."

Elysia stepped to Acky's side and leaned over to examine the boy. He was slim and graceful, delicate down to the arch of his stained, bare foot. It was a painful beauty, seeing something so broken that had been so full of the youthful potential of growth. The Vampire of Salzburg gathered up the small bundle of bones and carried it to the dusty settee in the corner. Elysia followed him, and then passed in front to seat herself and receive the offering. She sat down and opened her arms. She felt as if she were cradling a soft sack of skeleton and straw, some twisted doll of a boy. Even his bones seemed hollow beneath his rags. She took one of his hands in hers: his extended fingers did not reach beyond her first knuckle. The back of his hand rested smooth in her palm but the palm that faced her was scarred by cold, cut and healed in a hundred places, crooked in one finger to show an ill-healed break, and accrued calluses on its heel.

She closed her fingers around the small hand and let the head slump to her chest. Elysia lowered her nose into his curls and began to rock back and forth. If only there had been a way to comfort and save this child. Elysia wondered if she could save herself. Her own child had been taken from her. How could anyone abandon anything so precious to roam in the streets? The boy opened his eyes and focused his brown irises on her. Elysia gasped.

Acky sighed. "Liebling, it would be much better if you had been raised working on a farm. You had animals on the family estate, no?

Sheep, cattle, chickens?" Elysia nodded and Acky continued. They were not pets. You know that. They were either working animals or food. He is not a pet. Do not attach yourself to him. It will not help you do what is necessary."

"No!" Elysia cried out through her tears. "This is a thing I cannot do. I will die before I harm an innocent child." Her throat tightened and her face blazed with tears as her hands grasped the fragile side and shoulder of the figure in her arms.

"What manner of miraculous physician are you, that you believe you could save him? His back is broken, woman. He grows cold even now. Feel him." Acky leapt forward and placed Elysia's hand on the boy's forehead. His mouth opened and closed soundlessly. "The life is draining out of him as we speak. It can either go to feed your needy vessel, or be wasted on the ground, spilled into the ether. His death is an inevitability that has nothing to do with you, Elysia. Whether you take life from him or not, he will die. Do you really think that your deprivation will save him?"

The Vampire of Salzburg knelt by the edge of the settee and removed a small knife from his pocket. Elysia's eyes immediately read it as crude but effective—it looked like a small ice pick, perhaps something from the leather bag of a barber-surgeon who kept an array of blades, razors, piercing implements and jars full of leeches. He felt the boy's neck with his thumb until he arrived at the carotid, the steady small river thrumming beneath his hand with the fading rhythm of the heart. He cut the boy there, the blade forming the small sharp crease of a valley before the skin separated and blood rose from the crevice. Elysia cupped her hand beneath the child's neck and watched the red liquid collect in her palm. "The dragon is the blood..." Here, in her hand, was the fire of life, the liquid of everlasting health, the inescapable wellspring of animal vitality: there could be no life without it.

"Drink," Acky commanded.

Elysia raised her hand to her face. The blood was already thickening. It smelled like iron. She closed her eyes and lapped at her own palm, her chin grazing the boy's curls. She tilted her palm and slurped the final sip from beneath her upper lip. Her stomach grasped the arriving drops with relief, but the end of pain was not worth the price it exacted. It was unimaginable that she would put her lips on the neck of this child and suck the life from him. She removed her hand from his neck and held it out with horror. This was a stain she could never wash away. She tried to wipe her palm on the boy's trousers, but Acky groaned with annoyance and flung her wrist back at her. He sighed and buried his face in the child's neck, holding the slight frame firm against Elysia by its shoulder. This was a sight not unlike the slaughter of the spring lambs that Elysia had once seen as a child.

It was cold in the earliest of spring. Snow was still on the ground and the peasants were up before sunrise to tend the beasts. That morning she was awakened by a high-pitched screaming, long and thin, and went out past the courtyard in her night-dress to discover the source of the horrible noise. The men had gathered the first spring lambs away from their mothers and took the milky-skinned, doe-eyed creatures into the solid crooks of their arms and slit their necks. The other lambs in the pen smelled their siblings' blood and cried with fear. She turned and ran from the sight, wanting to cry out, but knowing better than to appear cowardly.

The boy was too near death to scream, but Elysia saw his eyes widen before a cloud cast over them and his lids slacked. Acky's head bobbed, and his shoulders rose and fell as he fed on the street urchin. Elysia sickened to hear the slurping noises made by her newfound protector. She looked away and saw a rat scuttle in the far corner.

Acky stopped and the spent body of the boy fell back into her arms. He was dead. Her hand wandered over his stained shirt and touched his skin, already grown cooler in an instant. The blood had held the last few strands of life within him: the skein unwound, and he was gone. This was some mother's son. Acky said he was a street child, but she was not entirely certain she believed him. Even if the child had been orphaned and abandoned, someone had birthed him, nursed him, cleaned him, and let him clasp her extended fingers tight as he took his first toddling steps. This boy would have been a heartbreaker as a small child; the carrot curls, the big brown eyes. Elysia traced his eyebrows with her little finger and then lowered each eyelid with the tips of her middle and index finger.

"Aha!" Elysia heard clinking as Acky rummaged through a canvas knapsack in the corner. He squatted over it and drew out an item with his left hand. "We have a clever boy here, indeed." He rotated a coin between his thumb and index finger, flipped it into his palm and then put it into a pocket beneath his cloak. "And do we have a surprise for m'lady?"

Acky's arm disappeared into the bag up to his elbow and reemerged holding a small silver box embossed with roses. He raised it to his face and flipped it from palm to palm, then turned a small silver key on the side. Tiny chimes emanated from within, vibrating off the chamber walls with sad, tinny plucks and whirs. Acky stood up and bowed toward Elysia, and then began a mincing dance: one, two, three side steps sliding, a little hop with a heel click, and then back the opposite direction. He smiled and revealed a red-stained mouth, thick liver-colored jam coagulating along his gums and between his teeth. Elysia recoiled, jerking against the settee. A little cloud of dust erupted around her shoulders.

"What?" Acky snarled and wiped his mouth on the back of his hand, licked it off, and then drew the thin gloss of saliva over the glaze on his cheek. Acky bared his vulpine teeth at Elysia, and then began to clean the front of his teeth with his long tongue, wiping the tip over the stained enamel with excruciating slowness. Then he stopped and smacked his lips. "Do not give me your airs; I know what I am. You cling to your ignorance like an infant to its nursemaid's skirts. Deny it all you want. The hunger in your stomach will grow and grow and you will wake up crying with the pangs of deprivation. Your blood will weaken and you will glow blue like an ersatz sapphire."

Acky crossed the room in two steps and picked up the boy, slinging the spent, broken body over his shoulder. "I'm going to take your baby for a little walk, if Madame permits." The sarcasm of his voice could have curdled milk. He bowed and the unshod feet of the boy's body bounced against his trunk when he stood upright.

"Where are you taking him?" Elysia asked as she pivoted forward. There were red droplets on the skirt of her dress from Acky's feast.

"To the wonderful garden where all his predecessors frolic." Acky's upper lip curled to the right in a sneer. "The bone garden. The little urchins are never cold, tired or hungry anymore, and instead of playing with dice, they use teeth. For marbles, there are eyeballs at first, then knucklebones. On nights when they want to skip and dance, they take out the long thighs and skinny shinbones of the remains of Salzburg's finest and beat a merry tune out upon the boxes that have yet to turn soft with dry rot. Did you for a moment believe that this is the first street child who has been brought to these chambers? We live in the catacombs and are surrounded by the dead. What is one body more or less?" He showed her his shoulder and the dark of the doorway swallowed him.

Chapter XXII
The Diagnosis

Any new factor can test a marriage: a change in career, a child, a move. It is unfortunate when tests come from things unchosen and are thrust upon us by the hand of fate. Claire and Stuart find themselves with such an unchosen element with Claire's diagnosis. That's how they refer to it around the house. "The diagnosis"—like a shoestring relative there for an extended visit or a homely dog who's always under the kitchen table and prone to licking the ankles of guests. The diagnosis is more complicated because it comes with a Siamese twin of eerie legend, the dramatic, seductive monsters of midnight movies.

Porphyria's association with vampirism may have been nowhere near as glamorous in its inception, but now the word 'vampire' brings to mind thin-membraned bat wings flapping past midnight as a newly ravished virgin writhes in white bedclothes, two puncture wounds on her neck exposed to the night air. It means dark, exotic, widow-peaked men hiding under satin capes as they prey on unprotected innocents, or likewise, a traveler astray followed by a trio of lamia, the female vampires who intoxicate with their voluptuousness and then drain the life-force out of their once-swaggering victim.

All of these associations are making Stuart nervous. They have nothing to do with a home, a garden, three kids, two cars, expanding business enterprises. The word 'vampire' should have nothing to do with their lives at all, unless they were watching a horror movie, sitting on the couch as a family, eating microwave popcorn. Or perhaps on Halloween, a junior vampire with dollar-fifty plastic fangs and lipstick blood trickling down his chin would come to the door and say 'trick or treat!' but that is the most he should ever be expected to deal with from some blood-sucking reanimated entity.

Claire does not notice Stuart's discomfort with her disease because her research into porphyria is relentless. She takes her career-honed skills of quality assurance investigation—fortunately within a medical discipline—and applies them to the question at hand. What is this condition? Was it manifested in her family in previous generations? What are its symptoms, causes, roots? How great is the genetic factor? Are the children at risk? Hours and days pass in the library; journals bound in thick green covers accumulate in her carrel. She submits special slips to circulation for inter-library transfers, needing the most recent information in the field; notes from a conference in Budapest, ancillaries from a research team in Ottawa. She has six weeks to find out everything she can, and if the samples test negative, well, then she would be relieved, and knowledge would be an end for its own sake. Research into her family history would also require a comprehensive investigation.

The disease is inherited and results from abnormal metabolism in the biosynthesis pathway of heme, the part of hemoglobin that carries oxygen to all parts of the body. The porphyriac has missing or defective enzymes, which would normally transform nourishment into heme.

Enzyme deficiencies cause key processes to go awry, including the little factories of heme production in the liver and bone marrow. A body sensitive to the sun and sulfur, tobacco, liquor and other allergens produces porphobilinogens, causing the patient to be devoid of life-giving oxygen and prone to attacks, spasms, seizures and even paralysis. But these symptoms rarely occur until after adolescence and are more evident in women. Claire imagines the myriad of ailments that could result from lack of oxygen to various organs of the body; a chill runs down her spine as she hears an echo of Bela Lugosi laughter. She remembers her last year in high school and how she was afflicted by gastric distress. She had always assumed her stomach upset was just because she was working so hard, between keeping her grades up and working at the drugstore part-time, but now she sees that those bouts could have been the first signs of porphyria. She remembers her terrible headaches, stomach aches, and nausea—such loud intestinal growling during conferences at her job when people would smoke around her. Now, she knows that the company no longer allows smoking on the premises. *Swell! After she suffered for so many years.* Eventually there are seizures, muscle spasms, tics. The vision may blur and weaken when the disease affects the cranial nerves, and if the nerves are affected more severely, delirium and comas may follow.

Claire notes that treatment consists largely of glucose administration and intravenous infusions of hematin. She recalls the legends—so perhaps some ancient porphyriac sensed that something was wrong with his blood and went to treat it with replacements taken orally. One discovery told her that Vlad Dracul was directing his alchemists to perform this surgical procedure of blood-letting with leeches on his family in an attempt to correct their problems. Who knows what fate befell the alchemist who didn't produce a cure and whose tremulous hesitation piqued Vlad's anger.

She recites her findings at home, telling Stuart about all of each day's discoveries, her growing notebook filled with information, raw data, conference presentations, and diagrams of enzymatic pathways. "So, Stuart?" she lowers her voice, breathing over his carotid one evening, "Vhat do you tink? How much are you villing to sacrifice to save your wife's life?"

"What do you mean?" He startles at the moist wind over his neck. "Don't be ridiculous, Claire." Her fingernail traces a straight line up and down his throat, from the underside of the chin to chest and back again.

"You know...vhat I mean, dear husband." Claire lowers her voice and exaggerates her breathing—rasp in, rasp out—"I vhant to bite your neck."

Stuart shudders and his arms flail out: "Cut that out! This instant!" Claire falls back into the couch and Stuart's elbow bounces off of her chest. She realizes with sinking dread that he is actually afraid of her. He is uneasy with the nature of her new knowledge, not proud of her initiative and drive.

"Stuart," she asks, "are you actually afraid of me because I might have an illness? We finally discover what could be causing the episodes after all these years, and you pull away from me?"

"Claire," Stuart is abashed, turning his hands around one another as he leans forward, elbows on bent knees. "Claire, how do you expect me to respond? We find out that you may have this rare disorder, and you treat it as a license to all this strangeness. I don't want to live with Elvira, with the midnight mistress of the late-late show. I want our regular lives to continue as much as possible; allowing that we may have to make drastic changes to avoid attacks of this disease is enough of a demand on our lives. You don't have to make it into summer stock theater. It's not right, this playing around with the idea of vampires, people walking around sucking the blood of others when they're supposed to be dead. It's not amusing...to me, anyway."

"Very well, then," Claire is sitting on the edge of the couch two cushions over. She rearranges a pillow made by her sister. 'God bless this house' reads the cross-stitching, words floating in a blue sky above a tranquil cottage with roses climbing up the side and daisies and a calico cat at the doorstep.

"The last thing I want to do is disturb you, darling. However, I was merely teasing you; I will tease you no longer. Would it make you feel better to know that porphyria is denoted as the disorder of royalty? In researching my family tree, I found that I am descended from an Austrian baron. Maybe you can look at me as a baroness instead of as Elvira!" Claire ends the conversation with resolve to speak no more of her condition to Stuart, and as the weeks remaining spin out until her diagnostics return, she wonders if she even has this condition that the enthused young doctor described in the emergency room. Perhaps she had imagined all those headaches, tremors, fits, bouts of gastric distress and general disorientation. Perhaps there was no such thing as porphyria, just as there was no such thing as vampirism, a medical metabolic mystery instead of an ancient legend of curses and immortal hungry nocturnal beasts.

Chapter XXIII

The Becoming

"Mother..." the cry was thin and distant although the child stood before her. The little boy was thin and pale. There were purple shadows beneath his eyes, the sort of stain of tiredness usually seen only on the faces of scholars or monks who spent long nights with manuscripts. His voice was thick and slurred. "Muth-errr." Elysia moaned and twisted in her sleep. This was the son she was given by Christoph, grown in the darkness like a mushroom among the undead and now returned to her. His little mouth gaped, fish-like, to expose two, too-sharp teeth. "I'm hungry." The little boy vampire protested, stamping a bare foot on the stones. "Feed me, Mother."

Elysia bent down to pick up her child, leaning over and lowering one arm behind his thin shoulders and the other one behind his knees in order to gather him up. She kissed his forehead. It was cold. The child grabbed a fistful of her sleeves and lunged at the base of her throat. She felt a cold 'o' on her neck and a pressure almost to the point of puncture, and then woke up gasping with her hand shielding the place where her pulse ran thickest.

Elysia was alone. Acky had put a tall taper in the candleholder before he left. Images of earlier dreams fell through her mind like a deck of foul cards cast on the gaming table in Odile's parlor; the orange tongues of torches danced nearer to her in the darkness, shouts mingled with barks, peasants sharpened stakes, fishwives brandished crosses, dogs ran at her with clear and viscous strands hanging from their wrinkled lips, and children with red smiles of injury across their throats were piled behind her like wood for a bonfire. A small fire still burned in her own stomach but she was afraid it would climb higher as she became more alert. Her hand groped for the edge of her macabre bed.

She saw the portrait of Christ lit by the soft and wavering flame of the candle in the damp underground air. His lips parted with bemusement behind his beard. A golden chalice almost as wide and shallow as a soup dish was suspended between the fingers of his right hand. With his right hand, he held back the edge of his robe as if to keep it from staining. A small stream of blood trickled from his chest into the vessel. Elysia remembered the stories of priests and nuns, the row of apostles at the last supper with wooden trenchers of coarse bread and rude jugs of red wine before them. Blood was the wine of Christ's veins, the most sacred communion, the blood of life and the bread of his flesh were the sacrament of life eternal.

Now blood was to be her sacrament in an eternal living death, but the painted eyes of this Christ did not seem to be judging her. Brooding lines surrounded his eyes, and the smile veiled by the dark beard was all-consoling. If the blood in the cup before him had been real, hot and holy, she would have walked up to it, lowered her right index finger into its wet vitality, and sucked the living broth off the tip, even licking the underside of her nail clean. She swung her legs up over the coffin's edge, and lowered her right foot to the floor first, skirts gathering up around her calf.

"Our Father, Who art in heaven..." she mumbled, reflexively turning to a phrase that she had been taught long ago. Who was this punishing God with this smug-looking, hemorrhaging son before her? They say that the sins of the father are carried for seven generations, but her father had been a kind, just man. Whose sins was she being punished for? Her own? She was tempted to take off her shoe and hurl it at the enigmatic fresco face before her, but then she heard the increasingly familiar tread approaching on the stones of the passageway.

"Hello, mein Schatz!" Acky stepped into their chambers with a bundle of dark fabric draped over his arm. He brandished it before her and presented it with a bow, suspending the garment over his forearms and wrists like a merchant displaying a rare velvet to the queen. Then he straightened himself and lobbed it at her chest. Elysia caught it with surprise, jerking her head back and wrinkling her nose at the dank of dust, cobwebs and mildew that emanated from its folds.

"My lady has a fine new gown for her presentation to Salzburg on the arm of Acky Hensel," he murmured with dark humor, wiping his hands clean on the thighs of his pants. "Put it on. We leave soon."

"You needn't resort to gathering rags to mock me." She pushed the bundle out into the air between them. "Your own good nature will suffice. This is unwearable—you were joking?"

Acky placed his palms on his cheeks in mock dismay. "Please forgive this most grievous transgression, Madame. I did not mean to insult you. Let me return to the wardrobe and select another ensemble for your debut. Perhaps a new gown from the Chateau de la Violette?" He loosened his wrists and fluttered his fingers in her direction. "Lavender, of course, with a shawl of embroidered tulle and matching slippers? Ah, but perhaps this steely gray thick silk with green undertones, like the stormy northern seas and m'lady's eyes, would better suit your coloring." His hands pinched invisible fabric, thumb to index fingers, little fingers extended, and he presented each dress for her inspection as he described it.

Elysia felt her face tighten with each insulting syllable. Acky continued to be correct about the most unfortunate things, but after a second of reflection it was obvious that she could not wander about Salzburg in her wedding gown. Something more inconspicuous was necessary, and the only unusual thing about the dull rag before her was the dust that enveloped it. She sighed and began to shake it, holding it on either side of the waist and flapping it out before her. Acky was soon obscured by the cloud in which they both choked and sputtered.

The vampire of Salzburg grabbed the dress's hem to still the little flecks flung everywhere. "Alright, alright. Forgive me indeed." He removed the dress from her hands and wrapped it into a ball shape which he promptly tossed to the floor. "There is another option, one that offers you fresher clothing and a truly ingenious disguise: men's clothing."

"Herr Hensel!" Elysia bellowed, "that is an indecent suggestion!"

"Please, Elysia." Acky rolled his eyes. "Your circumstances are complicated enough already: there is no call for making things even more difficult through particularity. You do not have the luxury. I will leave the chamber while you are changing. There would be no threat to your modesty. Will you reconsider?"

She turned her limited options over in her mind and agreed. Acky left the chamber and returned with the men's garments: long trousers, boots, belt, woolen socks, loose blouse, waistcoat and a large baggy jacket with square pockets sewn onto the front.

The damp air grew a crop of little bumps on her skin. She tried not to think of a hot bath. Who knew when she would see such decadence again? She held the pants by the waistband and inserted one leg and then the other. There was ample room for the shirt's tails: she cinched in the fabric with the belt and covered her bundled waist with the vest. The brass buttons had little embossed lions. Very pretty, but one of the buttons was missing. The coat added a slight comical effect; the cuffs hung down to her knuckles. She pulled the short woolly socks onto her feet and smiled at their contrast to fine silk stockings. She turned around in amazement: was something missing? What had she forgotten?

It was amazing how little time dressing took with only half a dozen items. Elysia spun around and raised her right leg in an experimental kick. Her limbs could fly when not curtained and weighed down by all those layers. Why, dressing as a lady, there were the requisite silken undershirt, the pantaloons, stockings, an underskirt, overskirts, underdress, overdress, gown and shawl or stole. Dressing required an assistant to arrange the bales of cloth. One had to be aware of the weight and swing of skirts to avoid staining or tearing the fine fabric. Never before had she realized how being beautiful could be a trap. She threw out her chest and flung her arms back from her shoulders, letting them fall back and slap to her sides. Her cheeks were lifted by her smile. This was a new beginning.

"Are you decent?" Acky stopped whistling to inquire from beyond the chamber.

"Yes, I am clothed and ready to go abroad." Elysia blew out the candle and stepped out into the passageway. She extended her splayed fingers into the darkness and felt Acky's broad, firm hand cover hers and wrap her in his grasp. His strength reassured her, even startled her, for only then in her relationship with Acky did she begin to realize the vast strength possessed by this man.

"Your vision and orientation in the dark will improve with practice, Elysia." He squeezed her fingers closer together in reassurance. "I have found that it is far better not to burn candles except when absolutely necessary. I do not wish to purchase or thieve any more than required, and more importantly, there is no call for drawing the attention of priests or sextons." They turned down the right passage.

"Discretion is the key to our valor, darling." His voice rose in front of her as they ascended the short set of stairs. "Now, pay close attention: these are the grates." The blue light of night came down upon them from between the bars. He showed her how the grates must be removed. First, she was to practice patience and wait for a minute, turning her ear to the air above to make sure that no caretakers, contemplative monks, or giggling lovers in search of a secret spot wandered above. Then, and only then, might she place the heels of her hands on opposite edges of the metal, scoot the rack of bars back slightly, and then lift them up. "Now keep paying attention." Acky whispered once they were above ground. He bent over and removed his boots, pointing them backwards and standing on top of them to make footprints going multiple directions. "Now, they will not know whether you are coming or going."

He winked at her. "I'm not joking, Elysia—no detail is too slight to ignore. The life you save may be your own; do you really want the gravediggers to know that people are climbing out of the catacombs and wandering about? If a trace of a footprint is left, it might as well point in a direction that suggests the less suspect, morally elevated grave robber, not a reanimated corpse." She understood and tugged off her own boots. They lost speed and grace, but left no clear trail. After reaching some hedges Acky signaled and they put their shoes back on.

"And now, Liebling," he whispered as he reached up to the iron spikes that topped the walls. "It is time for you to see the true nightlife of Salzburg." He swung one foot on the far side of the metal, then perched on the top to extend a hand to Elysia. She had not been allowed such immodest exertion since she was a child climbing trees in the orchard with Peter. She was still getting used to the chafing of the broadcloth shirt and the woolen trousers. Acky had provided her with quite a ridiculous hat to help obscure her features. It sat on her head like some sad felt pie, hair bundled up and knotted beneath, tied with a scrap of cord.

On All Saints' Eve a couple of the more daring girls on their estate had worn men's clothes for the revelries among the croppers, but this was something she had heard derided by the house servants: rumored, not witnessed. This was not a time for maidenly shyness—she would have to part her legs to climb and run in her introduction to her new world of darkness.

"There." Acky helped hold her steady on top of the wall. "Quiet and careful, as we must ever be. Do you have a firm grip?" He made sure that each of her hands was wrapped around a stake, squeezing his hands over hers. He leaned forward and their noses touched. Elysia could not respond—her balance was far too precarious for her to voice any protests. She nodded instead. Acky leapt down to the far side and then raised a hand to help her down. She lowered herself, keeping a firm grasp on each metal bar, and he held her calves to his chest and stepped back from the wall, releasing her so that she fell back onto his chest when she landed.

Acky's pride and enthusiasm were evident. "Now, my student, there is much for you to learn. Here, for example, to your immediate right, is the home of Georg von Strummel, a wealthy man whose family fortune comes from the jewel trade. Once, they were safeguarding a shipment of rubies from the far Indies, stones just cut and polished but not set. These stones never reached their destination in Amsterdam. Her majesty in England had wished a matched set for a necklace and was quite disappointed." His face contorted to a clown's frown, the tragedy mask displayed at the theatre.

"Acky!" Elysia was shocked. "*You* stole them?"

He continued without pause. "Now, the house further past—yes, yes that modest summer cottage of four stories of terra cotta stucco—the lady of that house has a rare hobby indeed. She grows flowers called orchids, from the tropics. They make butterflies look shy my dear, little wings and sacks of lurid fuscia and yellow. A whole conservatory of them. It's relatively easy to cut the panes of a greenhouse, you know? I'm afraid that a chill breeze kills orchids, and now her entire room of plants are gone. They used to have an amazing collection of silver, too. His arms swung out as his gait relaxed, each boot springing back from the cobblestones.

"Ooooh! That's the Carlotti's—the one with the steep-gabled roof. Very tricky to keep your balance upon, particularly in winter, but the ballroom has a window as tall as a cathedral's that faces the lake, and when they entertain they garland the place in a way that makes Odile de la Violette look subtle. Across the way, the Burchardt's. He's an architect for his Eminence, first one in the family to have a useful skill for generations, damned lazy gentry—present company excluded, of course. Plays at building palaces, yet they're quite pretty. His own home has the loveliest furnishings. The walls of the library are covered with calves' skin to match the chairs, and the fireplace is surrounded by tiles bearing quotations from the great scholars of history. Aristotle, Socrates, Pliny..."

"I realize stealing is a means of survival, Acky, but are all vampires spies and Peeping Toms?" asked Elysia. She had to double her stride to keep up with him.

"If that were the worst of it, my dear..." his broad smile melted to a soft shadow of itself. "A vampire is the ultimate outcast: neither living nor dead, consigned to roaming the darkness, far from the bosom of human companionship. It serves me well to prod my memory, even though it may cause an ache of envy. I can look, but I will never be invited in—not there, nor in the humbler homes we will approach. No one will ever say, 'Vampire of Salzburg, Herr Otto Henzel, I would be honored if you would take a stein of lager with me to celebrate the birth of my son.' Or even, 'Acky! There you are—the strawberries are ripe on my farm and we have them falling out of our ears. If I see another strawberry I will become ill. The wife has put some up as jam—could you do me the extreme favor of relieving me of some? At least a couple of jars? There's a good fellow—Ina, go fetch Herr Hensel two jars of the preserves.' No, I have only red meal jam for my bread, and no one would send their little daughter on an errand on my behalf. The child would scream and run away and her father would grab a torch and release the dogs. Looking in windows at least permits me to imagine." Acky shrugged. "I know their meanderings. Better to lift my necessities when they are enjoying a night out."

The street narrowed and the grandiose homes gave way to buildings with dark alleys between them, washing strung on lines like flags of requisite drudgery. Elysia's nostrils detected some rotting cabbage, and other pungent smells assailed her senses: wood smoke, festering leftovers, old cheese, night soil and horse manure. She stumbled and grasped Acky's cape for balance. "Careful, Elysia." He took the hand that held the fistful of rough woolen cloth. "Remember, vampires are supernaturally graceful. But these ruts would trip up Impaling Vlad himself. Here we are!"

"What is it?" Elysia looked around his arm at the gasthaus. The door fell open, emitting a square of yellow light and the suggestion of uproar. It opened again and a patron stumbled out, wandering to the alley to release a yellow stream. The next departing client was heaved out by two other men and landed very rudely on his rear. He did not rise to his feet immediately, but instead looked up at the eaves of the place and began to sing.

"A place to find prey, darling," he leaned down to her and placed a finger to his lips, "but first I must teach you how to move silently in the shadows, if only for your own safety. The shadows are our friends, guardians and companions. Remember that first." Second followed first, and then third, for the night was filled with lessons. How to blend in with a brick wall as opposed to a finished one, what posture to adopt if you want to be utterly forgettable, and how to choose a route of escape if you are afraid you will be remembered. Elysia was sore in her arms and legs, almost panting by the time he lead her back to the first tavern they had passed. Its window glowed warm amber, a small rectangle crossed by iron bars. Acky beckoned her forward to gaze inside. "Why do we skulk outside of such a place?" whispered Elysia.

"Did your father ever fish the rivers of your lands for trout? Did you ever go with him?" he whispered back.

"Yes," Elysia responded, "I was allowed to hand him weights and hooks, and he explained to me that the fisherman casts the line where the eddies run toward the middle, deep enough that the delicious silver quarry swim there in the delusion of safety, but not in the center, where the river runs too fast, nor under the dragging leaves of the willows near shore, for they do not venture there. So, *this* was a particularly good fishing spot."

Acky was impressed and pleased with her poetic discourse. He paused to show appreciation and bent down to look directly into her eyes. "Then you know that the successful fisherman is a patient, observant man." His eyes turned to the panes and he inventoried the crowd. "Don't cast in the middle of a school." He cocked his head toward a table near the fireplace where a large group called for more wine. One man had his arm over the shoulder of his companion, another friend slumped against his opposite side. The man calling for wine had received attention and was now trying to grab the rump of the serving lass as he ordered. "You seek solitary game, and these will limp off in pairs at the end of the night, but never alone. This is a shame—they tend to include the fattest, finest specimens: the salmon of our little pond. Look near the back door— there, beneath the stag's head." Acky pointed at a table of gamblers.

The table was of unfinished oak, planks thick enough for the deck of an ocean-going vessel, as rough-hewn as everything in the place. Froth-topped steins and empty bottles littered the table. One with an actual paper label was upended and had spilled a red trickle onto the sawdust floor. Candles sat on mantles, held to the surfaces in their own wax. The card players were not fancy, but rough and ready. They looked like palace guards slumming on holiday, by no means destitute, but far from ignorant about the ways of their tough milieu.

Elysia's breath sprinted back past her throat so suddenly that her head shook: there, like a parrot among hawks, sat Christoph de la Violette. Christoph turned his head over his shoulder and yelled something to a neighboring table, first careful to spread his cards face down on the playing surface and anchor them with his flattened left hand.

Acky's finger pointed a path right to the well-curled auburn tail of hair above Christoph's nape. "Now, consider that specimen. That would be quite a treat, and it would give me satisfaction to do in one who looks as if he actually has the means to commit wickedness and indulgence instead of some poor wretch just killing his pain in the only way he knows how. Can't pretend to be too high-minded about it, of course: the redhead would be clean, perfumed, seasoned game instead of something fatty, unclean, and rank-smelling, as are most of these tavern habitues."

Acky shrugged and furthered his speculation. "I call him Casanova, but if he were such a great lover, he would not have to buy company, eh? Definitely a regular, in here every night, knows all the cardplayers by name, knows all the whores a bit more intimately. He bundles one into his coach, sometimes more, at the end of the night but generally drops them off within blocks. Yes, I've followed. Last week he didn't even give one poor thing time to lace up her bodice before kicking her out. The gap-toothed wench almost tumbled out—I had to leap into a doorway with Godspeed to avoid getting spotted, not that it was anything to her if I followed. She was holding the top of her dress together with one hand, cap askew, shaking a fist wrapped around guilders as he drove off. 'Bastard!' she shrieked, and then some more curses in dialect—sounded like a Frisian. These country girls come to the city to be servants and are shamed and then..." He shook his head at the folly of human endeavor, the cycles spun out, the same play repeated every night with different actors. "Well, what do you think of him? Long, lean, clean, and healthy—would he not be a catch? With his last breath, he would insist that you serve his blood in cut crystal goblets, such a fancy pants. Perhaps the Baroness would deign to partake?"

"It's Christoph." she sighed, and then looked to the ground in embarrassment. Elysia's eyes betrayed her by rolling back up to consume the profile of the laughing figure, haughty chin raised, eyes narrowed, his lips pulled back from his teeth in mocking laughter at some unheard suggestion. One of the rougher-looking women present stepped from behind the table and he turned, pulled back his hand, and smacked her square on the behind.

"That's him?" Elysia looked to the side. The surprise on Acky's face seemed genuine; his eyebrows had leapt towards his hairline and his mouth hung open for a moment. "This is Christoph de la Violette? Your husband? I had no idea, Elysia," he lied. His brow furrowed in a parody of concentration. "You would have had quite a marriage bed—when he was home. Or perhaps you would have been expected to share it. Oh, I'm sorry, dear, I did not mean to be so blunt—this one is just legendary among the bars and the evening ladies that inhabit them. He is always hiring, never takes a night off, actually once ate a full silver tray of oysters at the Gasthof Schnelling and left with six girls in the carriage. It's a rite of passage for a prostitute to do this one, and he is none too discriminating, considers it a point of pride to sample all the goods. Why, Griselda, the old one who cleans up here, was once gossiping with the owner and I heard her say that he had bragged of finding a whore who was missing a leg, arm, and eye on the same side and doing her. He anxiously awaits the carnival that travels with its cursed oddities to come to the outskirts of town each spring so that he can hire the Egyptian dancer, the Indian contortionist, and the sisters born joined at the backside."

She did not want to crumple in front of Acky, but she could not control her tears. She had heard the stories told by Marie-Ange, but such evidence and such tales were too much. The vampire looked at the clear trails on her cheeks and pressed further. "All this excess might be one thing if he were clever, sweetheart, but he is randy and wealthy—not astute. See the girl tracing his right ear with her finger?" Elysia saw that the woman's breasts were still falling out of her dress, the top brown crescents of her nipples peeking above the red and white striped fabric. She leaned up against him, pillowing his ponytail into the crevice of her bosom. "She is working with the card player across from him, the fat one in the green vest. Yes, right there—the one who has just waved for another stein. They have so many signals and signs that they will rival a bishop at high mass in gestures. They are so elaborate, I am tempted to believe that they have it worked out to the suit. If she tugs her right ear, he has two or more kings. Left ear, it's queens. Pulls at her curls, aces. Scratches her lower lip, a run of ace through knave. Quite a system."

He gave his eyebrows a quick double-raise at Elysia to express his amazement. She was looking at the glass eyes of the mounted stag, no longer able to witness the lewd gropes beneath its patient brown head. Elysia felt as stuffed and mounted as the stag, stiff and hollow, tongueless, filled with sawdust. The eyes were laughing at her now. "Which of us has the better bargain?" the trophy asked her. "I am a decoration to drunkards, thieves, and whores, but I am welcome inside where it is warm and people do not run at the sight of me. More than you can say, Baroness von Eschenbach. See where your vaunted title has got you now? Where are the dozen servants to leap at the wave of your little finger? Where is the maid who pressed your fine gowns? The child who washed your gold-rimmed plates? The venerable grandmother who rinsed your chamber pot? And what of your fine wedding to the most eligible bachelor in Salzburg, a grand affair orchestrated by your loving mother-in-law-to-be?" The taxidermic creature continued peering over its dusty snout at the revelry beneath it. Christoph slurped a wine-stained lick on the chest of the pig-nosed harlot in the striped dress.

Elysia answered the trophy in silence. *After my fine wedding I discover that my father is dead; my aunt, captive; I am reviled and threatened with fire, bludgeoned with crosses, cursed in the name of God and driven away from my husband's home by his mother and one of his whores.* She swallowed the salt of tears in the back of her throat. *I have spent my honeymoon in a graveyard with a blood-drinking ghoul, the only one who has shown me kindness. He stands next to me in this alley, and I am his pupil, wearing the cast-off clothes of a man he killed, perhaps a man like one of the beer-stinking gamblers sprawled out on benches on the other side of this window. Among this human garbage sits my husband, groping whores, getting drunk, and losing amazing amounts of money.* Elysia closed her eyes. Perhaps she had died and passed on to a personalized hell, a pit which designed to display her every nightmare as a joke before subjecting her to an eternity of crasser torments.

Acky was not empathetic to Elysia's anguish. Now all that was necessary to dissolve her sentiments for her old life was to show her the truth of it. Her foundations were rattled; it was time to start the new buildings. He regained her attention, placed his index finger to his lips for silence, then pointed to an area opposite the gamblers, where a stout man had to push his chair back a foot from the table before taking leave of two companions. He swayed as he got to his feet, and stood still for a moment, bent over to support himself on the table. His eyes were closed and his mouth was a panting wet slit in his dark beard. Then he opened his eyes and righted himself, garnering a bid of farewell from the two men still playing at the boards.

Elysia was startled by the emptiness to her right. She did not remember Acky removing his hand. She craned her neck back around, looking at the darkness all around, and then saw him flush against the wall on the far side of the building's front, right at the entrance to the alley. A square of yellow flared between them as the departing patron fell out of the door and into the street on unsteady feet.

"Gustaffff, my friend!" Acky slurred the words and blurred his gestures, throwing open arms toward the man. "Gustav, I have been waiting on you. I need your help!"

"I am sorry, my friend. I am not Gustav," the man answered, scratching the long hairs of his stubble.

"Gustav? You old joker, it is exactly like you to claim that you are not Gustav, but you cannot fool me. We must go now." Acky's shadow snaked next to the pool of gray thrown down by the large silhouette of the man.

"I am not Gustav. I do not know any Gustav. My name is Bodo Fretzle." The man wrinkled his brow and nodded his head as if confirming he'd gotten the name right. "Are you alright, stranger?"

"No, I made a silly mistake. Can you believe it, Bodo? Bodo, let me tell you something: a secret, Bodo." He slumped forward and beckoned the drunkard with a crooked finger. "Over there, I thought that way led to the Gasthaus Green Boughs, but I was wrong, and when I turned to go back around to the square, I tripped." He slapped the upper arm of the man in front of him. "There was no Gasthaus there and I tripped in the alley on some garbage that some filthy wench left there. Garbage! And then my purse strings must have broken because I heard coins dropping on the stones, at least fifty guilders in gold, and when I reached for my purse it wasn't there!" Acky looked surprised and patted his belt where the purse had been for affirmation.

"Stupid garbage!" Acky slurred as he threw his arm around Bodo's shoulders and leaned against him as he staggered to the alley. "Don't tell anyone about this, Bodo. You can help me? Just you and me. We'll find it."

"I can help you," Bodo assured him. "Just tell me where this accident happened. It's our secret." Bodo raised his fingers in the air at the solemn oath. "Now, how many coins did you drop?"

"That is a good question, my friend." Acky shook his finger at Bodo. "I can tell that you are a thinker. I thought there were at least fifty guilders' worth, but some were single pieces, and some were five guilder pieces, and there was at least one ten-piece with an eagle on one side and the emperor on the other. Such a clumsy new friend you have, Bodo. And it is dark in the alley here, Bodo. Is this a five piece?" He stooped and pressed a coin into the man's hand. The two figures rounded the corner into the alley. Elysia left the square of pale light from the window and watched the men, leaning her back against the flaking paint of the building.

"Wait!" said Acky. "Were you going to keep that? Give me my guilder. I can't trust you."

"Of course you can! You yourself just said I was your friend. Now, show me where you tripped, and we'll find your money and go have a drink with Gustav."

"Gustav! You know Gustav? Let's toast Gustav! A drink to Gustav!" Acky rummaged beneath his cape and removed a silver flask. He pulled out the cork, mimed tipping it to his lips, wiped his mouth with the back of his hand, and pushed the metal bottle at Fretzle.

"To Gustav!" The man tilted his head up and sucked the flask. His Adam's apple bobbed. Then he lowered the flask and belched. "It tastes funny," he complained. "What is this stuff?"

"The elixir of the Gods, my friend. I have been drinking it all night. I may not do well in alleys, but I have spent the last three hours in the corridors of castles, talking with kings and dancing with their daughters. Woo, hee! The first sip, you knock on the door to the kingdom. The second, they come out and give you the keys." Acky slapped Bodo on the back. The man shrugged his shoulder and drained the flask.

"Now you are with me. To Gustav! Let me show you where I fell. It was over here. Or was it here? You help me, my friend." His hand was in the small of Bodo's back. The noise of the tavern faded behind them. Elysia stepped forward, eyes straining at their outlines in the darkness. Then she heard a thud. Acky stood over the collapsed mass of Bodo, his face down in the muck and mire.

"Elysia." Acky's voice was low and soft. She could see him bent over the unconscious form in the darkness. "Come out, come out wherever you are. Elysia?"

Elysia took ten steps to stand beside Acky. She put out her hand to orient herself in the dim. A rat rustled in the rubbish. "Is he sick?" she asked Acky. "How did he take ill so suddenly?"

Acky sighed through his teeth. "He is not ill, my darling. Do you not recall the potion I gave you?"

"Yes."

"Well, Herr Fretzle downed twice as much on a stomach already full of lager." His hands disappeared into his pockets and reemerged with a knife. Acky slid the blade beneath the man's cuff and pushed the knife up and away from him to slit the sleeve like a fish belly. Bodo's pale arm was exposed, the jagged cables of blue veins right beneath the skin. Acky placed the razor edge over a vein and sliced quick and sure. The blood spattered and speckled, sleeping heart pulsing it out into the air. Acky held the wrist and the knife together with one hand, and put his other hand on the nape of Elysia's neck. He exerted gentle pressure, as if pressing wine from a rare grape in the autumn frost, and guided her head toward the thick flow.

"This is not a street urchin. This man is not an innocent. Elysia." Acky's whisper continued, "This man was a sinner like us all. Now, how do you think I have managed to survive for so long?" She felt his breath on her ear. "Here is the life. Here is the means to survival."

As her lips fell to the blood, all of her senses were heightened. She could feel each hair from the tufts on his arm scrape her skin like a wire brush. He smelled of accumulated sweat, and with it the comfort of animal warmth, the smell of a stable on a summer morning. As if she had never held a human arm before, his weighed heavy and stiff in her hands, a rough log made of maple with its sap draining away.

She held her open mouth over the flow but hesitated. The pulse from his wrist bubbled to fill her ears like the rush of an underground river. The blood smelled of meat and iron. She grasped the wrist and closed her eyes; her lips curled to form suction to the skin as her tongue first lapped. The man's life ran into her mouth, coating each tooth and robing her tongue in its velvet-hot stream. Her mouth pulled harder, a hungry infant at the nursemaid's teat. She had never been so hungry, nor so relieved. A tremor started in her mouth and ran down the length of her body. She drew in her cheeks.

"Not so much." Acky's hand pulled her back. "Not so much the first time, Liebchen."

Elysia's breath shuddered and she clutched at the bloody limb. "I am not full," she protested. "I've had nothing for days. This is my first meal."

"There is a basket of root vegetables in the larder of our home."

"What is this? You tell me I need to drink blood, but when I do, you try to give me a carrot?" She wiped her lips on the rough, dark nap of the cuff of her coat. "Don't I need blood to survive? You lure me into this depravity when I never needed it?" Her voice rose at Acky. Elysia shifted her weight. Her legs were beginning to cramp. When feeding, she had not noticed the awkward squatting posture she held, crouching over the body. She rocked forward to her knees and sat on her heels.

Acky drew her toward him, while patting her for solace. "A child does not go straight to bread and sausage. When Becoming, the body must also gradually adjust. The blood is rich enough to keep you alive, but your stomach still wants to hold solid food. I will get you a nice rutabaga."

Elysia responded to her mentor with vehemence. "You spend every waking moment persuading me to take the blood of the living, and when I relent and give up everything, lose all chance of salvation because of your words," she sputtered in anger, "when I succumb to your temptations, then you pull me away, saying 'Tut, tut. Not too much'?"

"Elysia, lower your voice, please! This is a debate we can enter into in the privacy of our quarters." It was the first time that he said "our." His hands were in Bodo's pockets, removing items to a pile in between his knees with the brisk efficiency of a gesture oft repeated. "Or perhaps you would like someone else to join our conversation? Perhaps you could find a sympathetic ear to hear about the travails of joining the undead? You will make a compelling argument with that blood still smeared on your face."

"Where?" Elysia's finger flew up to her features. She moistened her fingertips with saliva to try to rub away the stains. "Do I really have blood on my face? How can you tell in this light?"

"Hey, now, Violette! Be sure to come back and win some more!" The tavern door flew open and shadows poured into the alley. One man guffawed and held his arm out to support a fellow drunk. The scent of tobacco smoke unrolled over them. A carriage arrived, polished brass plates on the harnesses and a small wreath of violets painted on the door. "Good night, old man!"

"Goodnight! Until next week!" Laughter echoed off the brick walls. "Don't forget your purse!" A figure stumbled up to the carriage and waved off the taunts with a deprecatory flap of his hand. The red-haired man was flanked by two garish women, their gowns laced like bales spilling straw, overstuffed as an old couch in a prelate's parlor, bright roses of paint blooming on their cheeks on top of the flush of too much drink. It was Christoph de la Violette with two whores. He opened the door and climbed in, followed by the first woman who gathered her skirts in her fist to step up on the running board. She wore purple stockings, one with a run widening over the knees. When the second climbed in, Elysia could see that she had no stockings at all, but did appear to be very proud of her feathered hat, which she clasped to her head with one hand as she pulled herself into the wagon. She tottered in the doorway, then fell in. A squeal of giggling erupted and the curtain on the carriage window closed the cabin from view.

Elysia retreated past the prostrate form toward the alley. That she would have competed with the likes of those! What was even more unthinkable was the conjecture that if she presented herself now, he would prefer their company to hers. One part of her chased the carriage, a piece of her heart racing behind in the muddy ruts, shouting, "Christoph, Christoph!" But she knew that this was a foolish yearning. She stood back from the street until the carriage rolled a safe distance away.

"The finest of Salzburg society." Acky spoke at her side. Elysia had not heard him approach; she was so engulfed in the pain of remembering. "The tales of your betrothal were not encouraging, Elysia. You have much to learn. A whole new way of living confronts you. You would do best not to waste your thoughts on one so obviously beneath you."

Elysia felt her composure dwindling. "I never loved before; he is the only man who ever touched me. No one else, ever..." Her voice trailed off. A sob caught in her throat as the last hammers of the horse hooves echoed to silence. Her back was to Acky; he had stepped behind her with a cape-draped arm offered to hold her close to him. So many changes in such a short time. The stubble of his beard scraped the top of her earlobe as he nuzzled her. "Oh, Liebling." He steered them to the wall, and then raised his cape to shield them from the sight of the street. He bent down to kiss her, first on the thin strip of hair behind her cheekbone. Then his dry, cool, puckered lips grazed the arc of her eyebrow. He paused as if trying to recall something, lips coming to rest on her forehead. His hand came up to stroke loose hair from her brow. Acky's mouth followed his hand and he planted a kiss on her hairline like a jewel on a tiara. With that she raised her mouth to find his; the metallic taste of the blood on her mouth jolted him. They fused in reverie, standing still with their lips together until they could hear the tempo of one another's hearts.

"Elysia." Acky removed his mouth to speak and then leaned forward again to stroke the space between her eyes. "It is time for us to go home." The words were simple, accompanied by a series of kisses down her neck to the collar, each longer and warmer than the other, the last one ending with a gentle pulling and a nip.

Elysia gasped, her eyes closed, but not resisting. Yes. Yes, to being held by a man who clearly wanted her, who paid her more sincere attention in three nights than her fiancé had in three months. It would help her to forget, to spread another memory over the knowledge that Christoph's hands were the only ones that had ever touched her, had ever molded the curves of her bare skin or delved into her most private places. She felt wanton for a moment, angry that he was the one she had given herself to. That he, who saw women as the servant views chickens in the barnyard, flinging shillings like feed among them, had seen her naked. "Yes." Her own hoarse whisper shocked her. "Let's go home now."

Never has a walk been so short and so long. The tread of the hanged man to the gallows, the measured steps of the young bride to the altar: these are journeys that are made once to an event from which one might never turn back. Elysia's throat was dry; her face flushed hot as Acky held her elbow and led her down the street. Then he laughed and leaned over to kiss her ear. "I cannot hold you here, darling—but soon, soon." Her eyes questioned, but Acky whispered an explanation. "Your clothes!" His hand gestured down her men's attire. "We do not need to be taken for sodomites and be beaten. Even at such a wee hour in this neighborhood, there are things not smiled upon." His lips brushed her ear again and his hand assumed a collegial pose on her shoulder.

When they approached the wall of the graveyard Elysia wanted to turn and run. She felt too bold with her consent. She knew the implicit meaning in this home they returned to. She was making a choice of her own will instead of having it eroded as waves thrashing away at the shore. Elysia watched Acky's stooped back as he removed the grate that covered the passageway into the catacombs. He stood upright and took her hand with a bow, and then preceded her down the stairs.

Their steps drummed unevenly in the stone hall. Acky stopped to kiss every part of her face except the lips, and Elysia could feel herself glow. They rounded the final sharp bend into their quarters, and Acky lowered her onto the couch. He lifted her chin, index finger curling under it, and turned her face to kiss each cheek. "Elysia," he said, and then melded his lips with hers.

Acky paused to light a tall taper, straightening the sheets in their bed. Elysia shifted on the couch, and a puff of dust rose into the still candlelit air like pollen of gold. Acky kissed her again, longer now, putting his hand under her shoulders to lift her to him. He stepped to the head of the bed and picked up each pillow, fluffing it by picking it up and moving each corner in towards its opposite. The most conscientious servant in the house of the Violettes or von Eschenbachs could not have prepared a bed with more meticulous speed. He returned to kneel by the couch. "Elysia," he whispered her name, a dry rustle in his throat. They tasted one another with the lingering charge of blood in her and she opened her mouth beneath his ear and released one word.

"Becoming." He pulled back his head to appraise her, almost imperceptibly, and returned his lips to hers. He lifted her by placing one arm under her knees and using the other to cradle her shoulders. Their faces did not unlock as he swung around to lower her onto the bed, and when her shoulder blades hit the resisting surface and she arched her back, she was gasping. He climbed into bed alongside her and rolled her onto her side to face him. Every step, every lace loosened or button undone, meant a pause for the tender part to be greeted and treasured with a kiss. Each series of kisses was leisurely followed with an investigating hand, Acky looking earnestly into her eyes to discern her response, adjusting the angle of his embrace or the pressure of his fingers. He would wait until her panting cries slacked and she took her hand to draw his face down to hers, fingers furrowing through the hair on the back of his head, pulling him down, down, trying to devour him from the inside. Sometimes he would resist, kissing her gently instead of giving over to the crush of lips and crash of teeth, resting on one elbow to watch her protest and dissolve. When she finally fell into sleep, it was just to enter a richer place in pleasure, like the invisible line where fresh water and salt water mingle when the river joins the sea.

A happier couple you could never meet. They loved when the dawn began to whisper its arrival, falling into sleep to rise with the dusk. The dark brought her continued education. He taught her how to tell a pleasant drunk from a mean one at twenty yards, how to pick a pocket in the closing melee outside a tavern, where to tread carefully and what paths were so deserted that they could move at quicker speed. Soon her reflexes were as quick as his, glancing over her shoulder before she sliced a wrist to bring it to her lips, ducking to hide behind a rain barrel at the sound of the nightwatchman's steps, flitting in front of the windows of the grand homes, stopping to eavesdrop. Nobody has ever tipped the undertaker. All valuables—coins, watches, rings—left the pockets or fingers of their previous owners to weigh down the canvas bag Acky kept knotted to his belt, a sack lined with cotton to muffle the clink of metal on metal. Sometimes they did not need to leave their home to find treasure. The dead would be buried with pomp and circumstance and the two would soon descend to collect the harvest. "She does not need this where she is going," he would shrug, unclasping an emerald brooch from the bosom of its owner, but soon those rationalizations were no longer necessary to her. Elysia gathered embroidered cushions from beneath the heads of the dead to cover the settee, their chamber's sole piece of furniture other than a chest and the box of a bed. She put her hands on her hips and laughed at herself when she realized what she was doing. "Acky, I am so domestic!" she said. As domestic as she could possibly be, living unmarried, undead, with a vampire in a tomb beneath the city and surviving by trickery, thievery, and murder.

One night was a splendid evening, indeed. They were in the shadows of the shadow, smiling silently to one another as they ran through the back ways without a sound. The kill was a Venetian merchant who had collapsed in their trail without ruse, leaving a brothel in self-disgust once he realized that he had consumed too much red wine to perform.

Amazingly, his purse was still full of florins and he wore three rings, one ruby, one sapphire, and then a ring of five diamonds. Acky and Elysia graciously accepted his contributions. There was freedom in her new life, a strength in agency, an awareness that she was beyond the protocol of station and duty, living in animal survival but with human cleverness. The baroness was dead; long live the baroness. Elysia von Eschenbach was Elysia, the Vampiress of Salzburg, happy and strong in the hunt with her mate, suffering neither fools nor weakness. Stomachs full of red vitality, pockets dragging with coins, at the end of the night they perched on a ledge and looked up at Orion, the hunter in the stars. "The laws of God, the laws of man," Acky whispered his favorite poem in her ear, "He may keep who will and can. Not I, let Gods and men decree laws for themselves, but not for me."

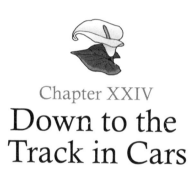

Chapter XXIV

Down to the
Track in Cars

laire and her sister Helena, without shame, have always doted on their brother, Richard. When he was young, they were hovering surrogate mothers, dressing him up and paying him constant attention. Now that he's older, they assist and support him however they can, and this entails going to the races. Richard has always loved speed. At age nine, he was quick to trade his new bicycle for a 125cc Yamaha Motocross bike and not amazingly won most races throughout the Midwest. In no time at all, he was dissecting and reassembling cars in their back shack before even possessing a driver's license.

This weekend there's a race at the Five Oaks raceway. Claire and Stuart pack their camper and drive through Dunbarton, Melling, White Acres, and then Smithville, and on to the track. "Claire," Stuart says, "do you really think it's alright for Victoria to spend all summer at Banff? Sure, it's a prestigious program, but it is so far away, in another country."

"Oh, for heaven's sake, Stuart, we couldn't possibly deny her the opportunity to study oboe with such acclaimed instructors. You know that Wojnarowicz teaches at Juilliard. Besides, Alberta, Canada is not the most desolate and dangerous foreign locale. Hmmm...was that house built the last time we drove down here?" Claire points to a beautiful example of Southern classic revival perched on top of a hill. Stuart is relieved to see Claire in the light of day, going to a regular place to do a regular thing—nothing further from vampirism than a motoring competition of Detroit's finest technology. This day would vanquish any traces of those gloomy memories. The field is fair and broad, the company is convivial, the sun shines so brightly as to eradicate any creature of the shadows that might lurk beneath the bleachers.

Stuart backs the camper in between the yellow lines and unloads the cooler. Claire gathers her bag and checks its contents: sunglasses, brush, comb, breath mints, note pad, receipts, keys and lotion in a turquoise plastic bottle. Richard's trailer is already parked and being unloaded. "Hey, you guys, good to see you!" Her younger brother gives Claire a hug, Stuart a hearty handshake. He raises his voice to make himself heard above the circling roar of the cars qualifying on the track. Richard's car rolls down its rack, gleaming with polished adoration. He springs the hood: the car's engine is as clean and shining as its exterior. His hands fly over the engine, double-checking a sparkplug, wiping an errant strand of grease from a filter. He and Stuart test the machine. At first it belches and sputters. The insides are manipulated with delicacy and discretion. The sputter becomes a stammer and then smooths to a purr, humming its buzz in a crescendo that promises power about to be unleashed.

Claire knows that the Ellises have their regular seats in section C5, so she begins to wend her way through the sunburned throngs of fans, punctuated by beer and hotdog vendors, when Richard barrels onto the track. She grasps the rail and leans to see where her brother is when she hears the announcer call his name and car number. Her knuckles barely have time to whiten from her grip on the guard railing as he shoots past— he's already gone. Watching the race is always such a thrill when Richard is competing. The hurtling ton of steel sailing by, but as delicately as a stone skipping over the surface of the water, belongs to *her brother*. The machine pageant is a testament to his expertise and skill: the years of study, the knowledge, the care poured into the engine and the calibration of its sensitive innards. Here is such a dedicated and accomplished young man commanding an oval at surreal speeds—and it's fun to watch.

Haley Ellis is a charming woman. Tall, slim, imperial, she blows the entire regal impression to hell the moment she opens her mouth. "Claire, honey!" Haley starts flapping her mouth and her hands at the same time, "How y'all doin'? I heard that Richard was racing and the first thing I said to Roger was, 'Roger, sweetheart, this means that I'm going to get to catch up with Claire Foster and hear about those three lovely children of hers! The—what is it again? Flute player?' Isn't that what I said, Rog, you tell her." Roger Ellis peers sagely over the edge of his beer glass and smiles at Claire. Haley does the talking for them both. "And how's the carwash coming along? Oh, sweetie, it's good to see you!"

After catching up with the Ellises, Claire returns to sit with Stuart. He finds them seats in the shade, but later in the day the shade shifts and sunlight falls on them. It's two o' clock and now the bleachers are fully exposed. But Claire will not acknowledge her condition in front of Stuart anymore. She cringes to remember the time he leapt back from her and wipes the sweat from her forehead with the back of her hand. No, she will not give Stuart any reason to recollect that he has ever even heard of porphyria.

Now Francine Moore has wandered over to their section to chat.

Claire recalls their last meeting, at a previous race. They had a fantastic potluck lunch from the back of the camper. Claire asks Francine for the pasta salad recipe.

On such a day it seems impossible to conceive of a disease that would drive people out of the sun. Claire leans back and feels the heat prickle her skin—the warmth is light, is life, is comfort. Her eyes become slits when she removes her sunglasses—the brightness penetrates the scrim of her eyelids, revealing them to be a rich liquid scarlet. When she opens them, a constellation of extra suns echo the one glaring down on them. The down hairs on her lower arms shine, bleached a paler blonde, almost white. The heat is unusually dry, but intense enough to feed a rivulet down between her shoulder blades. Stuart watches Claire from the periphery. Moments pass as he realizes she is experiencing the first excruciatingly painful throes of some sort of attack. Was Dr. Tynan's sophistocated monologue coming true? She begins to moan as her fingers knead her brow. With lips curling, she grimaces, her mouth agape. Stuart's heart beats with trip-hammer precision. My God! He thinks he is having a heart attack himself, he is so frightened. He yells at Claire, "Claire, Claire! Let's get to the car. Come on, give me your arm! Can you walk?" Pulling her up and supporting her with her clothing, he force-walks her out of the bleachers and to the car.

Gravel flies as Stuart creates a racetrack of the highway. Stuart whispers a prayer, "Dear God, save us!" But he starts to calm down, slowing the car when he notices that Claire is sleeping peacefully. The car swerves every time his eyes rest too long on Claire instead of the road. They arrive home. Claire is still weak, but mobile. Stuart tucks her into bed after much questioning and prodding. "Are you sure you're alright? It's not too late to go to the hospital."

The nightmare awakens Claire in the dark. They are about to cremate her: instead of a coffin, they are carrying her tethered body to a bier. She feels the chafing of the ropes, the growing heat. If only she could writhe or scream so they would know that she's alive—but she cannot move, encased in some rough burlap, bound and log-stiff as they lower her to the flames.

Flames! Her skin feels like it's burning up, covered with tiny, hard blisters still exuding heat. Her breath crackles as she tries to raise her voice. "Stuart!" Her throat is grasping the sounds, trying to pull them back—her lips retract from her teeth in a spasm. It takes all of her concentration to swivel her swollen knees over the edge of the bed. She has to lean against the wall each step down the hall. Her nails scrape the paint; it seems like her fingers should leave scorched tracks, smoldering smears of soot, to mark wherever her skin has touched. Stuart is watching TV. The well-modulated voice of the eleven o'clock anchor floats down the hall: "...Earlier today tragedy struck a Westside day care center..."

"Stuart." Claire is close enough now that her plea is heard above the television. "Help me."

Stuart wheels around in the easy chair then leaps up, knocking over a table. A bowl of peanuts scatters on the carpeting at her toes. "Oh, my God, Claire!" He steps over the end table and grasps her by the shoulders. Claire is amazed that he doesn't release her at once—her skin feels that hot: doesn't it burn his fingers? She collapses against his chest. Her mouth twitches open and she can taste a trace of detergent in his shirt. Speech requires the utmost concentration—her muscles are now linked to an electrical charge beyond her control.

"Stuart," Claire knows her throat will give birth to her heart at any second. "This is what it feels like to die."

"John!" Stuart calls down the hall. "Your mother is having a heart attack. I'm taking her to the emergency room. Call Dr. Land—now!" John murmurs, sticking his tousled head into the hallway and wiping his bleary eyes as he stumbles toward the phone.

Chapter XXV

Mortality

Elysia von Eschenbach stirred in her sleep and stretched awake. After rubbing the dry crust from her eyes and extending her limbs as far as they might go, first arms, then legs, she noticed something odd about her body. She felt as if she had become all breasts, two sensitive, independent masses on the front of her chest that she wanted to shield even to get up. And her sense of smell was terribly acute. She knew, for example, just through an inadvertent whiff inhaled with a yawn, that there was a hunk of bread with Maerchenburger cheese left on the table from the previous night's adventuring, and that the shirt Acky had taken from a victim, only slightly stained with a few red flecks, had been perfumed with an expensive combination of freesia and civet. Also, her own blood had not arrived for many weeks, and the new moon was almost waxed; enough days had passed since her appointed time to require some explanation. Elysia knew what explanation was the most reasonable and evident. "Acky," she rose on her elbows, "I believe I am pregnant."

"Don't be ridiculous. You are a vampire. Vampires cannot become pregnant, ergo—you are not pregnant." He twisted out of sleep and waggled his finger as if lecturing. "Is that not how the learned Jesuits would say it? I always enjoy eavesdropping around the monasteries. You must be dreaming. Talk to me when you wake up." His words were muffled with the thickness of a salted tongue. Last night they had fed, and Elysia sniffed the iron and animal odor from the dried blood within his mouth.

The red of the blood recalled dried red roses to Elysia, a bouquet abandoned or a memento pressed in the pages of a novel, and she was reminded of the dream-flowers in the garden where her father had last visited her. The Baron von Eschenbach stood in the garden and beckoned her. She wore her wedding gown and the white roses deepened to red after his blessing and his warning. He let her know that a rock path was before her, and that in the face of tribulations her own survival was paramount. She would bear a child to continue the line. Her heart warmed at the echoing memory of his voice. Elysia spoke to Acky's back. "And what manner of physician are you, Herr Hensel, that you are so certain I cannot conceive?"

"The most pristine and obvious logic, my dear, as I just presented to you in crystal-clear syllogism." He looked to the ceiling and spoke out of the crack of caked blood. "I do not need to be a medical man from the University of Stuttgart to tell you that the undead do not make life. You have survived your Becoming and are now a vampire. That means you will never be a mother. Now, please do not wake me up with such hysterical fancies in the future. I suspect there's still a good solid hour of daylight I could have slept through."

If they had a fireplace, Elysia would have liked to grab a poker and hit him with it. "You have established how to survive, in your own way, very well," she sniffed instead. "That much I will grant you. But by your own admission, you have lacked female companionship. This issue would never have arisen before. So, once again, I submit, how do you know?"

"Really, Elysia, I don't know why you persist in bothering me with such a ridiculous argument." Acky closed his eyes and put the thumb and index finger of his outstretched hand on the lids, massaging them gently. "We are immortals who do not reproduce. There are some legends of elder Nosferatu creating initiates by letting them feed upon their own fiery blood, but I find these tales suspect, the vengeful products of frightened, jealous little minds."

"You are the one who is afraid!" Elysia was becoming agitated. "You are afraid of the knowledge given to me by my own body, afraid of becoming a father, and afraid because I can create this thing and you cannot." Acky rolled to his side and propped himself up on his elbow. "I am certain you are right, dear. I am afraid. I am afraid of you losing the skills for survival if you continue to dwell in such fantasy. Now, tell me of a single story you have heard of a pregnant vampire? You are being absurd. You are not pregnant." He reached out and patted her stomach with his palm.

"Acky, I am pregnant."

"You are mad. Mad! Perhaps you fed too much last night—it gave you odd dreams and addled your mind altogether."

"This is not 'mind.' This is 'body.' My body." She batted his hand away from her belly. "When was the last time you were pregnant, Acky von Hensel? How would you know how it feels?"

"Now you are being completely silly. Your monthlies will be upon you any instant; you are frothing like all women do beforehand. If you can concentrate enough to hunt, I am going to the Hinter Brule." He sat up and let his feet slide to the floor.

"No." If Elysia were one of the female clients of the Hinter Brule, she would have spat on the floor at this point, but instead contented herself with crossing her arms in front of her tender breasts.

"Madame's choice." He snickered, proffered a fake bow, and turned to storm out. As he strode down the street, thoughts and fears dueled through the skull of Acky von Hensel. *What if Elysia were pregnant? How could such a thing be? Of course he knew how such a situation came about, but for a vampire?* His face creased and darkened. This had been his first row with Elysia, and in addition to the tawdry typicality of a spat, he shuddered to think that she might actually be right. The possibility of companionship, fine. He was delighted to have found that with Elysia, but he did not think it was possible for him to become a father. His imagination flew—all of a sudden an adjacent crypt had to be turned into a nursery, to be stocked with a little ebony cradle trimmed with lace lifted from the priests' vestments. He smacked his palm to his forehead at the thought of having to thieve toys, little spoons, tiny shoes, bundling clothes and rattles.

Acky saw himself bouncing a little boy on his knee, and the youngster sticking its pink sausage fingers out from its own little black cape to take a bit of raw, bloody beef from his father's fingers and gum the scrap in his toothless mouth, eyes crinkling up in delight. "Bye bye, baby bunting. Daddy's gone a-hunting," Elysia would sing in the dusk.

It could not be. In the back of his mind, a darker demon grew: *what if the woman was right? What if she was with child?* This would mean that their coupling had made her so. This would mean he was not, not a —! An iron gate clanged down to trap that possibility in the deepest recesses of his mind. He would put a stake through that beast's heart before he ever let it roam the honest truth of his thinking days. Elysia was not pregnant.

Elysia was all sulked out. She did not want to apologize to that thick-headed man. There was no reason to suspect for an instant that he was right instead of she. Really, of all the nerve, to make such accusation regarding her sanity and be so coarse in general. They had fought like commoners, the sort of battle that ends in flung crockery or waste pots emptied out of windows onto fleeing men. If she could occupy herself more in their chambers, perhaps she would have, but there was no call for a great mopping and scrubbing. Well, there may have been, but even if she had been so trained, Elysia knew she did not have brooms and brushes and might as well not make it a concern. Maybe if she caught up with Acky at the Hinter Brule he would know where to get them some. It was a small thing, but this was their home, as it was.

She flopped down on the couch and put her feet up on the armrest. The mural of the bleeding Christ gave her a sympathetic gaze. "Really, my child," his aching brown eyes relayed to her, "If I can forgive all of humanity, if I can be sacrificed for all the world, my father's only son, then surely you can give the man who has been kindest to you in your time of need some patient understanding." She sat up and put her elbows on her knees, to return the mercy of his eyes. She was giving Acky an odd piece of knowledge. Many an ordinary man would take such news adversely, let alone a couple in their incomparable circumstances.

If she did go to the Hinter Brule, it would be for the company of her man. But if he was undead, was he also an unman? Someone had made her in the family way. She rolled her eyes up at the mural of the Messiah. Cases of maternity under different circumstances were rare, indeed! She enjoyed the adventure of roaming the darkened, dissolute streets of nighttime Salzburg with Acky, a show and a carnival at every turn, the cat and mouse thrill of the chase, the challenge of making herself invisible. The delight was in the pursuit, which reminded her of playing hide-and-seek with her brother as a young girl. Elysia discovered she did not need to feed every night. As long as she ate the simple foods that she knew from her childhood, all seemed right. Her stomach did not twist and cramp. Very well, then: she would join Acky, perhaps have a skip down an alley, or a particularly exhilarating leap from roof to roof. Maybe they would set silly tests for one another, such as stealing the keys from the belt of a sleeping nightwatchman. Elysia smiled to think of such foolish risk. If she had a child, such shenanigans would have to go. She braced against her knees and rose. Her heavy woolen jacket hung on a metal hook stuck in a crack between stones. She put it on then grabbed the three-cornered hat that completed her costume. Acky and she had immediately seen the wisdom of cutting her hair, for both disguise and mobility, so now a discreet ponytail covered her neck from nape to collar. It shocked her as much as the clothing, at first: her head felt so light. Now she was used to it, and it amazed her that women did not wear their hair in such fashion in the course of regular life.

Above ground, snow began to collect on Elysia's cap. The wide white flakes were floating like goose down, soft drifts accumulating on all the gravestones and ledges. She smiled to see Acky's 'backwards' footprints filling up with flakes. Extra candles glowed in the windows of the church. A childish impulse grabbed her and she reached up to knock the fluff from the spidery branches of the chestnut overhead. It was the first week of Advent and the bells in the church tower called the early rounds of celebration with their echoing tones, covering up the subtle scrunch of the snow beneath her feet. The air was cool enough to keep the snowflakes from being sloppy, but not yet so cold that it stung the throat and nose. Elysia puffed out small white clouds in the air before her.

They had hunted at the Hinter Brule Gasthouse before. Rumored to have been built when Salzburg was but a village of three goatherds and a cleric, it was never short of drunkards and lay-abouts, slack-jawed men and sloshed-eyed stumblers, weary and bleary after revels. Acky saw no need to make a difficult situation more of a challenge. Just as it would have been foolhardy to attack the young, strong, or sober, it would be equally foolish to draw attention to their crimes with some display of the legendary vampiristic…a gaping neck wound, for example. Each assault was orchestrated and camouflaged in such a manner that it looked like an everyday robbery, and the wound from which they, or Acky, fed, just an incidental stabbing in the course of separating an unfortunate from his wallet.

Acky would hunch over the paler whiskered figure on the ground before him in an alley and spit on the wound to wipe away any untoward smears or suspicious lip-prints from the limb of his victim. Then his hands would fly with practiced efficiency, checking belts for purses, waistcoats for wallets, pockets for coins, and if the kill looked street-wise, he would even make sure they had not hidden valuables in their shoes. Elysia kept watch at the alley's entrance with an inward sigh, resigning herself to the knowledge that despite his daily kindnesses and attentions, Acky von Hensel was not only a bloodsucker but also a thief.

For all its twisted aspects, their macabre routine had become precisely that to her: routine. Whenever she accompanied him on a hunt, she would wait with Acky for a likely victim, watch the wretch be seduced into a dark recess with the promise of money or liquor—greed clouding judgment was such a dense and constant fog that she did not know whether to laugh or cry—and then the "robbery" would ensue. Their pattern never varied. Once Acky had cut the gold hoop out of an Italian's ear, and Elysia flinched to see the lobe sliced like a chunk of sausage. This was the most gratuitous violence she could remember, but now the scene on the alley's paving stones made her draw in her breath with terror. Her chest tightened and her heart leapt in her throat so suddenly that she slapped her hand in front of her mouth to keep it from jumping out onto the street and shivering on the ground. The sudden witnessing of Acky savagely attacking an unlikely victim released any thoughts of forgiveness and love.

Acky held onto a beggar woman from behind. Her thin limbs dangled from beneath a shawl, light papery fingers alternately fluttering in the breeze, then curling inward with a spasm of protest. Her neck looked no thicker than Elysia's wrist, shrouded as it was by straw-like strands of hair that straggled out from an ill-used cap. The hat was sliding to the front of her face, but one revealed eye rolled wildly in its hollow socket, sometimes half-covered by a lid succumbing to the drug, the flap of skin then opening in the remaining wakeful wish to fight. Her frail arms swung like twin pendulums. She was bent over, pinned to Acky by one strong arm, her waist in the crook of his elbow. His left hand drew her shoulder back, allowing him a better angle to her throat. The woman raised her arms as if attempting to flee the horror siphoning away her life, but they flopped to her front again as Acky worked the crepe of her neck with animal avidity. Elysia heard a slurp from where she stood. The woman moaned.

Elysia stepped quickly and placed her back flat to the wall to see whether Acky would try to salvage anything from the pockets of this one. The corpse draped over his forearm, his free hand rummaged the skirts and emerged with a couple of coins. He threw them up into the air with a whistle and they landed in his palm with the dull clink that Elysia knew was copper.

She tilted her head back against the wall and closed her eyes to take in the cool air. Her companion was killing out of bloodlust without any ritual of respect or consideration, fulfilling no need except the one for blood, or so he claimed, not even selecting a victim who would have a full wallet. He dropped the broken figure of the woman to the pavement.

Elysia saw the father of her child as a monster, no pitiable unfortunate driven to take out of necessity, but a beast cruelly preying upon the weakest creatures with the brutal logic of the pack. But this was worse, those who hunt on four legs take what they need with what is available to them—claw and fang. Acky could have prevented the woman's pain and struggles, sending her off to sleep down a dark river before draining the irrigation of her veins. Instead, he relished her weakness and her terror, lapping like a fiend with a twisted grimace stained red above her throat. His will hungered as much as his veins.

Elysia felt shame in her own memory. She had been here before: believing what she wanted of a man and having the illusion shattered. Christoph offered her family salvation: a financially secure future, restored manor, and continuation of the line. Acky took her in when there was no one else in the world to shelter her, and she had chosen to see him as a loving guardian, no matter what twists and convolutions were in his life. Now, she had been proven wrong twice.

Was Acky always like this, or was this what happened to a person who "Became," in his terminology? If she completed this Becoming, would she also relish the chance to grasp a weaker being and tear sustenance from their throats? Would she hunch over the twisted form of a street child with the same wanton abandon that she had seen in Acky, shoulders bent inwards and eyes closed?

He squatted next to the corpse and scraped a pile of glimmering snow between his hands, moving his mouth from side to side over the melting flakes. He reached behind his head to unfasten the band that held back his hair, shook his head and combed his tangles with rough fingers. Acky leaned against his thighs and levered himself up with such a sudden stride that Elysia gasped and darted back out of sight. He must hunger yet, to move so fast.

She followed his swift shadow. He did not tarry near the Hinter Brule, but passed beneath the swinging pretzel sign that marked a bakery. Snow collected in its wooden curves. He walked to the back of the building, passing a rain barrel and a pile of bricks.

Elysia's hand flew to her mouth to quiet her panting breath when a young boy stepped out of the bakery toward a woodpile. The snow collected on his dark hair as he entered the small yard behind the baker's. He was there to tend the fires and learn a trade, heaving doughy oblongs into the oven with big flat wooden paddles. If the fires were not lit at once, the bread would not be done on time. If the fires were too hot, the bread might burn. Either way, the baker would beat him with the shovel used for scooping flour. A lad of nearly twelve, he was solid in a way that promised future strength. He blew on his hands and rubbed them together as he approached the woodpile, and then for the split logs. "One, two, three," he called out singsong, piling wood into his arms, and then headed to the fire.

Acky leapt from the shadows and swung a log with practiced elegance, holding it by its furthest end and arcing it down in a gentle curve. It connected to the boy's skull with a dull thud and he fell forward. The vampire grabbed the youth's ankles to drag him behind the shack. His body scraped a trail in the snow. Snow angels...children should make snow angels in drifts, not be food for monsters.

"Rudolf, the lies you tell!" Elysia jumped up from her hunched watch and flattened her back against the wall. She had been so absorbed by the villainy before her that she had not heard the approach of the bakers. She cursed herself in silence.

"But it is true, Adolf, I swear that it is: the woman had teats as big as cider jugs and she wanted me! It was like she was in season." The man hefted the air in front of his own chest to indicate the mass of the bosom.

"If it is true, then, why were you at home when I came to collect you instead of in the arms of this temptress? Hey ho, what is that strange one doing skulking by our building?" Rudolf pulled his hat from his head and waved it in Elysia's direction. "Hey, you! What do you want? What are you doing?" Elysia pulled away from the bricks, taking care to sway. People expected to see lone drunks wandering away from the Hinter Brule at this time of the night. It would do no harm to fulfill their expectations. She took some rocking steps down the alley and then disappeared with a purposeful stride. Before they could follow her, Acky ran from behind the shed, roaring and flapping his cape. The surprise worked: they jumped back in alarm and he eluded capture. His intentions had not been chivalrous, for he had not seen Elysia and had not run to distract them from her path. Instead, the only routes available for his own escape were either the path between Rudolf and Adolf, or an attempt to hide in the bakery and locate the exit there. *Always head for the more open space.*

The two figures stared down the gangway again, heads tilting towards one another. "What in the name of Blessed Sophia was that?" asked Adolf, crossing himself. Rudolf was about to speculate, but then they heard a low moan from behind the shed. The men hurried over.

"God in heaven!" Rudolf exclaimed, crossing himself this time. "It must have been the work of that monster. And the first was his lookout. Uli is all bloody—the man-beast tore his throat! Quick! You go get Herr Doktor Apfel!" Adolf took flight.

Uli? Uli, can you hear me?" Rudolf turned the boy's chin up to appraise the wound and shook his head. He could not apply a tourniquet at the neck. He should have sent Adolf for a priest instead.

"Elysia, Elysia, my sweet!" Acky burst into the catacomb's innermost sanctum and threw his arms around her before she had a chance to remove her coat. "I was the nearest to complete fear that an immortal has ever known! Three strong thugs, drunk and bellicose, almost caught me, but I scared them so that they almost filled their pants. I became the demon of their feeble imaginations, leaping and shrieking and flapping my cape." Here he held the edge of his cloak up over his face and whirled around. "Flapping my cape like a great bat so that they scattered in my path like mice before the crash of a hawk in the barnyard. Ho hey! Let us have a waltz to celebrate! Such a display—you should have seen it." He stepped forward to wrap her in his cape but she backed up to the bed before she could become encircled. Elysia angled her face to meet the gaze of the mural and then turned it back a quarter-arc to evaluate the figure before her. "I did see it."

His pupils were shrinking in the candlelight. He recovered his thwarted attempt at an embrace by converting it to a comradely slap on the back. "You followed me? Well done, my girl. You are truly a 'Creature of the Night' now. What route did you take?" Elysia said nothing. "Well, aren't you going to share with your proud teacher?" probed Acky. He crossed his arms and tapped his foot like an impatient schoolmaster. Elysia still did not speak but only raised her eyebrows and averted her gaze.

"And what was this 'it' that you saw?" he inquired. "It would be odd if we have different accounts."

Her feelings vacillated in all directions. "Murderer! I saw you torture and kill a woman and a boy, not some rich fat sinful drunkard from whom you could line your pockets, not from a knife wound, but at their throats like an animal!"

"Anything else?" Acky was smiling.

"Else?" Elysia fumed. "What you did tonight transcends the criminal. It was monstrous: a crime against God and man. How dare you!"

"How dare *you*!" Acky replied with eyes rolled, knuckles on the pelvis points of his breeches. "How dare you call me a monster when you, too, have drunk the blood of the living. How dare you complain of my thievery when you have placed rings in your own pockets, and have eaten the roots and lit the candles that I purchase with our spoils." He threw his hands in the air. "Such comedy! Monster calls a monster a monster. Too receive such indictments from my student—and what an apt pupil you were."

"No!" Elysia shouted. "I believed in your 'Becoming,' but now it is all revealed as lies...*lies*...an excuse for brutality. Your 'Undead' is just a story that you tell yourself. What kind of beast are you?"

"The same sort as you, Elysia: deny it all you like, but you are a vampire. You, like me, exist beyond the circle of ordinary mortals." Acky stood straight and proud. "Your true nature will not be denied. You were meant to hunt the nights with me, Elysia. Be a true predator, not squeamish about it."

"Predator or parasite? You are a common thief with ghoulish pretenses. I am ashamed that it took me so long to see through you. You have taken necklaces, wallets, purses, bracelets, pocket watches, clothing and even furniture from your victims, in excess of what you yourself actually need. You steal belongings, and you steal the most intimate belonging: liquid life, the blood of others."

Acky 'tsked.' "Now, Elysia, you have done none of these things? I thought we had just gone over this. Do you need me to recount specific evenings?"

Elysia looked at the floor. She remembered her first night out with Acky, the excitement, and the mystery of initiation. *The shame of it all.*

"And who in this life does not take something from another? Perhaps vampires are but more honest and boldfaced about it, but no more/no less a thief or a parasite." He traced the cleft in his chin with his index finger. "Who stole your heart, a naive girl with an isolated life of duty?

Christoph de la Violette, perhaps. And why? Not even for himself, but to fulfill the social ambitions of his mother. Now there is an ogress: are you safer in my company or hers, Elysia? Who has displayed more concern for your well-being? Who has helped you more? That woman used you like a trained dog, a little white one wearing a ruff that is required to stand on its hind legs and dance at tea. She used you to enhance her own status, or tried to. The only one who does not take from anyone is the hermit living on grubs and residing in the desert rocks, and even he takes his breaths from the air and must scavenge some creature to feed upon. Really, Elysia..." Acky's face was twisted in a sneer. "Tell me who *is* pure."

He did not give her a chance to speak but plowed on. "I can tell you who is *not* pure. Your first true love, Christoph." He put his hands together and leaned the side of his face against them, lids fluttering in the imitation of a swoon. "That in itself may no longer surprise you, now that you, with your own two eyes, have seen him running off with his whores. However, you may be surprised to know that he is engaged to remarry—and his first dear wife is not even cool in the grave." Here his hands parted and he slapped his own face. Then he looked up and saw Elysia staring at the mural, upper lip quivering.

"Oh, my child. I am sorry. This was not the way to tell you. It would be so frightening to lose you, my companion, my sweetheart." He stepped forward and put his fingertips on her cheek. "You are my ally, Elysia, my one and only. We are together to serve as one another's guardians: their ways are not our ways."

"You did not guard me, you took from me," Elysia choked through her sadness and looked away.

"Elysia, my darling, what have I ever taken from you? I have given you all my time, my home, my knowledge. Did I not take you in and shelter you when no other would have you?" His open hand cupped the left side of her face.

Elysia's emotions were sapped. She could barely shake his hand away. "You robbed me of my innocence."

"I rescued you," Acky said in flat, low tones.

"Liar!" she hissed.

"This is ridiculous! You can keep yourself warm this evening, Madame." He threw himself down on the couch and put his booted feet up on the arm, wrapping his cloak about him. "Good night." Elysia did not respond, but promptly blew out the candle and went to bed.

The next evening offered no resolution. She awoke to his slipping out and did not ask him what he had done upon his return, nor did he volunteer any details. He went straight to the couch and rolled over to sleep, rough snores echoing in the chamber. To wake him would have required acknowledging him, shaking his arm, touching him, so Elysia tried to sleep through it.

When he returned the next night, Elysia resigned to her station in life. Acky looked so out of sorts that her heart ached. His skin resembled a thin layer of egg yolk, damp and yellow-tainted.

"Acky, you look as if you have a fever."

"I appreciate your concern" he sniffed, "but apparently you have forgotten that you are speaking to an immortal. I would not be affected by any common malaise."

"Well, then perhaps you are afflicted with an uncommon one, for you are clearly not well. Acky, the veins in your eyes stand out like red rivers on a yellow map. You are covered with sweat, and I can tell from here that your tongue is coated."

Acky extended a hand into the aura of the candle's glow and shrugged. "It is nothing more than the light from tallow that confuses you. When was the last time you saw a healthy creature in the daylight, that you should know how one looks?"

"I see you all the time, and you are not your usual hale, albeit vampiristic, self." She leaned forward to hear his response.

"Elysia! If I have indeed changed, it has to be the final stage of the 'Becoming.' Yes! That's it—this is but the final stage of my transformation to a vampire. Look at me and see what you will become." His arms flew out, hands clutching the edges of the cape, spreading the black cloth to impersonate a bat. Now the theatricality struck her as pathetic. His eyes glittered. His glare turned sullen and she knew he felt rejected. As well he should, because he was. Elysia turned her face away from this madman of whom she was once enamored and shuddered to recollect her crimes. He let the cape fall onto his shoulders and strode from the room. The scuffed heel of his boot entering the passage was the last Elysia ever saw of the Vampire of Salzburg—alive.

Chapter XXVI

Father Ronalde

Elysia lingered in their chambers, eating the last of the bread and reading a novel that had been on the well-padded person of a victim the previous week. The story concerned a medieval Duchess, Eveline de Crequette, who lived in genteel poverty with the memory of her saintly father. A band of young hoodlums invaded her castle the week after Lent, and while they respected her person, they did not pay such heed to her limited larder and the dwindling family wine cellar. Their leader was a whip-lean falcon-eyed trickster named Yarrow. He paid her court, and helped her decipher the riddle embroidered in a family tapestry: "The treasure is the vine." The embroidered tableau showed a fenced garden with rose trees in bloom, loaded grape vines, a fountain, lovers on a bench beneath an arbor, a bear doing battle with a unicorn in the background, all above the cryptic legend on a golden scroll.

The heroine had always assumed that the words referred to the family vineyards. Their rolling rows, partially overgrown and run through with brambles and foxes, were her greatest inheritance. Yarrow followed the mistress of the house and sang suggestive ballads, winking broadly and playing the lute of their deceased beloved jester, the one-eyed Demetrio. In the end, she reveals the secret of the tapestry, and Yarrow deduces that the vine in the garden proper is the marker for buried treasure. His broadsword uproots the fragile roots of the ancient muscat despite her cries of protest, and beneath they discover a chest full of coins and jewels. Her patient love has reformed him, and they marry and live in quiet contentment with his former cohorts now knights, and new vines planted in the garden.

Burning candles to read represented a luxury, but Elysia needed the distraction waiting for Acky's return. The next night she went out and scavenged a meal from the garden of a nunnery. Taking from the church did not perturb her: they had offered her no sanctuary from the de la Violettes. Also, small farmers were more likely to have hungry dogs that roamed the yard and barked when she neared the fence. The leftovers from wealthy households were too rich. Vegetables from a garden and the slightly burnt loaves rejected by a baker were sufficient repast. The second night ended with her return to empty chambers.

When the sun set and dusk brought her waking hour, Elysia decided to check their regular hunting grounds despite her lingering suspicions that Acky had another hiding place where he sulked. He would always be thinking of back routes and paths of escape—of course he would have another lair. Perhaps a deserted family mausoleum like the one in which she had been interred, or the farthest cellar regions of a deserted castle. He was probably just trying to scare her. Nonetheless, she set out to investigate all their old haunts: the Hinter Brule, the Green Oak, the Happy Friar, and the unnamed dives that alternated with the bordellos on Gertesgasse. There was no sign of him on the eaves or in the alleys. She would have almost welcomed the sight of him brutally tearing the throat of a beggar woman, if only to know where and how he was. The prospect of living alone in the dark and scavenging what she could was a bit daunting. True, there was enough spoil stored in the walnut-wood chest in their chambers to allow her to live for quite awhile, but it would be a lonely living without even a deceiving partner.

How much had he deceived her? Was Acky a liar, or was his own mind clouded by this tale called 'Becoming'? Elysia huddled in an alley, drawing the cuffs of the oversized coat down over her fingers. She shuddered, and raised her spine straight against the wall, vertebra by vertebra, to steady herself. This was no time for weakness, but her mouth grew dry and her eyes became wet at the thought of a lonely eternity as a soulless ghoul cursed to wander the edges of human habitation and scrounge for food. She had not eaten, but still felt queasy. Elysia put her two hands over her stomach, fingers laced together. With a final pressing on her woozy abdomen, she shoved away from the wall and began to trot back to her home, following the little clouds of her visible breath. At the wall, she grasped a low-hanging tree branch to pull herself up, and hunkered with her feet braced in between the iron spikes before swinging over to land with a quiet rustle of snow-covered vines.

"So, what have you got there?" Elysia ducked behind a tree and leaned her forehead against the rough ridges of the bark for a moment. There were some men between her and the entrance to the catacombs. But how many? This was the last thing she needed. She took a deep breath and edged her face around the trunk to take in the scene before her. Three men huddled around the tinkers' plots, the untended, weed-clogged section of the cemetery with its broken stones where the paupers and other unclaimed dead were buried.

"Fancy girl!" One man stood upright to brandish a small, flat object over an open box at their feet. It glinted in the moonlight. "A silver hair-clasp made it past the deacon. And look at this work: all those little curlicues and flowers in the metal. Yes, I'll definitely be able to get a few schillings for this."

"Oh, the deacon doesn't stop to waste holy water on this lot. You know that, idiot. Well, would you be ahead selling it for a couple of coins or making your old lady happy, Louie?" The second man took the barrette from his bear-like compatriot and turned it over in his hand. "Christmas is coming up: make a good present to her and the 'thank-yous' may last all year, eh?"

He handed the trinket back to Louie, who slipped it into some hidden pocket beneath his cloak with a grunt. A third man stood on the far side of the box and scavenged about the perimeter of its length. His movements were quick and neat beneath the outstretched arms of the others.

"The wife has her Christmas present already and it's so big she doesn't know what to do with it." Louie grabbed at his crotch with both hands and bent forward, first standing on his left foot and then his right, and then squatting to waddle back and forth with his hands interlaced beneath his basket. The third man whistled and shook his head. The one who had spoken put his hands on his hips and threw his head back to chuckle. They laughed far more than the jest merited, as far as Elysia was concerned.

"So, Mauricio, is there anything else for us?" He got serious and stooped to raise a lantern.

"'Us?' It is *my* lucky night, indeed: I have found this wonderful brooch." His hands stopped their burrowing through the wrinkled garments of the frozen corpse and lifted a lump of yellow metal into the torchlight. Elysia gasped. It was the brooch she wore for her wedding, the family heirloom that she had assumed lost in the chaos on the day of her marriage, death, burial, resurrection, and flight from the de la Violettes'. Mauricio held the ornament to the three good teeth on the right side of his mouth and gave it a bite, cringing to test his tender bleeding gums as well as the metal. He held the pin up to the light again and turned it back and forth in appraisal. "Yes, this is the real stuff, soft and pure." His fingers closed around it and it disappeared into his pocket.

Elysia hunkered further back behind the tree: she stepped forward with the surprise of seeing her old jewels discovered and treated with such indifference. Her hand rested on the rough bark and she leaned her face next to it. The three figures cackled and muttered. A black cloak formed a rectangle on the snow past big Louie. The hair ornament fell in the center, followed by a shirt, boots, silver-buckled belt and small dagger. The half-clothed corpse curled at the grave's edge like a kicked dog. Its exposed skin was yellow and waxy, the skin of someone cut down by illness, not an accident striking a man of robust health. The muscles throughout his body had set as the mortar used to mend old tombs: his arms curled up throwing a half-punch of defense as he left this world, his face was frozen in a convulsion that revealed his jagged teeth, canines outsized and sharp, his eyelids peeled up to reflect the moonlight. It was Acky von Hensel.

The moment of recognition rocked Elysia. She lowered her head in mournful contemplation, jarred as it crossed her mind that Acky could not be an immortal vampire.

"It's too cold to dig another hole." Louie stood upright and watched his smaller compatriots work, stepping back as Mauricio and the talkative one grasped Acky by the bare feet, the other by his elbows, and hoisted him up to swing him, one, two, three, into the pit. "Let's go sell one of these." He spat on the pile in the middle of his cape, "and hoist some steins at the Happy Friar."

"Come now, Louie," Mauricio grunted, "give us a hand with these, at least. We can't leave a full cart in the yard." A body with only a thin cotton shift to protect it on its final journey was unceremoniously swung on top of Acky's remains down the hole. Another followed.

"Well, aren't we the perfect examples of industry?" Louie put his extended index finger beneath his nose and held it up in the air before letting his hand fly from his brow in salute. "If you are all such hard workers, you will not hear my idea that we just throw a couple more in here, cover them with some rocks, and then refill it."

"Oh, there'd still be a pile of dirt to spread about—do you think the priest will believe that we were gardening?" The talker snarled as he pulled the empty wooden cart away from the edge. A branch snapped on the path to the south of them and all three jumped.

"Speak of the devil," Mauricio giggled, "and his sanctified self appears."

Louie pulled the belt from the pile of dead-scavenged goods and flopped the corners of the cape over the booty in an untidy bundle, fastening it all together with the strap. Elysia crept further behind the tree, leaning onto the trunk with only one eye revealed. She reached out to pull the branch of a neighboring shrub in front of her. A tall man in long dark robes approached the gravediggers.

"Good evening, gentlemen." He greeted them without a sign of command or condescension. "I hope that the chill has not made your work too difficult this evening."

"Good evening, Father Ronalde. No, thank you, Father Ronalde," they chorused as one.

"Are there three in that grave?" He took a step nearer the edge. Louie stepped to block his view.

"Only three.,Father." He mumbled, almost tripping over a shovel and changing the count to four.

"Then your work here is done," said the priest, swiveling to face each man individually. "We need two more plots turned at the west end of the sixteenth row."

"Why two. Father? There was only one, the boy." Mauricio asked, leaning forward to let the cart's handles rest on the ground.

"Another one will be needed by morning. A young woman has taken ill with the same affliction as the boy—it would almost be a blessing if the Lord does not let her suffer through another day, and it looks as if this night will be her last." Father Ronalde looked at the ground, hands held in front of his chest briefly in a gesture of supplication. The men knit their brows and silently exchanged looks of dread as they imagined the horror of the corpses' demise.

"You will not indulge these superstitions," the priest sighed. "These legends are the devil's work. I have heard the whispers. Do not let yourselves be so fooled and distracted."

The talker shifted from foot to foot, hands clasping one another behind his back. "With all respect for our Holy Mother the Church, Father Ronalde," his head bobbed like a toy at the St. Eitrude's day market, "the boy's neck was bitten, I heard torn out, even. What affliction is that?"

Louie chimed in agreement, his lower lips slack and thick. "Yes— Rudolf and his brother saw the fiend. The beast changed into an enormous bat and paralyzed them with its cries. If they were not such fighting men, they would not have lived to tell the tale."

Mauricio shrugged and added his knowledge to the others'. "They were too late to save the boy, but watched as his skin melted to the sheen of the undead, Father. It changed before their very eyes, as a snake molts, but more like a melting of color. The lad became a monster. To be safe, surely the rituals of garlic and the stake, with the precaution of holy water, should be performed."

"If there is another," Big Louie's eyes rolled from side to side and he whispered like a child told a frightening tale too late at night, "that means that the fiend is still near. Father Ronalde, the Wolters saw a lone creature in the bakery's alley as they entered, and it fled. Perhaps there are two of them that roam and kill. This is when we must turn to the church against the darkness."

"And the church will receive you in darkness and in light, my son." Father Ronalde shook his head and let his forehead rest in his hand. "But there is no greater darkness than a life of fear and ignorance. Perhaps if you concentrate on interring these poor souls you will have less time to be distracted by such drivel." Snow crunched beneath his heels as he walked to the small chapel. Father Ronalde sat on the last step. A gargoyle laughed over his shoulder at the departing diggers.

"Yes, Father Ronalde." Mauricio oozed sarcasm. Louie tossed his bundle in the wagon along with two shovels, a spade, and a pick-axe. The talker grasped the handles and the wheels creaked as they pulled the cart west to dig more graves. All was silent. Elysia could see the big and small bear dancing across the heavens from beneath the bare branches. She stuck her head around the trunk. The priest seemed lost in a reverie, tracing the shapes of the constellations with an outstretched finger. He was still too close for her to risk going to the catacombs. She would have to wait him out. What if the sun rose? She could see the rich blue bleeding into the black at the eastern edge of the horizon.

"They have left. You are safe here." The priest let his hand fall to his knee but did not move his gaze. "You may come out now, my daughter: I will not harm you."

Elysia swung from the tree and leaned against the wall. She was discovered. Not only could she not return to her safe lair, she must flee. But to where? In her mind's eye, she inventoried all the other cemeteries in Salzburg. St. Teresa's was far too small, St. Rupert's was too near the market, there was no way that she could make it to the parish of St. Umberto the Congenial before noon, and she didn't even know if they had catacombs. Was she to run to a lone family tomb like the one that almost became her grave? Likewise, it was miles to the far side of the de la Violette mansion. That mausoleum, at least, was not an option."

Chapter XXVII
Eschatology

D r. Land affirmed that Dr. Tynan is on duty in the ER and is waiting for Claire and Stuart as they arrive. He takes the handles of the wheelchair and pushes her down the familiar hallway to the emergency room. After oxygen and stethoscopes and EKGs and intravenous fluids, Claire is deemed stabilized and Dr. Tynan takes Stuart out into the hall. He removes some reading glasses from his jacket pocket, puts them on, and starts scanning an open folder. "Stuart, I want you to have a look at these. They're the results from the Mayo Clinic. Test results indicate that your wife has porphyria and those tests give us a specific type. It is imperative that we start preventive measures at once."

"Wait!" Stuart's eyes widen as he looks over Tynan's shoulder at columns of numbers and percentages, graphs with wavering lines. "Type? There's more than one? And she definitely has it?"

"Yes. There are possibly seven varieties of porphyria. All can prove fatal under specific conditions. Once we determine the type and the aggravating factors, the condition can be managed. But, the management must be rigorous—vigilant, even. Stuart, you need to take charge of your wife's care immediately. The damage to her system is due to cumulative exposure. Things that used to be tolerable, innocuous, have now become toxic to her. We can halt the damage if we end the decline now—but major changes in her way of life have to occur, beginning today. She may require hematin injections in the future."

The next day Dr. Land repeats as much to Claire and Stuart together in the hospital consultation room, with Dr. Tynan in attendance. A chart of internal organs hangs on the wall. Dr. Land's silhouette lines up with the diagram. "I'm glad you're feeling better, Claire. I've spent many hours studying this enigma of porphyria, but I have also taken advantage of Dr. Tynan's astounding knowledge and deep wisdom." Claire remembered that Dr. Tynan's family also grappled with this age-old disorder. "I'm going to let Dr. Tynan do most of the talking."

Dr. Tynan cleared his throat and began. "If you want to get back to feeling well there are some changes that are going to have to happen, and now. These may seem drastic, but the overall improvement in your well-being depends on them. I'm certain this will prove adequate incentive."

"First and foremost: no sunlight. Many porphyriacs are what we call 'photo-sensitive.' The complicated reactions from the rays of the sun to porphybilinogens are being studied as we speak. All I can say right now is that the sun's rays are poison to you. You are going to have to cover yourself. Maybe even wear gloves.

"But, Dr. Tynan," Claire protests, "How could I permanently avoid the sun?" Reflexively, she looks out the window for the yellow disk. The blinds are half-opened, so that the light falls on all of them in sharp-edged parallel blades.

"At the very least you should wear a hat and sunglasses at all times. There is a specific sun-block which is suggested by the American Porphyria Foundation. It is the only one that works. I'll get the name for you. Even bright windows are to be avoided; with the right exposure, sunlight can pour through glass." Dr. Tynan moves to the window and finds the clear plastic rod that controls the angle of the blinds hanging like an icicle. He twists it, and the blinds close entirely, leaving the three of them sitting under the hum of fluorescent tubes. He adds, "Even your car's windows."

"To run from the sunlight? Really, Dr. Tynan, this is ludicrous. I will feel like a vampire."

"Well, there is something to be said for the nocturnal schedule. The problem of further sun damage would be eliminated. Please consider gradually spending more of your waking hours after sunset."

Claire slumps against Stuart. "I am, and have always been, a morning person. Is this course of treatment truly necessary?" Claire lets her face loll against the comforting warmth of Stuart's chest. *Why do I have to face such drastic measures? This one suggestion cuts me off from people entirely.* "I'll be as pale as a ghost. No tanning, no color to my skin, getting up when everyone else is going to bed. This is a complete reversal of order. I can't imagine living like this."

"Well, others do, for many reasons, and they eventually adapt." Dr. Tynan sits down and places his clipboard on his knee. Dr. Land interjects: "Yes, much of our society follows the daily conventional clock of '9 to 5.' However, think of how much more you'll be able to accomplish when you are rid of the condition, of the actual attacks and the constant distracting fear of them. You've gotten so much done *with* this handicap. In fact, your strength and tenacity most likely inadvertently worsened the condition. You've become accustomed to the illness and your stoicism to its symptoms allowed it to progress." She feels Stuart's grip tighten on her.

"An interesting parallel to the vampire legends is the information that vampires do not drink wine. This is so entrenched that Stoker incorporated it in his Dracula after reading Polidory's version of the legends, all transcribed from folklore. But I digress—you're not here for a literary history of the myths of the undead; we're discussing what we need to do to keep you well."

"Well, I don't drink wine—that often, actually. Just an occasional glass at the holidays."

"Very good. One less thing you won't miss, Claire, because some of the dietary changes may prove daunting. But first, here's a list of substances that commonly cause reactions in porphyriacs." Dr. Tynan lifts the metal clip at the top of his board and removes a sheaf of papers, passing it to Claire. "Where food is concerned, definitely err on the side of caution. If you have a reaction to something, eliminate it, on the list or not. This guide is really just a starting point, suggestions regarding some of the most glaring offenders. Be sensitive to your body. If you suspect any ill effect after eating something, eliminate it from your diet. Reactions include headaches, nausea, indigestion, fever, discomfort, even vomiting. Wheat may be a major contributor. Keep track of how you feel after eating wheat products. Dairy foods cause mucous to increase and may be particularly difficult for your body to process. If your body is as food sensitive as I suspect it might be, your new diet will be very simple."

"What do you mean, doctor? This is absurd. It sounds as if the treatment entails leaving the human race—no sunlight, no bread." Claire can feel her throat tighten with concern. She puts a finger beneath her watchband and circles the circumference of her wrist.

"It is virtually impossible to find processed food without wheat or dairy. Fast food, pizza, pasta—these are all eliminated."

"Am I going to have to eat like a rabbit?"

"No, not at all. As a matter of fact, I've been testing a new diet. It is exciting for me to be able to tell you it has proven to be miracle-working. Not only is it a miracle for porphyriacs, but I'm discovering it actually reverses Alzheimer's, Parkinson's syndrome, neuropathy, diabetes and many other disorders that are difficult to treat or cure. My own father has recently been taken off insulin shots and is maintaining an extremely even blood sugar level. I'll see that you get my recipes and I want you to report back. In the meantime, while following the diet, you must follow my previous instructions. By the way, I call my new diet 'The Royal Diet' since porphyria is known as the disorder of royalty. You didn't know that you are possibly descended from a royal bloodline, did you?" Claire's response was immediate, "As a matter of fact, I did know that, Dr. Tynan. I just learned that little tidbit of info when I studied and researched my family tree."

"Ahhh, Claire, no need for further explanation now, but you may have descended from the most royal family of all. In the meantime, Stuart, we need your help." Dr. Tynan looks up at Stuart sternly. "Making this many drastic changes requires the support of everyone in the household. It is inevitable that these radical adjustments will affect you. I want you to sit down together and work out the details."

"Details?" Stuart shifts from foot to foot. "I won't make Claire get a suntan."

"It's more far-reaching than that, Stuart. London is now a more appropriate vacation destination than Lisbon; Halifax over Hawaii, okay? Or if you don't go on vacation at all but stay home, perhaps you'll want to sit out in the yard and have a pizza and a beer. It seems only logical to invite your wife to join you. And if you do so, it will be a cruel insensitivity, because I'm sure Claire would like nothing more than to keep you company, but she can't. Continued exposure to aggravating factors will send her right back here with another attack. Serious nerve degeneration will result from the cumulative effects."

"But why is this all a problem now? Claire's always been such a dynamo. What brought it on?"

"Porphyria has existed for centuries that we know of—it tends to be most prevalent among people with Celtic backgrounds. I'll spare you the ethnographies of central Europe, but between tribal migrations and wars, that includes Germans, French and British, as well." Tynan gestures at an illustrated DNA strand affixed to the back door. The braid of red and blue globes winds over a rectangular chart—a Punnet square. Claire knows that it is used to track hereditary dominance or recessiveness for specific genes.

"In order to keep this particular explanation from getting technical all at once, I'm going to avoid the most recent research on 'jumping' and modifying genes and refer to the classic diagram for genetic probability.

Gregor Mendel used it for the pea garden at his Austrian monastery."

"Porphyria is a dominant gene. This means the likelihood that any of your three children has inherited it is fifty percent, so there is a very strong possibility that one or two of your children will also be porphyriacs. Now that we know to watch for it, the good news is that changing how they live now could help them avoid the sort of suffering that a more advanced condition such as yours entails."

Dr. Tynan stands up and walks over to the poster, using the eraser end of his mechanical pencil to trace the individual components of DNA—guanine, adenine, cytosine, thymine.

"Considering the increased UV levels caused by ozone depletion, both you and the kids are executing changes that would benefit anyone. However, in your case it's not a matter of some long-term gain but of your immediate survival."

Dr. Land wants to assure Claire he's been on top of things. "My own theory is that porphyria isn't rare…but an accurate diagnosis is, which I've been unable to give you all these years. When it appears inconsistently across a range of symptoms, doctors are not going to be on the lookout for it. Also, if someone's having a mild attack—too much sun, for instance—and goes to bed, the time away from the source of deterioration will make them feel better."

Claire tastes vindication. "So, this would explain why I arrived at our cottage every weekend feeling fine but was exhausted and so ill by Sunday?"

"Precisely, Claire. The entire perception of the sun as a cure-all and a source of beauty does not apply to you. Attacks will only be exacerbated by exposure." Tynan is leaning up against the genetic chart now and the DNA diagram circles his head. Claire smiles to herself, thinking it is a halo.

"Previously, there have been broad catch-all diseases. Attributing a death to 'consumption' could mean anything from tuberculosis to cancer. I believe that 'heat stroke' is a similar category, a way of labeling a set of deaths with similar circumstances that covers for the medical profession's lack of knowledge."

"Now Claire," Dr. Tynan continues, "there are other factors involved here which may precipitate an attack- the stress of illness such as the common cold, extreme emotional stress or physical fatigue.

Environmental factors could provoke an episode. Cigarettes, insecticides or weed killers come to mind. You are definitely going to need to protect yourself."

Stuart's body sags. "I'll say one thing. Even though this is a monumental blow to our lifestyle, it's good to know what this mysterious ailment is and that we can now fight it."

"Well, I'll say another thing," adds Claire. "Eeesh!.... However, I've studied this enough to know that all this would be my future."

Chapter XXVIII
Arising

She stuck her neck out further. Elysia wondered if the priest had eyes in the back of his head, for he turned in her direction and nodded. He grasped the cuff of his gown and pulled the sleeve down over his wrist. He swept a patch of snow away, uncovering the bare stone of the step to his immediate left. Elysia closed the distance between them with four long strides. She cringed when she stepped on a twig but shrugged with the realization that silence was a moot point. He smiled and inclined his head as she sat, in a show of approval and greeting, one that two comrades would exchange if their paths crossed on the road. She did not feel belittled.

"I am Father Ronalde. It is my vocation to listen to the troubled at heart," his clasped hands rested on his lap. His beard was small and as pointed as if it had been whittled, and his nose was likewise sharp. There was nothing unkind about his face, though: the sharpness suggested a spare efficiency; practical angles, not cruel. "If you wish to talk, my daughter, it is my duty to listen."

"Are you suggesting that I perform confession?" Elysia scraped the snow from the step beneath with her shoe.

"Nothing of the sort. However, if confession would lighten your soul, please do." Creases appeared at the outside corners of his eyes. "If confession would make you feel worse, please do not. If you would care to tell me of your adventures—and I beg your pardon, but your costume and your previous posture lead me to believe that you live an unusual life for a young lady—I would be delighted to listen. A simple conversation is possible, but if you do not want to be so personal we could start with the weather."

"I may have to begin with the weather, Father Ronalde, for I am out in the cold." Her words were slow. Elysia felt out of practice in her speech: it had been almost half a year since she had spoken to anyone other than Acky, let alone a man of the cloth.

"I beg your pardon, Miss?" The priest raised a finger to stay her sentences for a moment. "You have the advantage of me. If I may be so bold as to ask your name?"

"My name is stained with sin." Elysia drew a breath and her chest rattled. She could feel water in her eyes. She did not want to lose her dignity before this stranger, but he seemed so safe, so reassuring.

"Every human name is the name of a sinner. This is why God gave his only begotten son to absolve us. Christ said, 'Forgive them, for they know not what they do.' Now, my daughter, whatever has happened to you, I do not believe that you have betrayed the Savior."

"I have betrayed all that I believed to be good and right and Christian, Father." Elysia could not hold back the tears that trailed down her cheeks. "I was betrayed, left for dead and then called a monster. Perhaps you have heard some of my story. My name is Elysia von Eschenbach." She sobbed with relief as she told her tale: the courtship, the betrothal, and the misadventures among the decadent de la Violettes. Father Ronalde sat in quiet stoicism throughout her purging. He did not reprimand or demand explanation, but merely nodded at appropriate intervals, or offered a word of encouragement when she faltered, repeating whatever word she had said before her voice trailed off.

"And this is how you find me, Father," she concluded, rubbing beneath her eyes with her handkerchief. "Deceived by a noble, misled by a ghoul, and made pregnant, one would assume, by a man." She held her stomach ruefully, eyes cast up to Ursa Minor. The white points of the little bear constellation were less defined, and the ink of the sky had gone from black to indigo. Bird chirps announced the imminent sunrise. The spikes along the top of the wall and the crosses atop the tombstones became more and more distinct.

The priest placed his hand on top of hers and squeezed it, his own wet eyes filled with emotion. For now, at the end of her mournful story, he became aware of who she was—the baroness whose wedding and interment he had witnessed months ago. Then he stood up, not releasing her hand. "Follow me." He stepped in front of her to lead her up the steps. Elysia climbed three of the stone steps and then halted. As kind as this stranger might appear, there was still a scrap of fear in the back of her mind regarding his intentions. What if this forbearance was merely a trap? What if he was to have her seized by unkind monks and thrown into a cell like a common madwoman, left to fester on a bed of moldy straw? Perhaps what Acky told her was true, all the old legends: that the place of blessing was anathema to her now.

"Stop!" She wrested her hand from his in protest. "If I enter a house of God I will burst into flame. There will be nothing left of me but a pile of ashes."

Father Ronalde's brow furrowed with concern. "Did the touch of my hand cause you pain? Pins and needles? A fever? A burning sensation?"

"No, Father." Elysia answered, looking down at her shoes.

"And am I not a man of God?"

"Yes, Father."

"Very well, then." He clapped his own hands together. "We will proceed cautiously. If warmth of the least degree overtakes you, or any other sort of pronounced discomfort, we will turn heel at once."

Elysia stood on the bank of a river of doubts. If she crossed it, she would know for sure. To follow the priest would determine whether or not Acky had told her the truth. Whether he had lied to her intentionally or had honestly believed he was afflicted with some demonic condition was something that she would have to decide in her heart. She had already died once and lost life as she knew it in all aspects. If she died a second time perhaps she might know mercy and go home to her maker, or at least have the opportunity to perform penance in purgatory. She glanced at Father Ronalde in agreement. He took her hand again and placed his free one on the heavy wrought iron of the church door handle. The wood panels before them were covered with carvings of cursed souls flung down before the feet of St. Michael. A serpent with bat wings circled around the flailing bodies while angels overhead clasped their hands together and looked to heaven. Naked bodies stood in open graves awaiting judgment. The door creaked on its hinges. Elysia held her breath. They stood on the threshold. She closed her eyes as the crack widened before them.

The priest's hand squeezed hers. "Are you all right, my daughter?" he whispered. Elysia opened her eyes and gulped. "Shall we go on?"

She hesitated, and then raised and lowered her head in affirmation. The time to run was through. Her first step beneath the doorframe was as if she were entering an unlit cellar with uneven steps, or had to navigate a bed of hot coals and glass shards. He led her up the aisle with a warm, dry grasp. Two steps and then a pause, waiting for her to join him at the end of each pew. Elysia waited for an itching beneath her skin that meant spontaneous combustion. There was none. Soon, they were standing before the altar.

The ritual table was heavy with elaborate gold. The priest pierced the surface of the holy water with his hands. Fat candles burned low, reflecting orange on this puddle in the vestibule. A drop fell back in and made rings. Father Ronalde held his moist fingers before her and crossed the air in front of her chest. Elysia tensed, still half expecting a cross of fire to erupt opposite the trail of his gestures. None did. *Did vampires not possess an aversion to godliness? Or was she not truly a vampire?* Her eyes made the climb from her unsinged chest to the sharp, calm features of Father Ronalde. This time the fingers of his hand made a small cup, and he removed holy water in the portion of a generous soupspoon.

He took Elysia's hand in his, turning it over so the palm was concave beneath the ceiling of the chapel. A minute fall of fluid filled the creases of her hand. "Do you feel any pain, daughter?" His mouth was a straight line, serious, but not unkind. She looked at her hand to see if there was any bubbling or hissing from the water within, perhaps a trail of steam snaking up from the center.

The priest's wet fingers again committed their geometrics in the air. Elysia held her breath and closed her eyes. Her jaw was clenched shut. A tightness constricted her throat. Her hands were fists in front of her waist. A damp hand touched hers, first a fingertip, then four wet cylinders closing over her knotted fingers. "What do you feel?" Father Ronalde whispered. Elysia's eyes sprang open and stared at his hand on hers. "Nothing," she whispered. "It feels like water from the washing basin." Father Ronalde smiled and held her hand over the font, then gently forced it to the bottom.

"Is your flesh on fire?" The priest's voice was quiet and serious.

"If it were, this would put it out. You are certain this is consecrated? It is holy water? It is blessed?" Father Ronalde smiled and nodded. Elysia wanted to dance up to the altar but felt that such an open display of her joy would be too irreverent. She never thought she would be welcome in the house of her maker: for the last half-year she had believed she would burst into flame and crisp to a cinder if she crossed the threshold. She faced the table where they blessed the host, flesh of His flesh. She knelt before it and lowered her head to her clasped hands. A wave of joy rose up from the floor and filled her as a vessel until the liquid peace reached the top of her scalp. Elysia felt like she would overflow. She threw her head back and opened her eyes. A triangle of light fell on her face, a slice of color from the rising sun piercing the rose window. Her eyes were damp as she stood up and turned to present herself to the priest.

"I am alive, Father," she whispered, and then her voice sang out deep and rich, "I am alive!" She raised her hands to the ceiling and shook her body. The edges of the priest's mouth reached his ears. This was a moment they never would have predicted in seminary, and it was the closest he had ever been to God. He'd heard hours of confessions, blessed unions, baptized babies, delivered extreme unction, rite after rite, but never before had he been so certain that he had led a lost soul back to all that is holy. He bowed his own head in humility and thanks at God's blessings upon him: faith and patient kindness, his heart and his ear.

The woman curtsied toward the circle of stained glass, as if reintroducing herself to the divine. "I am the Baroness Elysia von Eschenbach." Her head faced the ground and then she brought it back up to face the rainbow shards of light, "And I thank you, Holy Father, for the blessings of this child." Her hands folded over her belly and she thought she could feel the pulse of the tiny heart within, echoing in her stomach like a drum in a cave. If she was alive, and indeed, the holy water did not burn her, then she had a child to replace the one destroyed by her illness. Her hand shook as she lit a novena for Mary. She knelt and bowed her head to the Mother and the Son, in turn. Soon she would have a child, and even if born in a manger, he would not be born in the catacombs. New life would begin in the warmth of straw and bread, not blood and stories of the undead. Her lips flew silently over the words of the "Our Father," and then she paused and spoke aloud to the empty church.

"You are my heavenly Father, but on this earth, your kingdom, my father was Ignatz von Eschenbach and my mother, Dorothea," her eyes overflowed and she continued. "Please tell Father he was right, that their lives will live on through me as he promised and predicted. It was the dream when he came to me. I understand now." Then another thought cast a shadow on her blessings: Christoph. He was not the father, but he was her husband. From one shamefulness to the other. The only important thing was her return to the land of the living and the continuation of the von Eschenbachs.

"Father Ronalde, if I am alive, then I am the bride of Christoph de la Violette. We must decide what is to become of me, the marriage, and, God's will be done, the child."

"I will help you any way I can, Elysia," he replied. "But for now, I have no doubt we will both be better prepared to plan your future after sleep and a meal—or a meal and sleep, whatever order you prefer." Elysia opened her mouth to protest but a yawn filled it.

"Sleep first. You are right." He led her back down the aisle to the door. Her eyes fought to stay open. She felt like a numb column of fatigue steered to the oaken threshold. Father Ronalde cracked the door and she suddenly recoiled, as if someone had tried to cover her with a sheet of flame. "Too bright!" she cried, pushing the door shut before the priest had it halfway open. She blinked at the dark panels of the door and closed her eyes even at the memory of the low-angled winter rays of the sun bouncing off the frozen white drifts. "Too much light. Too bright. My eyes..." moaned Elysia.

The priest blinked in consternation. All other myths had withered with their inquiry, legend and deceit disproved as Elysia received blessings and touched holy water. Why did sunlight remain a bane? He turned the question over in his mind and then decided it was far better to determine what light she could tolerate in the short term. They could take the underground passageway. He took a lit candle and her hand and led her to the side stairs. "Is candlelight also difficult for you?" he asked as they descended to the cellar.

"No, Father. Thank you," answered Elysia. They turned at the foot of the steps and he opened a plain unpainted door with its hinges mellowed to a verdigris patina. The candle illuminated a narrow hall ending at a wall that they reached in ten paces. First, a sharp right, then a turn to the left. They must be beneath the priests' quarters. Cobwebs laced the tops of the walls. "I am sorry, Elysia," said the priest. "These hidden rooms were constructed as a sanctuary, and while they offer shelter, they do not offer many amenities beyond that. I will bring you your own candles, wood for the fireplace, water, soap, and something to eat."

"Father Ronalde, I am truly blessed among women," Elysia crossed herself. "Last night, I was sleeping in the tombs, alone except for the dead and my curse, uncertain of the blessing in my stomach and the divine love of God." She raised her head to the priest "You have brought me home to my maker, and now you give me a home. I thank you." She clasped his hand and kissed it, repeating "thank you."

She made a home in the hidden rooms, enlisting Father Ronalde's assistance even in bringing items from her old chambers to the new. Elysia stole into the catacombs, blushing to gather up the candlesticks and cushions that Acky had thieved. She constructed a pile at the mouth of the tombs, and Father Ronalde even borrowed the gravediggers' cart to move it to her new quarters. Each day she discussed things with the priest: his holy instruction, that week's sermon, the intrigues of Salzburg's wealthy families, the questionable content of the performance at the playhouse.

She debated with him on personal and general matters. He said that she must eat more meat than she liked for the health of the child. Elysia complied. She said that the divine right of kings was legitimate and that any peasant who would presume to usurp something so ordained was no better than a heretic. Father Ronalde was tempted to point out that this particular noble was now a dependent on the charity of the church. Was this divinely ordained as well? Even in their sibling bickering, he could not be so unkind.

She asked Father Ronalde to pray for Acky, the father of her unborn child. They spent hours discussing Acky's imagined or deluded—but convincing—belief that he was a vampire.

The bulge of her belly grew with each passing week, the first swelling grown to the size of a peck, then a bushel that she was tempted to carry with fingers interlaced beneath. Father Ronalde blushed to see the miracle of each ordinary family unfold before him, yet this was the closest he would ever get to being a father of an individual instead of a flock. He could plant the seeds of faith and scatter blessings, but that was all. He brought her children's cast-offs from the collection boxes. "Some contributions to the poor are quite generous," he said as he set the folded little squares of woolens and tiny leather shoes in an empty cradle. "You would be surprised by the sort of things I find."

Elysia's cheeks grew even more red than her proximity to the fire would suggest as she recalled the personal collections Acky had scavenged from the inhabitants of the town. She hoped that the sewing she did for the church repaid this debt.

The snow melted. Father Ronalde brought her a tiny bouquet of crocuses to keep in a glass on her table. Sometimes Elysia felt like a prisoner in the chambers, so the presence of spring was much appreciated. A handful of jonquils followed. The weight of her infant brought languor. Soon it was Easter. She covered her features with a heavy cloak and joined the back of the congregation for a midnight mass.

Hundreds of white candle flames swam before her eyes. The voices of the children's choir echoed off the saints on the frescoes above, the same saints that greeted her as she floated away during the ceremony. This was the church where she had died, and where her father met his end. She clasped her hands together in grateful prayer, for this was also where she had rejoined the living. The child kicked and she reached beneath her cloak to place her warm hand on the side of the natal globe. The high notes of the singing carried her spirit up to heaven. Their praise and thanks were her own. The stone was rolled aside from the tomb and the disciples saw that Jesus had ascended from the crypt. Elysia von Eschenbach raised her tear-soaked eyes to the ceiling above and saw the painted martyrs lifting their hands to bless the flock below. She had been lost and now was found. She was risen from the tomb, and this Easter, she carried the blessing of the Lord.

Chapter XXIX

Truth & Madness

"The mundane and the miraculous are two sides of the same," Elysia von Eschenbach could not help but think as she ran the tip of her little finger back and forth across the forehead of her son. A year ago, she would never have believed she would be in a church again, let alone in a church holding her own child about to receive the blessing of a man of the cloth. She resumed listening as Father Ronalde began the Latin chant. Little Ignatz furrowed his tiny brow, as if he were a Latin scholar in miniature. Perhaps he was hearing an explanation from some world still within his range but long lost to the rest of them—to his mother, the two nuns who had tended her during her confinement, and even the priest. His newborn's eyes cracked open, bearing an almost milky coat. Elysia resisted the impulse to clasp him even tighter to her bosom as Father Ronalde cleared his throat. "I baptize thee, Ignatz Ronalde." His eyes flickered up to Elysia's and they both grinned.

Odd to choose a priest as a namesake instead of an ancestor, but she believed Father Ronalde was like a brother to her, and he had given her new life. "Ignatz Ronalde, the fifth Baron von Eschenbach, in the name of the Father, the Son and the Holy Ghost." His fingers finished tracing the path over the child's head. "May the Lord keep you and protect you. Amen." The priest lowered the missal and held it in front of his waist with flat hands. "For God so loved the world that he gave his only begotten Son, that whosoever believeth in him shall not perish, but shall have eternal life." Elysia's eyes welled, despite herself. Once condemned to eternal purgatory, she now faced life anew, and not alone, but with her own son.

Later, in the sacristy, the priest removed the thick cotton fibers of the papers from his sleeve and provided them for Elysia. "The solicitors were quite explicit." His nail drew beneath the inky scrolls of their names. "These documents are legal and binding in effect. If you still wish me to be the guardian of your son, we need only sign at the bottom."

"Do you still consent?" The young baron woke and emitted a thin mewling cry. Elysia lifted his head and cooed to him.

"I would be honored." Their names were joined in signature at the bottom of the script. *"This,"* thought Elysia, *"is the best relationship I have had with a man outside of my family. He is my intimate without ulterior motive, and he is so completely of his word that he is willing to document it."* Once the ink was dry, he folded the sheaf and escorted Elysia back to her chambers.

Her room had been transformed from a drab monastic chamber to a warm and distinctly feminine abode. The stark straw sleeping pallet was replaced by a mattress. A carpet covered the bare flagstones of the floor. The brocade settee had been salvaged from the catacombs, given a thorough airing, and was waiting for its occupants in front of a friendly fire. Elysia moved aside the wedding gown draped over its arm and sat down next to Father Ronalde with little Ignatz at her chest. A skein of embroidery floss and a small ridge of pins etched one sleeve of the dress.

"You are not one to waste time. Are you repairing the dress out of your preference for order or for a special occasion?"

Elysia blushed, "Indeed, Ronalde. You are as perceptive as you are kind. I could not have chosen a better guardian for my son. I want my son to be raised in human society as the young baron he is: therefore, I must return to it."

"Are you certain of your welcome?" Father Ronalde wanted to be as kind as possible about the likelihood of Elysia receiving any sort of homecoming. First, she had no home to come home to—it had become Christoph de la Violette's, and, secondly, her only surviving relative was imprisoned. Far too much was at stake for too many to allow a gentle acceptance of her return.

"Yes. I am certain that I will *not* be welcome. Whether or not Odile de la Violette would greet me with open arms is immaterial. I know better than to expect a heartwarming intimate reunion with my husband. This is for my child, for Ignatz." The baby had quieted down, so she placed him in his cradle, first moving aside the counterpane embroidered by Sister Elizabeth. Little teal and blue flowers wreathed its border, each with a center of yellow French knots. So much better than violets. Elysia sighed and pushed the thin, dark cowlick back from his forehead. "The next Baron von Eschenbach must receive what is rightfully his. I will not raise him as either a ghoul or malcontent. He should not be hidden, and neither of us should have to impose upon your already considerable generosity any longer than necessary." She sat back down on the settee and gently rocked the cradle by putting the toe of her shoe beneath its curved edge.

"Elysia, you're dead to these people. They will prefer it if you stay that way. There might even be a chance they will make sure you become that way if you display your current condition." Father Ronalde stuffed each hand deep in its opposite sleeve. "Your son is a blessing from God: you and I both know this. However, it does not mean that a court of law might not call him a bastard. Without legitimacy, it is uncertain whether he could inherit the lands."

"Possibly, but technically, I do not exist, so how could I have a bastard?" she countered in defense.

"An intriguing conundrum. May I suggest that you approach this one step at a time?" He warmed at the memory of her timorous foray into the church many months ago. "I am not certain you want to begin your challenge to society with a child of questionable parentage on your hip."

"I know it may sound foolhardy, Ronalde, but my options are limited. In order to provide for young Ignatz and restore our estate, I *must* be accepted into society. This is not a matter of my vanity. If my survival were the only issue, I could thank my Maker for his forgiveness. I could return to the land of the living, enter a convent, or, with your generosity, stay here and meet my expenses through embroidery or other fine piecework." Elysia's expression grew somber. "My mother thought it unwise that anyone reach maturity bereft of some practical skill. However, my existence and subsistence are not the issues. I must provide for my child, and that means I must establish myself in my open identity, daughter of the late Baron Ignatz von Eschenbach and wife to Christoph de la Violette."

"Why must it be day or night with you always?" Father Ronalde closed his eyes and rubbed his brows together with the thumb and index finger. "There are myriad possibilities if you could find a sponsor to reintroduce you, perhaps, or if you could accept a life of reduced means within the church. The boy would be educated by the Jesuits, and there is no finer learning available for young men throughout Europe."

"Such resignation would be to concede defeat to the greedy and unjust." Elysia's jaw and constitution stiffened. "I was put up for auction like so much chattel, an unfortunate necessity,but we both know that the wealth of the de la Violettes was the factor that rendered them attractive as a family to 'freshen the bloodline.' I was taken advantage of, and the child that should have been cherished was used as an instrument of matrimonial blackmail. Once they were assured of receiving both land and title, I was paraded around Salzburg like a circus freak for the appeasement of that woman's avarice. As long as I am alive, which I now know that I am, and not some cursed wandering ghoul, my purpose should be the return of the lands to my son, and the guarantee of his rightful place in the world." Her breath was quicker.

"Very well, then." Father Ronalde settled into the couch. "What is your plan?"

"I thank you for your confidence and your information, Ronaldé: I recall that Christoph is engaged to marry again, of course to a contessa. Odile de la Violette will not be able to resist the opportunity to have a lavish celebration and invite everyone who she perceives as her superior in birth. Rene's roses will be gilded, the fountain in the courtyard will run with champagne, an entire flock of swans will have their wings clipped and be placed in the fountain, she and her daughter, Marie-Ange, will be packed into gowns more ornate than the filigree on the mitre of the Pope himself, and every surface will be garlanded with wreathes of those forsaken violets. Countess Lydia von der Vogelweide will be Christoph's new bride. All of Salzburg will be in attendance. I must re-enter society with a large and prestigious audience. If I approach them individually, it is entirely possible that I would be killed on the spot, if not with Odile's bare hands. Nothing must be permitted to interfere with that woman's social ascension," Elysia's body dances with nervous restlessness.

"Perhaps people will want to know what happened to you, that you could be mistaken for dead and falsely buried." The priest rubbed his dry lips. "People will not calmly accept that you have returned from the grave as from a pilgrimage to Lourdes or a retreat to the spas at a mountain spring. Some explanation will be in order."

"People will want an explanation, but people do not always get what they want in this life." Elysia's eyes rolled to the ceiling. "If anything, I should receive abundant and witnessed public apologies, elaborate rites of atonement, to make up for being so unjustly and publicly used. The la Violettes have been using my name like a ribbon, some banner draped over the chest of the cheese princess at the farmers' festival in the spring." She sniffed. "Their outrages consigned me to a life with Acky von Hensel and the atrocities I experienced, the trespasses, literal and moral, with this man of the catacombs. I am blessed that the mercy of the Lord is infinite." Here she bowed her head and crossed herself, but then raised her face to continue in defiance. "I will explain what may have caused my 'death' when Odile de la Violette explains why she was in such a hurry to bury me alive."

Father Ronalde's teeth shone through his beard. He had to grin with joy at her resolve and conviction. The gift of her son Ignatz also brought with it a strength, an inner iron that had been tested on the forge of the last year's travails, a purification for the purpose of regaining what was hers and protecting her son. "You may need some help, of course."

"I will have many favors to ask of you, adding even more to my debt of gratitude at your kindness. Ignatz should meet his Tante Sophia, his only other living relative. If I am attacked or shoved over the balustrade at this engagement reception, at least he will grow up with family. Also, I must know who is attending this grand function, the public celebration of my usurper. It will be most helpful to know exactly who is in attendance, and may affect my plans. Finally, I will need you to guard my child. Tante Sophia is not a young woman. Whether they turn on me immediately, or there is some ongoing campaign against myself and the comfort of the child, any threat to him makes me want to weep with outrage." Her eyes were iron, as far from weeping as any Father Ronalde had ever seen. "On this final favor, I must request your most solemn oath. Nothing is more important to me than the safety of my child."

The priest looked at the floor, weighted with the knowledge that this duty was a gift of God, a chance to know the fundamentally human obligation of being a father. His gaze lifted to Elysia's face. "I swear it," he announced, his head giving one nod.

A week passed, and then another. Elysia attended to her wardrobe as the date of the gala drew close. She repaired the lace, and scrubbed the last traces of catacomb dust from the bodice. She re-gathered the draped cuffs, and loosened some seams at the torso to allow breathing space for her fuller maternal figure. The gown was indeed glorious: she considered of the possibility that the de la Violette's fortune and acclaim was not entirely undeserved—they knew how to make a dress, or at least how to find the people who knew how. She spun around and arranged the skirts from the nave of pleats at a bustle in the back, head straining to see the folds. Father Ronalde searched a week for a mirror, finally finding one in storage quarters in the retreat section of the convent. Such totems of vanity as full-length mirrors were not commonly requisitioned by priests, but no one around St. Michael's was going to question his requests. Elysia turned in profile and swung her arm back and forth to admire the fall of the lace. This was not a matter of decorative frippery: she was dressing for combat. To appear lovely, if possible, and thus garner sympathy, but also to wear the wedding gown and remind people of her final appearance with the de la Violettes. She studied her reflection in the glass, rising from a curtsy to her full height, fingers curled into one another at the base of her ribs.

"It would be wasteful for such an exquisite gown to be displayed on only one occasion," she considered, turning to examine her profile on the other side. "Odile de la Violette's attention to detail should not be so wasted."

"Elysia?" The priest's voice was on the other side of the door. "Elysia?" he asked again, rapping with his knuckles against the wood. "There is someone here to see you." The door cracked open and in stepped Tante Sophia. Elysia was stunned. Father Ronalde had told her that her dear aunt was still alive, but seeing her proud, warm flesh was an entirely different matter altogether.

Seeing Elysia standing before her, resplendent in the gown she had worn on her wedding day, caused the old woman to lean on the doorframe for support. Father Ronalde wrapped an arm around Sophia and sheltered her as she sobbed. She straightened and then tottered forward several steps to fling herself upon Elysia's neck. Her body shuddered, and then she took a breath that stretched her ribcage as she began to speak.

"Elysia, Elysia von Eschenbach, my darling child, let me hold you!" She kissed Elysia's cheeks and held her face, stepping back to scrutinize her before she embraced her again. "My child, my nearest to a daughter, I did not believe them. I did not believe them! I tried to keep them from burying you."

Elysia held her aunt as she guided the weeping woman to a chair. Tante Sophia wiped at her cheeks and beneath her nose with a yellow scrap of fabric. "I know of the perils of the blood. I knew that you were not dead. I was not going to let them bury you alive. I would have sooner wrested your body from the coffin, had I been strong enough, and flung myself inside it to be buried instead. Oh, my sweetheart." Tante Sophia wailed again and clasped Elysia's hands in hers.

"It's all right, Tante Sophia, it's all right. We're together now." Elysia knelt at her aunt's side and leaned up to stroke the woman's hair.

"My child, I was kept in a prison called a convent, bread and water to eat and a straw pallet to sleep upon. It was not to be believed. Prayer and meditation are good, but I never took the vows to be a bride of Christ. My every prayer was that you had somehow managed to free yourself, that you would have a miraculous recovery and escape. Elysia, I feel like a failure. It is all my fault for not having watched you more closely to begin with, or looked after your health right before the wedding. If there was any way I could have escaped and helped you...but the doors were barred; the locks, brass."

Elysia consoled her aunt. "I know you would have rescued me if you could, Tante; do not cry. That Violette woman set thugs on you; nothing would be allowed to inconvenience her plans. Here, you must meet someone. I have a surprise for you." She raised the woman up and rotated her so the cradle fell into her line of sight. "This is your nephew, Tante, my son, Ignatz Ronalde von Eschenbach." Elysia gathered her skirts and knelt by the cradle, scooping Ignatz out with her hand beneath the soft dimple on the back of his head. She balanced him on her forearm and then loosened the blanket that wrapped him in order to expose a tiny hand. She let the four small fingers grasp one of hers before she lifted the child up to Tante Sophia's embrace.

Sophia crumbled with joy. "This is truly a gift from God." The child was shaken slightly by her heaving arms. "And you named him for your father. Oh, the Baron would have been so proud—a grandson, and a continuation of the line. Who is Ronalde?" Elysia's eyes directed her to the priest, who bowed by clasping his hands in front of his cassock and inclining his head.

"Your servant," he said. Tiny Ignatz opened his eyes to his aunt's sobbing and joined his cries with hers. She quieted, but the child's yowls continued. Tante Sophia rocked back and forth, patting the baby on different parts. Suddenly she whispered to Elysia, "Is this priest the father?"

"No, Tante." Elysia reached over her aunt's arm to stroke her son's red cheek with the back of her forefinger. "Ronalde is a godsend, a lifesaver, and this child's namesake, but his father is dead. Her aunt leaned forward and brushed the tip of her nose to the baby's crown, inhaling a lock of down. "I will have to hear all about him," insisted the great-aunt. She sat up straight and the baby gurgled and closed his eyes.

"And you will. But first, we must regain for Ignatz what is ours from that accursed Odile de la Violette."

Days flew by as they prepared for the momentous event. No debutante had faced a ball with greater anticipation. Elysia may not have had minions scurrying to lace her corset or press her gown, plait her hair or find her matching gloves, but Tante Sophia and Father Ronalde buzzed with the energy of a servant army. In order for Elysia's plan to work everything would need to be in order.

If Tante Sophia flitted and fluttered, as nervous and erratic as a butterfly that has dipped its spiral mouth in absinthe, Father Ronalde displayed his vexation only by wringing one hand with the other. Elysia wanted to look impeccable, not only to garner sympathy through admiration, but mostly to create the impression of utter normalcy. This was a challenge, indeed, appearing after a year's absence after a supposed death and burial, but she would not let any aspect of her appearance indicate the mishaps and disasters of the last year. Only with the infant did she let her steely visage drop, for shortly before the requisite hour of departure for the ball, radiant in her refurbished wedding gown, she patted the child over her shoulder. She listened for the soft air bubble, and then held him before her, hands wrapped around the fragile torso, and bobbed him up and down. "My little dragon," she whispered, and rubbed her face to his. "Blood of my heart." She chanted the words of the family legend like a nursery rhyme, but she repeated them at a slower cadence. "Blood of my heart. Heart of my life. You are the life of my blood."

She pursed her lips and blew like a trumpet against the pudding dome of his stomach. Ignatz gurgled and squealed. Elysia turned her head and put her ear against his chest. His little heart thudded. Elysia remembered her father saying that each creature had a heart the size of its forepaw, so for humans it would be a hand, a heart the size of one's fist. She wondered if the baby's heart was the size of his little fist, fingers curled around her pinky finger, working so hard, or if the heart was larger and to be grown into, like his head, almost a quarter the length of his body. She smelled the warmth and milk of his skin, the waxy scent with a trace of the eiderdown that he slept in.

There were three short, sharp raps at the door. "Elysia, Elysia, the coach is here!" warbled Tante Sophia.

"Thank you, Tante." Elysia put the child down in the crib. She straightened the sleeves of her overdress and collected her gloves and her fan. Her gloves could have been gauntlets, and her fan, a sword. Elysia was entering battle to defend everything she knew and loved, to reclaim what was hers, and to secure a future for her son. It would be much more interesting for her to arrive at the de la Violette's in a chariot with wheels of fire, but the hired coach would have to do. Every detail had met with her attention. The coach was to be respectable, but not ostentatious. Her entrance would be gripping enough.

Tante Sophia knocked on the door again. "Yes, it is time," Elysia said to herself, and then opened the door and followed her twitching aunt up the narrow stairs. Father Ronalde, resplendent in his hand-tailored woolen cossack, waited for them at the door to the courtyard. The complement of finery displayed by both him and Sophia was not ignored by Elysia. She tilted her head in humility at the honor, and said, "I will not fail you."

Instead of escorting her to the carriage, Father Ronalde locked eyes with Elysia as he reached for her hand and coaxed her to be seated on a nearby bench. His command was explicit, "Elysia, sit."

"At this juncture, Sophia and I believe it will be an important aid for you to learn the truth." He continued, "Our fine trappings are less to give you a rousing dispatch for your imminent journey of madness than to herald the magnificent truth I am about to relate. Sophia was at his side, smiling and nodding in agreement.

Elysia, as guileless as the child she had just kissed goodbye, sat speechless.

"It is time to treat you as the mature woman you are." He plunged his hands into the pockets of his elegant new vestment, which the nuns had crafted with such skill. He proceeded to pace back and forth, all the while delivering a soliloquy.

He began, "Tante Sophia and I have had ample time these past few days to converse and thereby compare notes. She has divulged plausible historiography which reinforces my own revelations of discovery. We believe the time is right to inform you of the secrets of your heritage. My words will no doubt shock you but we believe this knowledge will shore your resolve for the undertaking on which you are about to embark. It will supply you with a purposeful objective in life. Reasons for God's guidance will become clear to you as you venture forth."

Elysia was frozen by Father Ronalde's demeanor. Something remarkable was about to happen. The quizzical look on her face softened as the magic of the moment permeated the air. Sophia, to Elysia's wonder, prevailed at remaining immobile and silent. Her lovely face, that of an elder lady, was lined with the soft creases of age. Sophia's peaceful countenance mirrored her thoughts: *The secret is out. At long last, Elysia will now be privy to the mystery of the dragon...but only if Father Ronalde will calm himself.*

Father Ronalde searched the courtyard with his eyes in the hope of finding the appropriate, sensitive verbiage with which to deaden the blow from this treasure-trove of new information. Finally, he threw his hands into the air, yelling "Saints preserve us; there is no easy way." He shifted position, stood still for a moment, then stated professorially, "You are a special human being, as you are descended from the greatest king of all. It is true...but the greatest secret of all eternity is God's intellectual interjection amidst the march of humanity. Solomon, David, Moses, Noah, and yes, Jesus Christ—these are exceptional beings who procreated a higher intelligence. Jesus was the epitome of this endeavor."

Yes, Jesus. At this, Father Ronalde's knee bent in genuflection, and his hand marked the sign of the cross. He murmured a respectful "Yes, Jesus Christ, our Lord."

Elysia allowed the shock to sink in with gradual acceptance. "You are my priest and trusted friend. You would not, I know, lie to me."

"Oh no, Elysia, hear me out," he continued with the same soft voice. My theory is reinforced by secret Church documents to which I have had access. It is based on empirical knowledge of the Merovingians, Carolingians, and more recently, the Conversos, Marranos, and New Christians. Sophia has added fuel, fire and solid alloy to my own findings. This lineage has suffered beyond comprehension. My very own family of priests initiated the dreaded Inquisition. The Jews of the Conversos were the true Christians, as they were the purest-of-blood descendants. And Elysia," here he stopped in front of her to emphasize his point, "thus was borne your physical ailment of appearing to be dead while still truly alive…in some…some *suspended* state, only to return to life, for the most part, unharmed.

The effort to keep the bloodline pure for generations produced physical anomalies. The resulting "risen" body would be shunned as a ghoul, a vampire…and the solidifying fear was used to sway the masses. Concocted stories of the undead promoted terror of the royal lineage of Jesus Christ. My beautiful Church was corrupt during the Dark Ages. They wished to retain the dogma that Christ was unmarried. But Elysia, it's obvious he did marry. You are a result of that heritage. Oh, but now I'm rambling."

Father Ronalde, having finished his explanation to the best of his ability, stepped back and crossed his arms, surveying Elysia's response. "It must now be apparent to you that there are no real demons in this world and that is why I was not afraid of you in St. Michael's Cemetery many months ago.

If this paradox of Christianity and former belief were a truism, then Elysia accepted it as a blessing. And she had been assured of truth by her friend and confidant, her priest—the one who saved her life. She must learn more upon her return from the ball…if God would allow her to return. "But Father," Elysia could not wait to ask, "why would you continue as a priest if your beliefs have been altered?"

"I cannot leave." He touched her shoulder with the gentleness of the ewe nudging her baby lamb. "It is my calling; my devotion is steadfast. Were it not for my beloved Church, I would not have received such a profound education. The many posts to which I have been relegated have allowed me to assess and assimilate much information. I must support the sanctity of this spiritual seminary. God did not show me these signs without wishing me to work for peace and love among mankind. He sent me you, didn't he?"

Sophia could not contain herself any longer. "It is true, Elysia," she blurted, rushing to her side. I have seen them—the holy relics, in their resting place—the Holy Grail, which is the fossilized womb of Mary Magdalene, the Ark of the Covenant, and the Tablets of the Ten Commandments. These are the secrets your father, Ignatz, wanted to pass on to you. Peter saw them as well. They are magnificent, Elysia."

Sophia's exultation turned to rapture as she signed the cross while genuflecting.

Elysia rose from the bench not at all sure she could stand. The three of them formed a circle as Father Ronalde prayed. Elysia, being empowered, broke away. "I must go. My timing for arrival at the ball is crucial."

Father Ronalde took her hand and helped her into the carriage. She kissed his cheek through the open window as he shut the door. The brass lever on the exterior clicked with pressure, and then he placed his hand over the sill and sought her gloved fingers in the darkness. He clasped them together. "Be careful..." He meant to say "Be careful, my child," out of reflex, as if addressing one of his parishioners, but there was no way he could call such a woman 'child,' even in blessing. Instead, his blessing was in the form of encouragement. "Go, my daughter, with love and purpose in your heart. You must regain your rightful place in life, to carry on God's work. Godspeed, and God's blessing go with you.

"Watch after them." Elysia gave Ronalde a staunch grin. She continued, "I know that they will be safe in your care."

"Oh, darling child!" Tante Sophia clambered up on the running board. Elysia leaned forward and kissed her on either cheek. She did not wave good-bye but sat straight against the unpadded leather covering of the bench. "Hie!" called the coachman to the horses, who snorted and took tentative, resigned stamps on the paving stones of the churchyard, but then gave into the rhythm of motion and jerked to haul the carriage out into the night.

Chapter XXX
Vampire????

The days speed away from Claire after the definitive diagnosis from Dr. Tynan, like time always does, but they are falling away in even larger chunks as she rearranges her life to suit her new regime. She attends the races swathed from the sun, slathered with sunblock, and carrying a parasol. At first she feels ridiculous but soon realizes that if this is what she needs to do to survive, a bit of discomfort or perceived oddness is no great burden to bear. What small minds judge things only by appearances, anyway? But the changes from family routine are much more daunting than the quizzical glances from strangers.

August comes and goes without additional trips to the cabin. September, she plants bulbs at dusk, saddened by the thought that she would not enjoy the blooming of the daffodils or stark pride of the tulips through the spring in the sunlight. The shortening of the days distracts her from her new limitations. Besides, there are all the dietary changes to consider. Claire becomes fully acquainted with the health food section of their local grocery store. Organic vegetables—the contaminants in conventional crops could be an irritant to porphyriacs—chopped up and steamed with lively herbs. It's not the sort of dish that she could have sold the kids on, but it will do very nicely for her now and they'll all be the healthier for it.

Thanksgiving, she makes a wonderful turkey, for which she receives endless compliments. Dr. Tynan's new diet is a resounding success and at Christmas the holiday is celebrated without the usual cookies, cakes and pies. Claire devises creative recipes for treats and each is delicious. She was never one to imbibe on New Year's Eve anyway, but the festivities seem a bit more somber with the added explanation of why she cannot. Everyone is supportive and understanding, though, so the changes pass into their lives with less difficulty than she anticipated.

She begins to cherish the quiet late hours alone and puts them to as productive a use as her old private hours before dawn. Most importantly, she is feeling absolutely rejuvenated and has no more attacks. Soon it is summer again, and Richard is starting his circuit of races.

"Claire," Stuart intones, "I can't help Richard set up a paddock space today for Saturday's race. I have to supervise the final details on the Thomason account. Could you please go for me? I might not even be able to make it to the race itself."

"Oh, really, Stuart, couldn't you have planned ahead?" Claire knows that running errands and directing traffic in the increasing sun is something she should avoid.

"I'm sorry, dear, but they really dropped the ball on the technical aspect of the report and we can't possibly release it to the client without my review. I may be there all day." Stuart leans back in his chair and scratches the end of each armrest. "I don't mean to let you down, but I know that you'll be happy to help Richard. If you wear your protective clothing, I know you'll be fine."

Claire is nervous about so much time outdoors in the daytime. "John, could you come along and help?"

"Sorry, Mom, not today or this weekend." Her son takes the last plate from the dishwasher and places it in the cupboard. "Baseball practice." He steps out of the kitchen, squints, adjusts the bill of an imaginary baseball cap, and then squats, swings an invisible Louisville slugger, and makes a knocking sound in the hollow of his cheek. "A home run! Quick, to first!" He raises his fists in the air and trots upstairs. Claire sees him wink at Stuart as he jogs by.

She looks at him with her head at an angle "You are certain neither of you can make it?"

"Absolutely no way. All tied up today. Come on, you could stand a break from your old bear of a husband." Stuart pulls himself up to kiss the top of her head, then rubs his cheek against her hair. "I know that you won't let your little brother down. You can tell him I'll be out there next weekend and I'll change the oil in the tow trucks if he wants me to. I'll do any little grease-pit monkey job that he can come up with. Next time."

The drive passes more quickly than she expected, just Claire and her thoughts and Debussy on the radio. Corn has barely broken through the fields; ankle-high green shoots stripe the fields like corduroy for miles around. She sees a white horse in a pasture along with a swaybacked bay and a young Appaloosa and remembers the childhood rule, "See a white horse, make a wish." She and her sister Helena used to squabble for wish privileges if they passed a white horse on a Sunday drive to their aunt's. Only one wish per horse, so whoever saw the white horse first had to call out "Horse!" Occasionally the other would quibble and say that the horse was really gray, or that it was too dirty, or that a certain spot or change in mane color made it ineligible as a wish horse. Well, today the choice was obvious, to wish for Richard's victory, or the safety of all the drivers. She wishes, then cringes, thinking that an effective treatment for porphyria would well be wished for. Too late now. One wish per horse. Funny how some things stay lodged in memory.

The entry to the track is well-marked, with arrows to the specific parking areas—one for drivers, another for the public. Bright plastic triangle banners strung from pole to pole mark the periphery. Traffic is bumper to bumper and the cool morning temperature is just beginning to rise. The bumper sticker on the car in front of her reads, "I race and I vote." Very good to see such civic-minded drivers. Then again, the sticker on the other end of the bumper says, "This truck insured by Smith and Wesson." An adjacent rectangle of white bears the text in red, "Horn broken. Watch for finger." Well, it takes all kinds. The gun-insured, voting, finger-flipper veers to the left and Claire drives on the worn ruts of the drivers' field, a square mile hemmed by scrub oak and maple. She'll set up in the shade.

Every driver reserves space for his car and the necessary equipment by using flags. Claire opens the trunk and takes a breath before slamming it shut. There are only five flags. Well, she'll mark what she can with the ones she has available, go to the gate, collect some more, and return. A regrettable errand, but there's nothing to be done about it now.

She is already wearing loose clothing covering her skin to her wrists and ankles—a caftan with an elaborate embroidered yoke...actually something vaguely ethnic and fun. It complements the wide-brimmed straw hat, trimmed with a long scarf trailing behind, a friendly accessory that is now her constant companion. She shades herself further by opening a large umbrella and holding it over her head. Does she look like Mary Poppins? Claire begins to hum as she walks across the field: "A spoon full of sugar makes the medicine go down, the medicine go down..."

Walking back from the flag stand Claire anticipates an uninterrupted stretch in the shade with a pitcher of lemonade. Fresh-squeezed for extra vitamin C, and perhaps some extra ice, too. Thirty feet from her car Claire stops and looks at the car parked next to it. She reads the license plate on her vehicle. Yes, indeed, she knows her own car, but why would anyone remove the flags, and then park close to her, so brazenly? She would figure out who had taken the adjacent markers eventually, of course, but a certain degree of gall was demonstrated by doing it so shamelessly. The car was conspicuous, too: a slick red Porsche Targa. The presumed owner creaks the door open and steps out to lean both forearms on the roof. He doesn't say anything, but just snickers behind his little rat moustache. "Heh-heh-heh." He sounds like a Chihuahua with asthma.

It's Vince. She remembers his poor sportsmanship from when Richard won the Moline 150, skulking away to pout instead of having his picture taken with all the other drivers. Even before his bad behavior, Richard was wary of him. "He's so wasteful, Claire," he complained to her one day after a race. "We all know there are some poor little rich kids in this field, grown boys who have a hobby their daddies have given them to keep them out of trouble, but this guy seems almost proud of that." Richard takes a sip of his soft drink, then rotates the bottle for a moment. "Vince Cabrone seems to like destroying equipment, but more through misuse than actually risking himself. It's not that he gets caught up in the race—it's more like watching him break his toys so that they'll have to be replaced." Too charming. Well, Claire knows what caliber of individual she's dealing with.

"Vince." No need to introduce herself pleasantly to this thorn in the collective side of the racing community. "I marked off this area for Richard von Eschenbach's crew. They'll be arriving soon. Someone moved the flags. I selected the shade for health reasons that must be obvious by my attire."

"Yeah, right." Vince won't step around his car door. "I don't know anything about your five markers." He tries to curl his lip up like Elvis but the effect reminds Claire of a gopher. Vince steps away from the Porsche, slams the door, and struts towards his crew like a bantam rooster. "Roger! Where's the new tires? Well, why aren't they mounted yet? When did I tell you to have them changed? Why isn't it being done now?"

Back at the car Claire decides to costume herself further. For additional protection from the sun, yes, but also to make it clear to Vince that her need for shade is mandatory. Her caftan and straw hat are replaced by a long skirt; a black top with full bat-wing sleeves; a full high-collared cape over all, and then black boots more suited to the rutted terrain of the field than her earlier sandals. A refreshing coat of sunblock on her face won't hurt. She taps her fingernail against the side of her sunglasses as she puts them on. Now, to top it all off with the appropriate chapeau: Claire leans into the back seat and retrieves the large flat black circle of a bolero hat, the cords on either side joined beneath the chin with a blue bead that the Greeks use to keep away the evil eye.

She gazes around Vince's work site. The young man needs to be reminded of manners and common courtesy. The edge of her cape rustles over a patch of grass as she strides up to his crew. The crew boss, the beleaguered Roger, stands to the right with a checklist clamped to a clipboard for desperate review. He raises the board to cover his chest as Claire approaches.

"You're in charge here?" she asks him. "Could you do me a favor?" Her voice carries the honeyed rising inflection usually associated with women asking the help of men. She doesn't need to explain anything further, but merely points a finger to the area that she had initially marked.

"We'll move the car." Roger tips the brim of his STP cap. "I'll have someone do that now. Steve!" A young dark-haired man tightening the lugs on a tire looks up. "Get the Targa out of the lady's space. Here are the keys." He removes a ring from his pocket and tosses them. "Do it now."

"As long as you're moving the car," Claire has to ask, "would you happen to know where my flags are? I put out five to mark the space. I can't imagine who would remove them: it was very clearly staked."

The crew boss removes his hat and scratches his head. "Well, ma'am, whoever did it just probably didn't appreciate who was going to get upset."

"No one should have their markers moved." Claire moves a half-step closer. "It's quite distressing to experience such disrespect." She straightens back up but lowers her voice. "I'm not asking you to move the car out of the space that I marked out of petty spite or vengeance. My health concerns are serious. If I am exposed to too much sunlight, I could die." She raises both eyebrows over the top edge of her shades, pulling them down slightly with one finger to look Roger directly in the eye. "Even if you can't expose the guilty party, I am certain you can appreciate my concerns. If someone happens to ask why his car was moved, you could remind him that he moved something earlier. Every mean-spirited act receives an exponent and boomerangs back to its origin."

Claire returns to the stand of bushy young oaks to place the stakes again, but a full set this time. She surveys the clearly demarcated area. She will stay with the site for now. There will be no grounds for misunderstanding if she stays and watches it. Claire strolls to the deepest patch of shade, lowers herself to a hollow between two roots, and sits to read her book. It is an informative historical review of the wars in Scotland centuries ago. The cool of the moors and the bloodthirsty clans swarming over ridges seem diametrically opposed to the controlled competition being played out that day: the set rules, the extensive equipment, the judges watching cars shoot by in carefully painted concentric rings.

Vince Cabrone's car whizzes past. It squeals to a halt, and parallel clouds of dust hang in the air behind him. The little man is having a tantrum: his car door hangs wide open and he throws his helmet on the ground as he fumbles to unstrap himself from the safety harness. His arm catches as he stands up and he bumps his head against the top edge of the door. Ooh, that always smarts. Rubbing the top of his head, he wheels around to glare at Claire.

Roger and Steve lead the way to the vehicle, with the other crew members behind them. Vince spins back around and begins to talk to them, wind-milling his arms, pointing at the car, gesturing over his shoulder with his thumb towards Claire, stomping his foot in the dirt more than once. Little snippets of squeaking float in her direction; she continues to enjoy her book. The MacKays battle the Campbells and the losers move to the south. Claire's mother was a MacKay, and of course they won. The women were more fierce than the men, noted the Roman historians who first documented the peoples of the region. The detail is so engrossing that she does not notice an hour has passed until she sees Vince's crew boss, Roger, walking toward her and she glimpses at her watch.

"This space is all yours, Ma'am. We're all cleared out now." He says no more and turns to go.

All hope for quiet regained is blown when Haley Ellis walks up. "Claire! Sweetheart! Do you know what they're saying about you, you naughty girl?" Haley is next to her now, and leans against the tree, extending her arms from the elbows to wave her fingers over Claire's head as if sprinkling pixie dust.

"No, what is it?" Claire places the bookmark between the pages and rests the closed book on her lap.

"Vince Cabrone's crew claim that you cursed his car!" Haley leans over, lifting her fingers to eye height and extending them straight out to waggle her nails at Claire once more. "A hex! Some serious mojo!"

"Well, so *that's* why the kid was glaring at me. Of all the ridiculous, superstitious nonsense. Does he think I sacrificed a chicken? Drew a pentagram in the dirt under the engine block?" Claire sighs. "Is the problem with the car serious?"

"Don't you know, honey?" Haley tilts backward and looks at Claire askew. "You're the one who cursed it."

"Haley Ellis! Surely you must be joking." Claire pushes herself up. It is time to move, anyway—the shade is diminishing as the sun begins its long, slow descent.

"Well? Did you put a curse on it?"

"Oh Haley, please. Don't be silly. I have to dress this way for my health, to completely avoid exposure to the sun. But believe what you want." Claire shakes her head as she returns to the car. The persistence of myth despite science is absolutely amazing. People think what they like, no matter how much evidence accumulates to the contrary. It's amazing that any progress has ever been made in the face of so much ignorance and gossip. No one would ever want to face facts.

Chapter XXXI

Restoration

Everyone attending a gala event must arrive fashionably late. The newest nouveau riche delay their arrival to enter with the greatest pomp and circumstance to the largest possible audience, but generally cannot restrain themselves in their giddiness at being invited at all. The de la Violette mansion looked like a burning barn of limestone, solid squares of flickering candles displayed in every window. A dozen carriages waited in the circular drive ahead. Matching teams of polished Lippizan steeds stamping in impatience, jet black stallions with yellow ribbons woven into their manes, roan mares with ostrich feather plumes fountaining on their harnesses: not even the beasts were allowed to escape vanity.

Elysia knew to arrive no earlier than an hour late, and the line of disembarking guests, each attended by a footman to keep gentlemen from staining their frock coats or women from—oh, ultimate tragedy—tearing the lace of an overskirt or cuff. Elysia swept past two such couples as she climbed the stone steps to the entrance. One couple she recognized. "Why, hello, Kari-Friederich. Lucretia. I hope you have a splendid time at my husband's party this evening." The two stood slack-jawed and then the short, stout woman toppled into her husband's arms. A footman took the stairs two at a time to help them.

"Baroness!" yelped a doorman. The partner to his right blanched whiter than his powdered wig and departed to spread the news. Elysia turned to the major-domo and handed him a card, dense curlicues of her name in black ink on the thick cream parchment. It was a nice touch; Ronalde had remembered everything. The man's cheeks flapped and then he stumbled a bit, tipping his head back to take a deep breath, and clearing his throat to announce her. "Madames et Monsieurs, permit me to announce the arrival of the Baroness Elysia von Eschenbach, wife of Christoph de la Violette."

The room became a tableau. Raised glasses of champagne were held in mid-toast, ornate canapes were suspended before parted lips, dancing pairs stopped mid-gavotte in assorted bows and postures, wandering hands frozen in errant gropes on others' bodices. The room was silent, except for the crepe conversation held by the folds of Elysia's gown as she wove through the still figures to seek her husband.

"Louis-Jacques St. Cloud! Welcome!" She greeted everyone she could by name, having reviewed the guest list in front of the fireplace as she nursed Ignatz on countless evenings in rehearsal for precisely this performance. "I will have to make the most charming acquaintance of mademoiselle shortly." Those she remembered only by personal quirks received curtsies of welcome. Then she saw her first target, his slow-moving eminence, Bishop Finzi.

He stood surrounded by deacons, as a battle frigate might find its hull skirted by the sails of many smaller cruisers, but this Christian navy was in perpetual doldrums. She was careful not to increase her pace as she steered herself over the parquet. Her curtsy was long, elaborate, and low, as she knew would appease the pride of this man. Elysia bent one knee, lowered herself at the waist, and let her left arm sweep out until her cuff almost touched the floor. "Your Eminence, how good it is to see you again." The greeting caused the reflex reaction in Finzi, hand with ring extended, but his eyebrows were chasing one another around his face as his mind searched for the appropriate way to acknowledge the greeting of a woman who was officially dead. The hairy ropes above his eyes rolled up his forehead, and then fell to meet again over the bridge of his nose.

Elysia remained bent at the waist and moved her mouth to audibly pucker above the ring. "The ring bestowed by the Pope himself, your Eminence. I kiss it and beg for you to give me your blessing."

Finzi retained his passion for the rote, and another element of Elysia's plan slipped into place. When asked for a blessing, he would provide. His hand was extended over the coiled braids and curls at the back of her neck and a stream of Latin began to dribble from his lips. His eyes shifted to note the frozen audience staring at him, and the resultant stress married him more firmly to ritual. Why did they gape in disbelief? If anyone knew how to bless, this Bishop did. He embarked on the next stanza of some beautifully elaborate and arcane verse stretching his memory back to seminary to add a codicil, a caveat, and a paean to the particular salvation of the blessed's ancestors, may all their souls be purchased out of purgatory with many indulgences. Elysia felt her knees creak on the floor but stiffened her legs to keep from swaying and smiled down at the top of her skirts. Such public association with the divine was exactly what she needed, worth a week of sore knees.

If she were one of the undead, the mere touch of the Bishop, let alone all this protracted contact and the drapery of holy words, would have caused her to incinerate instantly. The la Violettes stood in rapt attention. She smiled with gratitude that things were going so smoothly and then raised herself up to a standing posture, giving Finzi another bow of deference.

"Thank you, your Eminence. I am revived in the Lord. Perhaps you have seen my husband this evening?" Elysia reigned reticence in a coy mimicry of Finzi's still-broadcast surprise. The Bishop's ringed finger pointed at the fireplace, its marble frame the size of a stable entrance. The crowd hummed like a hive of newly smoked bees.

"There is my husband. I see him now. I thank you again for your kindnesses, your Eminence."

Her path was instantly cleared as she continued to nod and smile her way across the room. The phalanx of satin, taffeta, organza and velvet parted to let her pass, and the gaudy hall closed up behind her. They stood as spellbound as the impresario in the loge at the opera.

"Christoph! My darling!" Elysia managed to bring true sweetness to her voice by holding the picture of burbling baby Ignatz in her mind. She held out her arms to him. "How I have missed you!" She delighted at having no feelings for the man at all. For the first time in their acquaintance, there was no physical or emotional response to this vain and obnoxious creature, no liquid longing, no fizzy-groined speculation, no gut-stabbing pangs of resentment. She was free from more than the catacombs or the comfortable confines of St. Michael's. Her mouth broadened as she neared him, but then Odile blocked her path.

"This is not your husband." The woman's hands were fists and her eyes were narrow.

"Mama, do not be absurd. He uses the name von Eschenbach, he tends our family lands." She reached past Odile to hold the sleeve of Christoph's jacket. He turned milk white, then green, then shuddered. "How could he do such things if we were not husband and wife?"

"You died!" Odile screamed.

"Madame? You are wrong again."

"We left you in the tomb."

"And I found my way out. Although I will not dispute that you were one of the last to see me there. You wear my wedding ring." Elysia grasped Odile's mitt and raised it for the crowd to see. The universal buzz quieted to a murmur. "Was this a memento for your fond heart to keep of me? Or perhaps a manifestation of your heart's true desire, for I know you would never sink to grave-robbing."

Odile's face ran red like the Calcutta dye-vats that stained the satin for her slippers. The crimson unfurled and traveled to her roots. She looked to note the frowns, open eyes and mouths, and bemused twitches upon the features of the guests.

Elysia released her hand and Odile stepped down to let her pass, leaving Christoph ill-equipped to enter a battle of wits. First she addressed Marie-Ange. "My sister, do you still like my gown?" Elysia lifted the wings of the overskirt to display the embroidered brocade. "I have a question for you that I might as well ask you now. When I escaped the premature burial orchestrated by your mother, I came to this house hoping to be welcomed as miraculously resuscitated and ready to start a new life with my husband. Never mind the details of my disappointment, except that you did keep gasping and shrieking that it was all your fault. Whatever did you mean?"

The girl's fingers knotted around one another again and again. Her skin began to flush, freckles darkening into blotches as she blubbered. "What are you talking about? You must be mad. Mad! I would never say any such thing. What could I have done?" One of her fingers darted up to wipe her nose. She sobbed as she walked backwards to flee. No one stirred to witness her departure.

Elysia turned her gaze to her true target. "Christoph." Her voice was as sweet as the whistle of the first robin in spring. "You must introduce me to your new friend." An attenuated blonde to Christoph's right was shaking like a willow. "Who is this woman? What is the meaning of this? Christoph, answer me!"

His eyes flickered from one woman to the other. "She was my wife. I mean, we married. But now, now she is a vampire. A vampire!" Christoph gained volume and confidence as he recalled the accusations from the night Elysia returned. "This is no woman, but a monster. She is a mistress to demons and kills Christian children. She sucks the blood from babies and consorts with Satan!" By the end, 'Satan' was a word he was shouting.

Elysia whirled to the bishop, her face torn with hurt. The Bishop faced a quandary. If Elysia were a vampire, she could not have received the blessings of himself, a man of the church, without bursting into flame, or at least withering and dying a ghastly melting death of the undead at his feet, leaving nothing but a puddle of smoking goo with a few bone shards and teeth. So, if she was a vampire, and had received his blessing, he could not be a truly sanctified agent of the Lord's holiness. This was not a possibility. The bishop stood straighter. He felt queasy. This required initiative and spontaneous thought, two of his least favorite things.

"No, wait!" he called. Every eye in the room rotated toward Finzi—even the glass eye of the Duke of Schlessigstein.

"This woman has received my blessing. She received the blessing of a man of the cloth without ill effect. She cannot be a vampire." He lifted his nose in the air and deepened and slowed his tone. "A minion of Satan could not kiss my holy ring and remain unfazed." The gathering hushed and turned its gaze to Christoph and Elysia.

"You are confused, Christoph." Elysia's confidence leaked through her mask of contrived wifely concern. The countess bit her lip to keep back tears of humiliation. "I cannot marry a married man, Christoph de la Violette." She sneered the 'la' with emphasis. Her hand groped at the left to remove the ring. Elysia smiled, the article of cachet, that single syllable designating his theoretical nobility, was already up for dispute.

"But she cannot be my wife, she did not complete her vows. She collapsed on the church floor in the middle of the ceremony," Christoph explained to Lydia. "You will be my first wife, my true and only bride." He placed his hands on hers in an attempt to keep her from removing the ring. Countess Lydia von der Vogelweide tore her hands away from his.

"I will never be your bride. Even if you do not aspire to bigamy, then you have adopted the title and property of the von Eschenbachs without legal claim. I thought that you were tragically widowed, and here your wife is before me. She is either your wife, or a woman whose property you have stolen, or conceivably both. Well, make up your mind. Which is it?" With a final wrench, she removed the lavender diamond from her left hand and flung it at him. Christoph winced, but then bent to retrieve it. "You are either a married man or a scoundrel of the most common variety, exceptional only in your gall. There is no engagement. There will be no wedding. You will hear from my family's solicitors tomorrow. Early."

The crowd stirred and parted as Countess Lydia stalked out of the parlor, half the crowd following her wake as if her skirt were hemmed with magnets of disgust. Odile rushed to the door to stem the flow, almost standing in the doorframe, but then stepped aside. Even the servants had turned to openly gawk. Countess von der Vogelweide did not even offer a perfunctory "Madame," but disappeared into the night. The following guests were not much more civil, most only offering Odile that they suddenly "did not feel well," or that "something had afflicted them." The footmen did not have time to close the door after each departure, so steady was the stream, each trussed and fussed-up couple leaving with their noses in the air.

Those still inside the home were not so much guests as an audience whose curiosity and desire for scandal outweighed the appeal of actively snubbing the hostess. Their wish for a performance, for some obnoxious finale, was not disappointed.

"Monster!" Odile shrieked in humiliation. She turned to Elysia with clenched fists shaking in the air. "Fiend! Beast! Leave now, before I kill you!"

Elysia ran to the side of Bishop Finzi, finding a crack in the ring of deacons and attendants to hover at his elbow. Bishop Finzi cleared his throat before he began. This speech would be orated in the direction of Odile, but was intended for the entire room. He knew his words would be spread from house to house tomorrow, exchanged as readily as calling cards, whispered over cups of tea and little crystal glasses of schnapps, punctuated by low mutterings. His chest expanded with the huge breath that he drew in to fuel his discourse.

"Madame de la Violette." When she heard her name, she sat down and buried her face in her hands. The bishop continued, enunciating as if he were biting through old tackbread. "Given the unforeseen and extraordinary events that have occurred since the wedding, the only appropriate action of the church is a prompt, complete..." he paused for effect, "and absolute annulment of any claim to marriage between your son and Baroness Elysia von Eschenbach." Odile de la Violette kept her face covered.

Elysia squeezed the Bishop's elbow and gave him her most pitiful look. He continued. "Also, Madame de la Violette, Elysia von Eschenbach will be compensated for the use of her name and lands for the last year. Some restitution is in order."

"Thank you, your Eminence. Our holy mother the church does not forsake the faithful." She glanced back at Odile, with some difficulty concealing her grin. Her glee was detected by Odile and acknowledged by the most murderous glare possible, two beams of hateful sight trying to drill into her own sockets. Elysia turned her head back to bob in front of the bishop.

There was no reason for Elysia to stay with this happy family. Marie-Ange had returned and was cowering behind the servers, gnawing on her fingernails. Christoph leaned against the mantel, unsuccessfully attempting to mimic nonchalance and appearing quite ill. Odile was hunched on the settee, rocking slightly and gathering knots in her hair. The only decent one was the one missing, of course. Where would he hide during Odile's grand fetes? The garden: Rene would be tending his roses. It was a shame she could not visit him, but she somehow suspected that news of the night's events would reach him soon enough.

She rose and bowed to each of the la Violettes before she prepared to leave. Elysia struggled to avoid feeling completely righteous, like some sort of Pied Piper of justice, for the bishop, the deacons, and a neat line of the remaining guests followed close behind. The parlor was empty within minutes. Odile leaned her back into the sofa and pounded the cushions with her fists. Christoph looked into the grate as if the flames were about to give him an answer to some universal dilemma. They soon presented an answer to his immediate quandary. He turned to the wreck of Odile de la Violette.

"Mama, I am going out." Yes, indeed, if there were ever a catastrophe that called for getting drunk, this was it. He could already see the warm comfort of the Hinter Brule, his seat beneath the trophy head, a few hands of cards and then a jaunt to the bordello.

"You are going out?" Odile almost spat the words on the carpet. "Go out and do not come back. I am no longer the endless purse to indulge you." Christoph stood straight with surprise.

"Christoph, I have kept you in liquor and licentiousness for years in the hope that you would, one fine day, keep your pants up long enough to make it through a wedding ceremony, marry well and make me a proud woman." Odile rose to her feet for emphasis.

"You *are* a proud woman, Mama." interrupted Christoph.

"I *was* a proud woman. Now I am the laughingstock of Austria, accused graverobber and mother to a would-be bigamist. If you had tended to Elysia like a good groom-to-be, minding her health instead of your whores, none of this debacle would have transpired."

Christoph shook his head in disbelief. "Don't be ridiculous, Mama. Am I a veterinary doctor, that I should have faithfully watched whatever cow you found for me? You can't blame me for this!"

"But I do. Be a man, for once in your life. Take responsibility."

"You are absurd!" he protested. "I will do no such thing!"

"Your options are limited. You heard me earlier: you can go out and stay out. Yes. You will never see a single pfennig from my coffers again. I managed, in my youth, with charm, guile, and considerably more wit than you possess, unfortunately, to make my way in the world from nothing. One would hope that a son would be equal to the challenge. You are disowned. Good luck. It will be interesting to see how you manage to keep up your drinking, gambling, and other derelictions."

Odile sniffed with the realization that Christoph was no longer her golden boy but her favorite scapegoat. The only way she had any hope of salvaging a shred of dignity was to throw herself on the collective bosom of the community, as it were, clammy and viperously gossip-ridden that it might be, and present herself as the victim of that universal bane sharper than a serpent's tooth, an ungrateful child. If she presented herself as the scandalized martyr in every parlor that would have her, perhaps she could gradually rebuild. Her gaze shifted to the huddled figure of Marie-Ange, cuticles now bloodied by gnawing. If the girl could be married off suitably, there might be some hope.

"Mama..." Christoph had deepened his voice—the irony of trying to sound more manly as he demanded his subsidy. "No more?"

"Leave before I have you thrown out." She walked to the window. The lone figure of her husband had just emerged from the box-hedge maze.

Chapter XXXII
Magic

Stuart joins Claire at the end of the race and they drive home together, with Victoria following in Claire's car. She tells him of the day's events, minimizing her costume change in the middle of the day to be better obscured from the light. No need to make her husband think he's married a female Bela Lugosi. The hills fade to black as they wind their way home. Stuart seems a little more animated than usual. "Where's the fire?" Claire asks.

"In my heart, for you." Stuart shoots her a warm, loving glance. Claire responds with a slurpy smooch to Stuart's cheek. By now the sky is completely dark. Claire is relieved to be able to toss her hat and sunglasses in the back seat, the folded shades landing on top of the bolero with a thump. She misses the sun but gains her health and skin. Bright pairs of headlights pass them in the oncoming lane, twin dots growing larger and whooshing by. Traffic slows by the time they reach their neighborhood, and as Stuart steers the car around the bend onto Emerald Avenue, she can hear the bugs beginning to buzz. Stuart whistles an accompaniment as he parks the car in the driveway, resting both hands on top of the steering wheel. "Claire, I have a confession to make."

"And what might that be?" She can see his profile because of the full moon hung behind him in the sky. So many stories for the moon: the jealous sulking sister of the sun, Diana the Huntress, a mirror in the night. Ancient Samurai saw a rabbit in the moon instead of a man. Right now it just shines on *her man*. Claire feels a pleasant bepuzzlement at this confession, but knows that it can't be anything too serious. That he's been spending too much time at his job? That he lost a hundred bucks in the football pool? Uncharacteristic, but not unforgivable.

"The kids and I needed you out of the house today to finish a surprise for you. When we go into the house, don't turn on any lights."

"Oh, Stuart, what's going on?" Claire opens the car door and stretches her legs. None of the stiffness or achiness that would have plagued her after a day at the track last summer, nor the nausea and headache that always followed a trip to the cabin. Her eyes adjust rapidly to the evening after the modest glow of the car's interior bulb, and the sidewalk shows the dim creases to the front door. Stuart opens it to the foyer and takes her by the hand into the living room. A tape is already in the stereo. He leans over to check the treble and bass—John is always turning up the bass—and then presses the "ON" button to its acute click.

The stereo speakers on the porch outside begin to emit the soothing strains of Debussy's "Clair de lune." Stuart takes Claire's hand and raises it to his mouth, grazing her fingers with closed lips. Then he slides the patio door open and leads her outside.

He flips a switch and a light shines from within the waters of a newly installed lily pond. Lotus flowers float on the surface, coronas of golden pollen-tipped stamens making sheltered crowns within the long, pale petals. Claire gasps, and Stuart flips another switch, causing a jet of water to squirt from the pond's center. It bubbles softly, jetting a curve a foot high that returns in ripples to make little waves up against the rough-hewn rocks that encircle the pool. Stuart steps behind her and wraps his arms around her, pressing her to him before he speaks again. "There's more to show you, you know."

He squeezes her for a moment more, resting his face on her shoulder, and then straightening up to kiss the back of her head. The sweet smell of her hair, even after a day at the track, brings him a rush of passion. He retreats to the back of the patio and returns carrying a large Navajo blanket. Stuart unfolds it and shakes out the heavy wool as if he's preparing a cloth for the ground at a picnic. Once the square falls to the grass, he tugs each side to make certain it is straight and to his satisfaction, even kneeling to smooth dunes of parallel folds that marred one of the corners. He raises his eyes to Claire and pats the center of the blanket. "Are you going to join me?"

Claire cherishes this lovely gift and is ready to sit and admire it with her husband. Stuart has been paying attention and knows she's been spending her evenings out on the porch in the cool of midnight. Stuart shushes her and waits until she's seated. He pauses to hold her hands in both of his before standing up again. Tiny wafts of sulfur drift to Claire's nose as Stuart lights candles around the garden with cardboard matches. Each pale taper is anchored in a bag with sand, and their cumulative glow begins to reveal a bed of new plants stretching before her. Some have lacy, silver leaves. One stretches tall and bears several white trumpets unfolded to reveal apricot centers. A vining plant with small blossoms releases a perfume delicate and sweet. The wavering light of the candle flames dance on the plants, swaying slightly from their rootstocks, proffering the different fountains of flowers and foliage that stretch up in a graduated bank to the fence. Claire is so entranced that she doesn't notice Stuart until he sits down beside her.

She places her lips on his cheek, and then moves them further up to his temple. "Thank you," she whispers in his ear. "I have never seen anything as beautiful as this garden. It is sheer magic. Enchanting. What plant smells so wonderful? It's like vanilla, but not for a kitchen, and not as sweet as roses...?"

"Night-scented stock. It is a plain and sturdy plant except for its perfume. There—in the border. Other flowers here have a scent, of course, but not as strong. This is a garden of night-scented and night-blooming plants just for you, Claire." Stuart's voice is almost a whisper as his head leans against hers. "During the day, it rests. At night, it flourishes. More proof that there is beauty after the sun sets." He sits up straight and turns to her, taking both of her hands in his again and looking her in the eye. Claire can see the scar on his left eyebrow from when he was playing catch with Holly and the ball hit him over the eye.

"I said I had a confession. Well, the garden and the surprise are probably the least of it. I just want to tell you that I know I'm not the best with words: I may act brusque to hide my discomfort, I may even be silent instead of offering the support you deserve."

"Claire, I've been too silent for this last year. I've been too selfish, also, thinking of these changes as an inconvenience to our old schedule instead of something you have to do, something where I should be there for you. You're trying to save your own life, and there I am on the sidelines sulking because you aren't there to make me breakfast. It sounds ridiculous, I know." Stuart leans forward and plucks a small flower from the new bed. It has five petals, each one tipped in pink. He brushes it against the end of Claire's nose and then places it behind her ear.

"It's funny how when life gets difficult, we're reduced to cliche. Maybe people say these things over and over again because they're true. Well, instead of lemons and lemonade, glasses half full or half empty, this is about types of light, your sensitivity to sunlight. Looking at this garden, as lovely and surprising as yourself, I realize that this is really a splendid new opportunity for both of us. Forgive me for not thinking of this earlier—this is my chance to go from sunlight to starlight with you, if you'll still have me."

"Stuart," Claire pauses to listen to a whippoorwill call. "This is the best thing I've ever received in my life; the most thoughtful and incredible gift, yes, but it also shows how right I was all those years ago to marry you." She leans against him and he arcs an arm around her front, holding her to him. Claire caresses Stuart's hand. Frogs keep time to the counterpoint of crickets, little rubbery brass trumpetings interspersed with the singing strings of insects rubbing their legs together. The candlelight dances on as Claire and Stuart listen. Her head is on his shoulder as her mind reviews the events of a lifetime: schooling, graduation, their leaving home together for the city, years of keeping body and soul intact as they established a household and a family; so soon, the three children, one right after the other; the litany of minor terrors and childhood diseases; her own employment; Stuart's career. Throughout it all she had been beleaguered by this disease and had never known.

Sometimes fate tests us, and in testing us shows us what we're really made of—what mettle, what solidity at the core. Claire has been given this condition, but prevails in spite of it, revealing herself to be even stronger than she thought possible, and relishing how much her husband understands and loves her. This is not a vampire's curse, but a different light that has been shown on her world. Claire remembers a girlhood Christmas choir and a visitor on the staircase, the words of her father:

"You must have faith and believe. Hope springs eternal. There is a reason and purpose for all things. I tell you now that you must always be a good person, honest and kind. There is a heavenly secret that has been entrusted to us. In time it will be revealed to you. Have courage. I will always be with you."

Claire takes a deep breath, closes her eyes and lifts her face toward the night sky. The deep security she feels in her soul tells her he will always be with her, but her inner perception stirs within, causing her to look questioningly at Stuart. "Might there be more secrets? Have all the wonders been revealed to us? Do you suppose there is additional magic afoot?"

THE END

Epilogue

Porphyrias are inherited metabolic disorders whereby defective enzymes are involved in the bodies' manufacture of heme. Heme is a vital substance for all body organs and consists of an iron atom surrounded by a porphyrin molecule and is part of hemoglobin which carries oxygen to all parts of the body. The manufacturing route or "biosynthetic pathway" of heme was not ascertained until 1988. However, the disorder is of ancient origin. Not only is the biosynthetic pathway extremely complicated, where there are eight enzymes involved, but symptoms are of a variable nature. Symptoms can range from one or more of the following ailments: Stomach ache, nausea, vomiting, constipation/ diarrhea, muscle weakness, pain in the extremities, insomnia, emotional difficulties, rapid pulse, high blood pressure, paralysis, coma and respiratory failure. Attacks may result in paralysis mimicking parkinsonism. Skin manifestations may occur and can include burning, blistering and scarring of sun-exposed areas. Sun sensitivity can occur in all but two types of porphyria. The degree of sun sensitivity to sunlight varies considerably. Because these symptoms suggest other diseases, the correct diagnosis is often delayed.

Symptoms are initiated by the presence of "allergic" producing compounds which the body of a porphyriac (or porphyric) cannot tolerate. These compounds can run the gamut from one or a combination of substances depending on the porphyric's condition at the time of exposure. Tobacco, alcohol, coffee, MSG-monosodium glutamate, which is added to almost all canned soups and many other foods to enhance flavor, chemicals used to concentrate juices, etc., hormones added to meats, sun exposure and drugs. A list of common drugs follows, but by no means includes all offending drugs.

Partial list of unsafe drugs: Barbiturates, sulfonamide antibiotics, griseofulvin, anti-epilepsy drugs, birth control drugs, alcohol, ergots, metoclopramide, rifampin, diclofenac danazol, and almost all tranquilizers, sedatives and anti-depressants.

FOR FURTHER INFORMATION CONTACT:

The American Porphyria Foundation
4900 Woodway Drive
Houston, TX 77056
(866) 273-3635 / Fax (713) 840-9552
www.porphyriafoundation.com